LINEAR ALGEBRA

LINEAR ALGEBRA

AN INTRODUCTORY APPROACH

CHARLES W. CURTIS
PROFESSOR OF MATHEMATICS
UNIVERSITY OF WISCONSIN

ALLYN AND BACON, INC.   BOSTON

First printing ....August, 1963
Second printing ....May, 1964
Third printing ....August, 1965

Library of Congress Catalog Card Number: 63-18178

PRINTED IN THE UNITED STATES OF AMERICA

To Timothy, Daniel, and Robert

PREFACE

Linear algebra is the branch of mathematics that has grown out of
a theoretical study of the problem of solving systems of linear
equations. This problem is one of the oldest questions in mathematics, and is still of fundamental importance for an understanding
of the elementary parts of most of the other, larger branches of
mathematics and for applications to the sciences and engineering.
The abstract ideas of vector space and linear transformation which
are suggested by the study of linear equations are today of far
greater importance than their parent, and have become an essential
part of every science student's early mathematical training.

In this book the subject is presented from the beginning as a
strict deductive science, and is intended to encourage readers to work
independently on theoretical questions in mathematics. A deep
understanding of the proofs of theorems in linear algebra is important, not only for beginning mathematics students, but for pro-
spective science and engineering students who will be concerned with
theoretical questions in their later work.

The book follows the historical, or evolutionary, development
of linear algebra. It begins with the real number system, systems of
linear equations, and matrices and determinants, motivated by the
connections with analytic geometry. In the second half of the book,
vector spaces over arbitrary fields and linear transformations are
studied from an abstract viewpoint, after the reader has enough

examples to appreciate the power of the abstract approach. The theorems of linear algebra are especially satisfying in that most of them contain more or less explicit computational procedures for solving numerical problems. The importance of numerical problems as an aid to understanding the theorems, and as an important facet of the course for persons interested in the applications of linear algebra, is stressed in the exercises throughout the book.

This book is presented as a first introduction to higher algebra. It presupposes only a standard analytic geometry and calculus course, and is intended to precede courses for mathematics majors in modern algebra and advanced calculus. Linear algebra offers significant examples of the abstract systems of algebra such as groups and rings, as well as vector spaces. Included in Chapter 6 is an introduction to finite groups via a detailed study of symmetry groups in two and three dimensions. A course based on this book may profitably be followed by a thorough treatment of elementary group theory, rings, fields, and modules in a semester or a year course at the junior-senior level.

Matrix and vector methods in differential equations, and the idea, used in modern advanced calculus texts, of approximating differentiable transformations of Euclidean spaces by linear transformations, show that a course in linear algebra is desirable as a background for advanced undergraduate courses in differential equations and advanced calculus. The theory of linear transformations is carried far enough to give significant applications to analysis, and an optional section on vector differential equations and the exponential of a matrix is included in Chapter 5.

A text in linear algebra, designed to be understood by students in a short course, cannot include all the desirable advanced topics in the subject. In the theory of linear transformations, there are stressed the theory of the minimal polynomial, conditions for a linear transformation to be diagonable, the primary decomposition of a vector space relative to a linear transformation, and applications of these results. Not included are the important topics of factor spaces, duality, and elementary divisors and invariant factors, all of which, I believe, are properly treated from the more advanced standpoint of modules over rings, and can be studied advantageously in a later course.

I have found that the material in this book, not including optional Sections 14, 25, and 30, can be covered successfully in one semester by a class of sophomores or juniors who are willing to work hard. The exercises form an integral part of the course and contain important theoretical material as well as applications to numerical work. Hints for some of the theoretical problems are included. No answers to the numerical problems are included because I have tried to select numerical procedures that may be checked efficiently, and students will learn more and gain confidence, I believe, by learning to check their numerical work in spite of the extra time it takes. The theoretical problems are intended to give the student the excitement and the challenge of doing original work on a worthwhile task; he must learn from these not only the satisfaction of seeing a good idea lead to the solution of a problem but also the disappointment of having ideas lead to blind alleys and failure. These experiences are all part of the training of a scientist, and are enriched by an instructor who is willing to read in detail the work of his students, giving them the benefit of his own experience and critical insight.

My chief acknowledgment is to the students in Math 115a whom I have taught at Wisconsin while the plan for this book matured. Their contributions are implicit on every page, and the project could not have been carried out without their encouragement. I have also profited greatly from the reactions to lectures I have given on parts of this book.

A preliminary version of parts of Chapters 5 and 6 was presented in lectures to teachers participating in the Summer Institute at Bowdoin College in the summers of 1959 and 1960. I lectured on the material in Sections 17, 26, and 30 to a wide audience of college students while I was a Visiting Lecturer of the Mathematical Association of America in the spring of 1961. Section 25 was presented to mathematics majors at Oberlin in 1961 and Section 26 to high school students in Racine in 1961. Finally, I owe a great deal to the interest and encouragement my family has shown at every stage of the work.

CHARLES W. CURTIS

Madison, Wisconsin
December 3, 1962

CONTENTS

LINEAR ALGEBRA

CHAPTER 1

THE REAL
NUMBER SYSTEM

1. INTRODUCTION

This book is devoted to the theory of vector spaces, or linear algebra, as it is sometimes called. The special problems which led to the concept of an abstract vector space come from the theory of linear equations, matrices, and analytic geometry. As a first course in the subject, we shall follow the evolutionary development of the theory of vector spaces, starting with linear equations, matrices, and determinants and working toward abstract vector spaces and linear transformations later in the book. It would be inefficient and a waste of time, however, to develop matrices and linear equations, for example, in exactly the way they were studied in the nineteenth century. We have made free use of modern developments in vector space theory to present the old material in an economical and efficient way, and to prepare the way for the abstract approach.

As we shall see, linear algebra is a rich subject, full of unexpected twists and turns. It would be a mistake, even in a first course, not to see on the one hand the powerful influence linear algebra has had on mathematical research and on the other the adaptability of linear algebra to computational procedures and its usefulness in numerical work and analysis. Thus, we have included in this book some problems on applications and numerical computation, and also optional sections which take up special problems, sometimes of an advanced nature, but which require only the tools developed in the course. The optional sections may be used for outside reading or special projects for interested students.

2. REAL NUMBERS

In this book much attention will be paid to presenting mathematics as a strict deductive science. In other words, we shall try to convince the reader that all our theorems can be proved by the methods of logical reasoning from certain clearly stated assumptions made in advance. As a matter of fact, the student and reader of this book will be asked to supply many of these arguments himself.

If we have any hope of putting the subject on a sound logical basis, we must have a clearly defined starting point. As the primitive concept of our subject we shall adopt the system of real numbers, which should already be familiar to the student from his earlier mathematical work. To remove any doubts, we shall list exactly those properties of the real numbers which we wish to use. We shall use this chapter also to introduce the reader to methods of proof in algebra, and shall give a somewhat more detailed exposition of the subject than may seem necessary at this point, in order to develop a number of concepts which will be needed later in the course. Some readers may wish to skip most of this section and the next one, and begin with Section 4 or Section 5, coming back to Sections 2 and 3 if they need them.

Before starting, we make a remark on the terminology. *Real number* is a technical term, and the real numbers are described exactly by the properties we assume concerning them. The fact that there are also complex or imaginary numbers should not lead the reader to believe that one sort of number is any more or less mysterious or more or less down to earth than the other.

Everyone is familiar with at least one intuitive description of the real numbers. For example, the real numbers may be described as the collection of rational numbers a/b, where a, b are integers and

$b \neq 0$, together with all "numbers" which can be approximated arbitrarily closely by rational numbers. They may be described also as all numbers represented by writing finitely many digits (preceded by a plus or minus sign), then a decimal point, and then an unending sequence of digits. Still again they may be described as labels for the points on a line. This is not the place to explore the connections among all these ideas; we seek a precise and usable description of the real numbers. To accomplish this we shall give a set of axioms for the real numbers.

The axioms for the real numbers will be given in three groups: first the *algebraic axioms*, which can be summarized in the assertion that the real numbers form a *field*, then the *order axioms*, which introduce the concepts of positive and negative real numbers, and finally the *completeness axiom*, which guarantees that enough real numbers exist for us to do business.

Let us first make a general remark about sets* and the notion of equality. The real number system is a set of objects, and these objects are represented by symbols $\{a, b, c, \cdots; 0, 1, \cdots\}$. The symbol representing an object may be thought of as the *name* of the object. We shall assume that with any set of objects we are given a means of distinguishing whether two objects are different or not. In other words, given an object with name a and an object with name a', we assume that exactly one of two possibilities holds: either the objects are really the same, in which case we write $a = a'$ (read "a equals a'" or "a is equal to a'"), or the objects are not the same, in which case we write $a \neq a'$ (read "a *is not equal to* a'"). Thus, if we happen to have assigned the same object the different names a and a', we indicate this fact by writing $a = a'$.

We assume that the "equals" relation has the following properties:

(1) $a = a$ (in other words, we cannot use the same symbol in a given context to stand for different objects).
(2) If $a = b$, then $b = a$.
(3) If $a = b$ and $b = c$, then $a = c$ (this is a precise statement of the notion that things equal to the same thing are equal to each other).

If, as in the case of the real number system, we have certain operations defined on the elements of the set, then by using these connectives we can form expressions such as

---

* A fuller discussion of sets is given in Section 3.

$$\left(\frac{a-b}{2+x}\right) + \left(\frac{3+ab}{2}\right).$$

Such an expression, provided that it satisfies the grammatical rules governing the use of the connectives $-$, $+$, etc., represents a real number and is called a *formula*. As a further property of the relation of equality we assume the following:

(2.1) Substitution Principle. *Let F be a formula representing a real number in which the symbol a occurs. If a′ = a, then a may be replaced by a′ in the formula F, and the new formula F′ will represent the same real number as F; in other words, F = F′.*

Now we are ready for our definition of the real numbers.

(2.2) Definition. The *real number system* is a set $R = \{a, b, c, \cdots ; 0, 1, \cdots\}$ together with two operations, called addition and multiplication, which assign to each pair of real numbers (a, b) unique elements $a + b$ and ab of R, called the *sum* and *product*, respectively, of a and b. This system is assumed to satisfy the *algebra axioms*. We assume also that in R there is a subset P, called the set of positive real numbers, which satisfies the *order axioms*. Finally, the system is assumed to satisfy the *completeness axiom*. A system satisfying the algebra axioms alone is called a *field;* a field satisfying the order axioms is called an *ordered field*. Thus the real numbers may be described as a complete ordered field.

ALGEBRA AXIOMS.   For all a, b, c in R, we have the following:

(A-1) $a + (b + c) = (a + b) + c$ and $(ab)c = a(bc)$ (associative laws).

(A-2) $a + b = b + a$ and $ab = ba$ (commutative laws).

(A-3) There exists an element 0 such that $a + 0 = a$ for all a in R, and an element $1 \neq 0$ such that $a \cdot 1 = a$ for all a in R.

(A-4) For each a in R, there exists an element $-a$ (read "minus a") in R such that $a + (-a) = 0$.

(A-5) For each $a \neq 0$ in R, there exists an element a^{-1} (read "a inverse") such that $a \cdot a^{-1} = 1$.

(A-6) For all a, b, c in R, $a(b + c) = ab + ac$ (distributive law).

ORDER AXIOMS

(O-1)   For each a in R, one and only one of the following possibilities holds:

$$a \text{ is in } P, \qquad a = 0, \qquad -a \text{ is in } P.$$

(O-2)   If a and b are in P, then $a + b$ and ab are in P.

Before stating the completeness axiom, we shall derive some consequences of the algebra and order axioms. The statements appearing with starred numbers [for example, $(2.7)\star$] are not proved in the text, and the proofs should be worked out by the reader.

(2.3)   *If $a + b = a + c$, then $b = c$ (cancellation law for addition).*

Proof.   We should like to say "add $-a$ to both sides." We accomplish this by using the substitution principle (2.1) as follows. From (2.1) and the assumption that $a + b = a + c$, we have

$$(-a) + (a + b) = (-a) + (a + c).$$

On the one hand, we have by the algebra axioms (Which ones?),

$$(-a) + (a + b) = [(-a) + a] + b = 0 + b = b \,*$$

Similarly,

$$(-a) + (a + c) = c.$$

From properties 2 and 3 of the equals relation, we have $b = c$, and the result is established.

An argument like this cannot be read like a newspaper article; the reader will find that he must have paper and pencil handy, and write out the steps, checking the references to the axioms, until he sees exactly what has been done.

(2.4)   *For arbitrary a and b in R, the equation $a + x = b$ has a unique solution.*

Proof.   This result is two theorems in one. We are asked to show, first, that there exists at least one real number x which satisfies the equation and, second, that there is at most one solution. Both

---

* A statement of the form $a = b = c = d$ is really shorthand for the separate statements $a = b$, $b = c$, $c = d$. The properties of the equals relation imply that from the separate statements we can conclude that all the objects a, b, c, and d are equal to each other, and this is the meaning of the abbreviated statement $a = b = c = d$.

statements are easy, however. First, from (A-1), (A-2), and (A-4) we have

$$a + [(-a) + b] = [a + (-a)] + b = 0 + b = b,$$

and we have shown that there is at least one solution, namely $x = (-a) + b$.

Now let c and c' be solutions of the equation. Then we have $a + c = b$, $a + c' = b$, and hence $a + c = a + c'$ (Why?). By the cancellation law (2.3) we have $c = c'$, and we have proved that if c is one solution of the equation then any other solution is equal to c.

(2.5) Definition. We write $b - a$ to denote the unique solution of the equation $a + x = b$. We have $b - a = b + (-a)$, and we call $b - a$ the result of subtracting a from b. (The reader should observe that there is no question of "proving" a statement like the last. A careful inspection of the algebra axioms shows that no meaning has been attached to the formula $b - a$; the matter has to be taken care of by a definition.)

(2.6) $-(-a) = a.$

Proof. The result comes from examining the equation $a + (-a) = 0$ from a different point of view. For we have also $-(-a) + (-a) = 0$; by the cancellation law we obtain $-(-a) = a$.

Now we come to the properties of multiplication, which are exactly parallel to the properties of addition. We remind the reader that he must supply the proofs of the starred statements.

(2.7)★ *If $a \neq 0$ and $ab = ac$, then $b = c$.*

(2.8)★ *The equation $ax = b$, where $a \neq 0$, has a unique solution.*

(2.9) Definition. We denote by $\dfrac{b}{a}$ (or b/a) the unique solution of the equation $ax = b$, and will speak of $\dfrac{b}{a}$ as the result of *division* of b by a. Thus $\dfrac{1}{a} = a^{-1}$, because of axiom (A-5).

(2.10)★ $(a^{-1})^{-1} = a,$ if $a \neq 0$.

Thus far we haven't used the distributive law. In a way, this is the most powerful axiom and most of the more exotic theorems in elementary algebra, such as $(-1)(-1) = 1$, follow from the distributive law.

(2.11)   *For all a in R, $a \cdot 0 = 0$.*

Proof.   We have $0 + 0 = 0$. By the distributive law (A-6) we have $a \cdot 0 + a \cdot 0 = a \cdot 0$. But $a \cdot 0 = a \cdot 0 + 0$ by (A-3), and by the cancellation law we have $a \cdot 0 = 0$.

(2.12) $(-a)b = -(ab)$,   *for all a and b.*

Proof.   From $a + (-a) = 0$ we have, by the substitution principle, $[a + (-a)]b = 0 \cdot b$. From the distributive law and (2.11) this implies that
$$ab + (-a)b = 0.$$
Since $ab + [-(ab)] = 0$, the cancellation law gives us $(-a)b = -(ab)$, as we wished to prove.

(2.13) $(-a)(-b) = ab$,   *for all a, b in R.*

Proof.   We have, by two applications of (2.12) and by the use of the commutative law for multiplication,
$$(-a)(-b) = -[a(-b)] = -[-(ab)].$$
Finally, $-[-(ab)] = ab$ by (2.6).

As a consequence of (2.13) we have

(2.14) $(-1)(-1) = 1$. (It is interesting to construct a direct proof from the original axioms.)

We come now to some consequences of the order axioms. First of all, we introduce the notion of inequality, "$a < b$."

(2.15)   **Definition.**   For all a and b in R, $a < b$ (read "a is less than b") means that $b - a$ is in P. We write $a > b$ (read "a is greater than b") as equivalent to $b < a$. We write $a \leq b$ to denote the statement that either $a < b$ or $a = b$. We define $a \geq b$ similarly.

We note in particular that a is in P if and only if $a > 0$. Note also that $a < 0$ means $-a > 0$.

(2.16)★   *For any two real numbers a, b, exactly one of the following possibilities holds: $a < b$, $a = b$, $b < a$.*

(2.17)★ *If $a < b$ and $b < c$, then $a < c$.*

(2.18)★ *If $a < b$, then $a + c < b + c$ for all c in R.*

(2.19)★ *If $a < b$ and $c > 0$, then $ac < bc$.*

(2.20)★ *If $a < b$ and $c < 0$, then $ac > bc$.*

(2.21) *If $a \neq 0$, then $a^2 > 0$. (Here, of course, a^2 means $a \cdot a$.) In particular, $1 > 0$ since $1 = 1^2$.*

   Proof. By (O-1) we have either $a > 0$ or $-a > 0$. If $a > 0$, then $a^2 > 0$ by (O-2). If $-a > 0$, then by (2.13) and (O-2) we have

$$a^2 = (-a)^2 > 0.$$

(2.22)★ *If $a \neq 0$, then $a > 0$ if and only if $a^{-1} > 0$.*

We conclude this section with a statement of the completeness property of the real numbers.

(2.23) Definition. A set S of real numbers is said to be *bounded above* if there exists a real number M such that $s \leq M$ for all s in S. The number M is then called an *upper bound* of the set S. The set S is said to possess a *least upper bound* L if L is an upper bound of S and if, for any other upper bound M of S, $L \leq M$.

(2.24) Completeness Axiom. If S is a nonempty set of real numbers which is bounded above, then S has a least upper bound.

EXERCISES

1. Prove that if a, b, c, d are real numbers, where b, $d \neq 0$, then:

a. $\dfrac{a}{b} + \dfrac{c}{d} = \dfrac{ad + bc}{bd}.$

b. $\left(\dfrac{a}{b}\right)\left(\dfrac{c}{d}\right) = \dfrac{ac}{bd}.$

c. $\left(\dfrac{a}{b}\right) \Big/ \left(\dfrac{c}{d}\right) = \dfrac{ad}{bc},$ if $c/d \neq 0.$

2. For each real number a, we define the *absolute value* of a by

$$|a| = \begin{cases} a & \text{if } a \geq 0 \\ -a & \text{if } a < 0. \end{cases}$$

Prove the following statements:

a. $|a| \geq 0$ and $|a| = 0$ if and only if $a = 0$.

b. $|ab| = |a| \cdot |b|$ for all a, b in R.

c. $-|a| \leq a \leq |a|$.

d. $|x| \leq b$ for $b > 0$ if and only if $-b \leq x \leq b$.

e. $|a + b| \leq |a| + |b|$.

3. Prove that if $a < b$ then a real number x satisfies the inequality $a \leq x \leq b$ if and only if there is a real number λ, with $0 \leq \lambda \leq 1$, such that $x = \lambda a + (1 - \lambda)b$. For example, we have $a \leq \frac{1}{2}(a + b) \leq b$ where $\lambda = \frac{1}{2}$.

4. Prove that if $a \geq 0$, $b \geq 0$, and $a^2 \leq b^2$, then $a \leq b$.

3. SETS, INTEGERS, AND THE PRINCIPLE OF MATHEMATICAL INDUCTION

A knowledge of the principles of set theory is essential to an understanding of higher mathematics. While it is true that much of it can and must be learned by experience, it will be convenient to collect in one place explicit statements of some of the concepts and facts that will be needed later in the course. The most important of these is the principle of mathematical induction, on which the proofs of almost all the main results in this book are based.

We begin with the concept of a *set* of objects. We use the word "set" as synonymous with "collection," or "family," but from a mathematical point of view "set," like "real number," is a technical term which takes its meaning from the properties we assume sets possess.

Let X be a set of objects. For a given object x, either x belongs to the set X or it does not. If x belongs to X we write $x \in X$ (read "x is an element of X" or "x is a member of X"); if x does not belong to X we write $x \notin X$.

A set Y is called a *subset* of a set X if, for all objects y, $y \in Y$ implies $y \in X$. In other words, every element of Y is also an element of X. If Y is a subset of X, we write $Y \subset X$. If $Y \subset X$ and $X \subset Y$, then we say that the sets X and Y are *equal* and write $X = Y$. Thus two sets are equal if they contain exactly the same members.

It is convenient to introduce the set containing no elements at all. We call it the empty set, and denote it by $\varnothing$. Thus, for every object x, $x \notin \varnothing$. For example, the set of all real numbers x for which the inequalities $x < 0$ and $x > 1$ hold simultaneously is the empty set. The reader will check that from our definition of subset it follows logically that the empty set $\varnothing$ is a subset of every set. (Why?).

There are two important constructions which can be applied to subsets of a set and yield new subsets. Suppose U and V are subsets of a given set X. We define $U \cap V$ to be the set consisting of all elements belonging to both U and V and call $U \cap V$ the *intersection* of U and V. Question: What is the intersection of the set of real numbers x such that $x > 0$ with the set of real numbers y such that $y < 5$? If we have many subsets of X, their intersection is defined as the set of all elements which belong to all the given subsets.

The second construction is the *union* $U \cup V$ of U and V; this is the subset of X consisting of all elements which belong either to U or to V. (When we say "either . . . or" it is understood that we mean "either . . . or . . . or both.")

Finally we have the concept of *function*. A function $f: X \to Y$ (sometimes called a *mapping*) is a rule which assigns to each element of a set X a unique element of a set Y. We write $f(x)$ for the element of Y which the function f assigns to x. The set X is called the *domain* or *domain of definition* of f. Two functions f and f' are said to be *equal*, and we write $f = f'$ if they have the same domain X and if, for all $x \in X$, $f(x) = f'(x)$. The function f is said to be *one-to-one* if $x_1 \neq x_2$ in X implies that $f(x_1) \neq f(x_2)$. [Note that this is equivalent to the statement that $f(x_1) = f(x_2)$ implies $x_1 = x_2$.] The function f is said to be *onto* Y if every $y \in Y$ can be expressed in the form $y = f(x)$ for some $x \in X$; we shall say that f is a function of X *into* Y when we want to allow the possibility that f is not onto Y. A one-to-one function f of a set X onto a set Y is called a *one-to-one correspondence* of X onto Y.

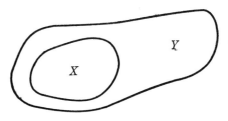

Figure 1.1

It is frequently useful to illustrate statements about sets by drawing diagrams. Although they have no mathematical significance, they do give us confidence that we are making sense and sometimes will suggest important steps in an argument. For example, the statement $X \subset Y$ is illustrated by Figure 1.1. In Figure 1.2 the shaded portion indicates $U \cup V$, while the cross-hatched portion

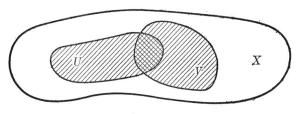

Figure 1.2

denotes $U \cap V$. Mappings (or functions) may be visualized by pictures such as that in Figure 1.3, which illustrates a function that

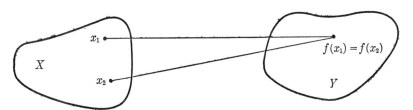

Figure 1.3

is not one-to-one. The reader will find it useful to construct far more diagrams than we have given in the book. It should be emphasized that a correct mathematical argument can never consist of a diagram alone, but must be a sequence of English sentences with whatever symbolic abbreviations are appropriate to the context.

Now we are ready to discuss some important subsets of the system of real numbers.

(3.1) Theorem. *There exists a subset N of the real numbers R with the following properties:*

(1) $1 \in N$.
(2) *If $x \in N$, then $x + 1 \in N$.*

(3) *N is the smallest subset of R which has the properties 1 and 2; that is, if $N' \subset R$ satisfies properties 1 and 2, then $N \subset N'$.*

Proof. Consider all subsets of the real numbers which satisfy properties 1 and 2. There is at least one such subset, namely the set R of all real numbers. Let N be the intersection of all such subsets. Then N satisfies properties 1 and 2 and, by its construction, N is a subset of every set N' which satisfies properties 1 and 2. This proves the theorem.

Using the fact that the set of all real numbers ≥ 1 satisfies properties 1 and 2, the reader may prove that

(3.2)⋆ $x \geq 1,$ *for all $x \in N$.*

(3.3) Definition. The uniquely determined set N satisfying properties 1 and 2 of theorem (3.1) is called the set of *natural numbers.*

Intuitively we may think of N as the set of real numbers $1, 2 = 1 + 1, 3 = (1 + 1) + 1$, etc. It is because of the vague "etc." that we must take the trouble to state and prove theorem (3.1). We have adopted this definition of the natural numbers only for the sake of economy. A more satisfying approach is to give axioms for the natural numbers and then to construct the real numbers from them. For this (rather lengthy) construction, the reader is referred to the book of E. Landau, listed in the bibliography.

We come next to the most important theoretical tool in algebra.

(3.4) Principle of Mathematical Induction. *Suppose that for each natural number n there corresponds a statement E(n) which is either true or false. Suppose, further, (A) E(1) is true, and (B) if E(n) is true then E(n + 1) is true, for each $n \in N$. Then E(n) is true for all natural numbers n.*

Proof. Let N^* be the set of natural numbers n for which $E(n)$ is true. Then $N^* \subset N$ and $1 \in N^*$. If $n \in N^*$, then $n + 1 \in N^*$. By theorem (3.1) we have $N^* = N$ and the theorem is proved.

The statement $E(n)$ will often be called the *induction hypothesis.*

(3.5) Definition. A set X is *finite* if for some natural number n there exists a one-to-one correspondence of the set of natural numbers m, such that $1 \leq m \leq n$, onto the set X. If, for all $n \in N$, no such correspondence exists, the set X is said to be *infinite.*

(3.6)★ *The set N of all natural numbers is an infinite set.*

Let X be a finite set. Then there is a natural number n and a one-to-one correspondence f of the natural numbers m, such that $1 \leq m \leq n$, onto the set X. Let us write $x_1 = f(1)$, $x_2 = f(2)$, $\cdots$, $x_n = f(n)$. Then we may write

$$X = \{x_1, x_2, \cdots, x_n\}.$$

The number n is called the *number of elements* in the set X.* Of course, for a given finite set there may be many choices of the function f. For example, if X is the set consisting of 3, -1, $\sqrt{2}$, when we write $X = \{3, -1, \sqrt{2}\}$ we are selecting the function $f: \{1, 2, 3\} \to X$ such that $f(1) = 3$, $f(2) = -1$, $f(3) = \sqrt{2}$. In other words, $X = \{x_1, x_2, x_3\}$ where $x_1 = 3$, $x_2 = -1$, $x_3 = \sqrt{2}$. When we write $X = \{-1, 3, \sqrt{2}\}$ we are selecting the function g such that $g(1) = -1$, $g(2) = 3$, $g(3) = \sqrt{2}$.

(3.7) Definition. An *n-tuple* is a fixed mapping f from the set of natural numbers m such that $1 \leq m \leq n$, into a set X. We usually write $\langle x_1, \cdots, x_n \rangle$ to denote an n-tuple where $f(1) = x_1, \cdots, f(n) = x_n$. An *ordered pair* is a 2-tuple $\langle x_1, x_2 \rangle$. Two n-tuples, $\langle x_1, \cdots, x_n \rangle$ and $\langle x_1', \cdots, x_n' \rangle$, are said to be *equal* if and only if $x_1 = x_1', \cdots, x_n = x_n'$. A *sequence* is a fixed mapping from the set of all natural numbers into a set X. We denote a sequence by $\{x_1, x_2, \cdots\}$. Note that functions defining n-tuples or sequences are not assumed to be one-to-one. For example, $\langle 0, 0, 0 \rangle$ is a 3-tuple which maps $\{1, 2, 3\}$ onto the single real number zero.

As a first application of mathematical induction, we prove the following statement.

(3.8) *If m and n $\in$ N, then m + n $\in$ N and mn $\in$ N.*

Proof. For the first statement, let us take as an induction hypothesis the statement

$$E(n): \quad \text{For a fixed } m \in N, \quad m + n \in N.$$

Then $E(1)$ is true by definition of N. Suppose $E(n)$ is true. Then

$$m + (n + 1) = (m + n) + 1 \in N$$

---

* It can be proved that n is uniquely determined; that is, it is impossible to set up a one-to-one correspondence between the sets $X = \{1, 2, \cdots, n\}$ and $Y = \{1, 2, \cdots, q\}$ unless $n = q$.

by the associative law for addition and by the induction hypothesis $E(n)$. This proves that $E(n)$ implies $E(n + 1)$, and the first result is established. The second is proved in a similar way.

As another illustration of the use of the principle of mathematical induction, we prove one or two facts about exponents.

Let a be a real number, and define

$$a = a^1, \qquad a^2 = (a^1)a, \qquad a^3 = a^2 a$$

and, in general, $a^{n+1} = a^n \cdot a$ for all natural numbers n. Then by mathematical induction a^n is defined for all positive integers n. Next we may prove

(3.9) $a^m a^n = a^{m+n}$ for all $m,\ n \in N$.

Proof.   The result is true for $n = 1$ by definition. As an induction hypothesis we take:

$$E(n): \quad \text{For fixed } m \in N, \qquad a^m a^n = a^{m+n}.$$

We have already said that $E(1)$ is true. Suppose $E(n)$ is true, and consider $E(n + 1)$. The associative law together with $E(n)$ gives us

$$a^m a^{n+1} = a^m(a^n \cdot a) = (a^m a^n)a$$
$$= a^{m+n} \cdot a = a^{m+n+1}$$

which is $E(n + 1)$. By (3.4) we conclude that $E(n)$ is true for all n, and (3.9) is proved.

(3.10)★ $(a^m)^n = a^{mn}$ for all m and $n \in N$.

(3.11)★ $(ab)^n = a^n b^n$ for all a and $b \in R$, and $n \in N$.

Another important fact concerning the natural numbers, the Well-Ordering Principle, is presented in Section 16, and is used in the discussion of unique factorization.

We conclude this section with the definitions of some other important subsets of the real numbers: the *integers* and the *rational numbers*.

(3.12)   Definition.   The *system of integers* Z is the union

$$N \cup \{0\} \cup N^-$$

where N^- is the set of all real numbers $-n$, where $n \in N$.

(3.13)★   *If a and $b \in Z$, then $a \pm b$, $ab \in Z$.*

(3.14)★ *There is no integer x such that $2x = 1$.*

Finally we come to the system of rational numbers.

(3.15) Definition. The system of *rational numbers* Q is the subset of the real numbers consisting of all real numbers a/b where a and $b \in Z$ and $b \neq 0$.

(3.16)★ *If q and $r \in Q$, so are $q \pm r$, qr, and q/r, where $r \neq 0$.*

(3.17)★ *If q and $r \in Q$, $q \neq 0$, then the equation $qx = r$ has a unique solution in Q.*

From (3.16) it follows that the system Q satisfies all the algebra axioms; in other words, Q is itself a field with respect to the operations of addition and multiplication defined in the real numbers R of which Q is a subset. We may express this fact by the assertion that Q is a *subfield* of R.

(3.18)★ *The field of rational numbers is the smallest subfield of the real numbers; that is, if F is any subfield of R, then $Q \subset F$.*

Note also that Q inherits the order axioms because $Q \subset R$. Therefore Q is an ordered field. We remark finally that there do exist real numbers which do not belong to the field of rational numbers. Perhaps the simplest way to prove this is to establish the following two results.

(3.19) *There exists no rational number x such that $x^2 = 2$.*

(3.20) *There does exist a real number r such that $r^2 = 2$.*

For a complete and painstaking discussion of the real number system the reader may consult Landau's book, listed in the bibliography. Later in the book we shall need the fact (which can be proved by a fairly straightforward application of the completeness axiom) that every real number $a > 0$ has a unique positive square root $\sqrt{a}$.

EXERCISES

1. How many distinct subsets are there in the set $\{1, 2, 3, 4, 5\}$? Can you give a formula for the number of subsets of $\{1, 2, \cdots, n\}$?

2. How many distinct mappings are there of the set $\{1, 2, 3\}$ into itself? How many one-to-one mappings are there? How many n-tuples $\langle x_1, \cdots, x_n \rangle$ are there such that $x_i \in \{1, 2, 3\}$ for all i?

3. Let X be a set and let F be the set of all mappings of X into X. If f and $g \in F$, define $fg \in F$ by the rule

$$(fg)(x) = f[g(x)], \qquad x \in X.$$

Define the mapping $i \in F$ by the rule

$$i(x) = x, \qquad x \in X.$$

Prove that the mappings in F satisfy the associative law

$$f(gh) = (fg)h, \qquad f, g, h \in F,$$

and that

$$fi = if = f, \qquad f \in F.$$

Do the elements of F satisfy the commutative law $fg = gf$?

4. Let X be a set, and let f be a mapping of X into X. Prove that f is onto if there exists a mapping g of X into X such that $fg = i$.

5. Prove that a mapping f of X into X is one-to-one if there exists a mapping h such that $hf = i$.

6. Prove that there exists no natural number x such that $1 < x < 2$.

7. Use the completeness axiom to prove that if r is any positive real number, then there exists a natural number n such that $n > r$. (This property of the real numbers is usually called the *Archimedean order property* of R.)

CHAPTER 2

VECTORS, MATRICES,
and LINEAR EQUATIONS

4. INTRODUCTORY REMARKS ON
ANALYTIC GEOMETRY*

The system of real numbers R defined in Chapter 1 can be interpreted geometrically as the set of points on a line. With this idea as a starting point, it is possible to develop the analytic geometry of two, three, and more dimensions. Analytic geometry differs from synthetic or Euclidean geometry studied in high school in the following fundamental way. Both are concerned with the properties of points, lines, planes, and other figures, but rather than taking points, lines, and planes as undefined objects and assuming certain axioms concerning them, as in Euclidean geometry, the approach in analytic geometry is to define them in terms of the real number system and then prove the statements that appear as axioms in Euclidean geometry. Thus analytic geometry appears as a model of Euclidean geometry. It

---

* This section is optional.

shows that there does exist a set of points, lines, and planes that actually do satisfy the axioms of Euclidean geometry. To put it still another way, in analytic geometry we replace the axioms of Euclidean geometry with the axioms concerning the real numbers.

We shall use analytic geometry in this chapter as a motivation for the results we shall give on vectors, matrices, and linear equations. As we shall see in Chapter 5, all the results on vectors can be treated from a more abstract point of view, and can have applications to problems quite different from those arising from geometrical considerations. Nevertheless, Descartes' discovery that the theorems of elementary geometry are equivalent to the theory of systems of linear equations is of sufficient importance, in view of the current interest in algebraic geometry, to justify the concrete approach to vectors given in this chapter.

Let us begin with the simplest case. A *point* in two dimensions is defined as an ordered pair, or 2-tuple, of real numbers:

$$p = (\alpha_1, \alpha_2).$$

The real numbers α_1, α_2 are called the *coordinates* of p; two points are the same if and only if they have equal coordinates. A *line* L is defined as the set of all points $p = (\alpha_1, \alpha_2)$ which satisfy an equation

$$L: Ax_1 + Bx_2 + C = 0$$

where A, B, C are fixed real numbers, not all zero. A point $p = (\alpha, \beta)$ lies on the line L whenever

$$A\alpha + B\beta + C = 0.$$

Now let us examine the algebraic meaning of a familiar axiom from Euclidean geometry.

(4.1) *Two distinct points lie on one and only one line.*

This result involves two different algebraic problems. First let $p = (\alpha_1, \alpha_2)$ and $q = (\beta_1, \beta_2)$ be two points. The problem of the existence of a line containing the points p and q is equivalent to the problem of whether there exist real numbers A, B, C, not all zero, such that

(4.2)
$$A\alpha_1 + B\alpha_2 + C = 0$$
$$A\beta_1 + B\beta_2 + C = 0.$$

This is a system of two equations in three unknowns A, B, C, and we are asking for a solution $\{A, B, C\}$ such that at least one of the numbers A, B, C is different from zero.

The system of equations (4.2) can be written more compactly if we define operations on pairs of real numbers, or 2-*vectors*, $\begin{pmatrix} \alpha \\ \beta \end{pmatrix}$, as follows:

$$\begin{pmatrix} \alpha \\ \beta \end{pmatrix} + \begin{pmatrix} \gamma \\ \delta \end{pmatrix} = \begin{pmatrix} \alpha + \gamma \\ \beta + \delta \end{pmatrix}, \qquad \alpha \begin{pmatrix} \beta \\ \gamma \end{pmatrix} = \begin{pmatrix} \alpha\beta \\ \alpha\gamma \end{pmatrix}$$

where $\alpha, \beta, \gamma, \delta$ are real numbers. Then (4.1) asks whether there exist numbers A, B, C, not all zero, such that

(4.3) $$A \begin{pmatrix} \alpha_1 \\ \beta_1 \end{pmatrix} + B \begin{pmatrix} \alpha_2 \\ \beta_2 \end{pmatrix} + C \begin{pmatrix} 1 \\ 1 \end{pmatrix} = \begin{pmatrix} 0 \\ 0 \end{pmatrix}.$$

The second problem raised in (4.1) is that of the uniqueness of the line containing p and q. We have first of all the result:

(4.4) *Two lines,* $Ax_1 + Bx_2 + C = 0$ *and* $A'x_1 + B'x_2 + C' = 0$, *coincide if there exists a real number* $\alpha \neq 0$ *such that* $A = \alpha A'$, $B = \alpha B'$, $C = \alpha C'$.

To prove (4.4), let (α_1, α_2) be a point such that $A'\alpha_1 + B'\alpha_2 + C' = 0$. Then $\alpha A'\alpha_1 + \alpha B'\alpha_2 + \alpha C' = 0$, and hence $A\alpha_1 + B\alpha_2 + C = 0$. On the other hand, if (α_1, α_2) satisfies the latter equation, we obtain $A'\alpha_1 + B'\alpha_2 + C' = 0$ upon multiplying by α^{-1}.

The uniqueness assertion of (4.2) is exactly the statement:

(4.5) *If* $\begin{pmatrix} \alpha_1 \\ \beta_1 \end{pmatrix}$, $\begin{pmatrix} \alpha_2 \\ \beta_2 \end{pmatrix}$ *are 2-vectors such that either* $\alpha_1 \neq \beta_1$ *or* $\alpha_2 \neq \beta_2$, *and if* A, B, C *and* A', B', C' *are two sets of numbers, not all zero, such that*

$$A \begin{pmatrix} \alpha_1 \\ \beta_1 \end{pmatrix} + B \begin{pmatrix} \alpha_2 \\ \beta_2 \end{pmatrix} + C \begin{pmatrix} 1 \\ 1 \end{pmatrix} = 0,$$

$$A' \begin{pmatrix} \alpha_1 \\ \beta_1 \end{pmatrix} + B' \begin{pmatrix} \alpha_2 \\ \beta_2 \end{pmatrix} + C' \begin{pmatrix} 1 \\ 1 \end{pmatrix} = 0,$$

then there exists a real number $\alpha \neq 0$ *such that*
$$A = \alpha A', \qquad B = \alpha B', \qquad C = \alpha C'.$$

A chief purpose of this chapter is to develop both efficient methods of treating these results and their generalizations to higher dimensions. The other propositions of Euclidean geometry can also be translated into algebraic theorems. Some of this is done in the exercises.

EXERCISES

1. Find the equations $Ax_1 + Bx_2 + C = 0$ of the lines passing through the following pairs of points:

   a. $(1, 2)$, $(-1, 3)$.
   b. $(-1, 0)$, $(1, 4)$.

2. Prove that the two equations

$$A\alpha_1 + B\alpha_2 + C\alpha_3 = 0$$
$$A\beta_1 + B\beta_2 + C\beta_3 = 0$$

   always have a solution $\{A, B, C\}$ such that at least one of the numbers A, B, or C is different from 0.

3. Is the converse* of (4.4) valid?

4. Prove that the lines

$$Ax_1 + Bx_2 + C = 0, \qquad A'x_1 + B'x_2 + C' = 0$$

   have a unique common point if and only if $AB' - BA' \neq 0$.

5. Define the lines

$$L: Ax_1 + Bx_2 + C = 0, \qquad L': A'x_1 + B'x_2 + C' = 0$$

   as *parallel* if $L \cap L'$ is empty. Prove that $AB' - BA' = 0$ if and only if either $L = L'$ or L and L' are parallel. (*Hint:* Use Exercise 3.)

6. Prove that two distinct lines are either parallel or have a unique common point.

7. Prove that if p is a point not on the line

$$L: Ax_1 + Bx_2 + C = 0$$

   then there exists a line L' containing p and parallel to L.

8. Prove that two lines with at least one common point, which are both parallel to a third line, are identical.

---

* The statement (4.4) has the logical form "p implies q" or, what is the same thing, "if p then q" where p and q are certain statements. Actually, (4.4) is expressed in the form "q if p," where q is the statement "two lines $Ax_1 + Bx_2 + C = 0$ and $A'x_1 + B'x_2 + C' = 0$ coincide," and p is the statement that "there exists a real number α such that $A = \alpha A'$, $B = \alpha B'$, $C = \alpha C'$." The *converse* of the statement "if p then q" is the statement "if q then p." If both the statement "if p then q" and its converse are true, then p is said to be *equivalent* to q. In this case we sometimes say "p if and only if q," the statement "p if q" being one assertion and "p only if q" its converse.

5. THE VECTOR SPACE R_n

In the last section we saw that for certain algebraic problems it is desirable to study pairs and triples of real numbers with certain operations defined on them. These ideas lead to the following general definitions. To help keep the notation clear, we shall denote points and vectors with Roman letters and real numbers with Greek letters.

(5.1) Definition. The *vector space* R_n over the field of real numbers R is the algebraic system consisting of all n-tuples $a = \langle \alpha_1, \cdots, \alpha_n \rangle$ with $\alpha_i \in R$, together with the operations of addition and multiplication of n-tuples by real numbers, to be defined presently. The n-tuples $a \in R_n$ are called *vectors* and the real numbers α_i are called the *components* of the vector $a = \langle \alpha_1, \cdots, \alpha_n \rangle$. Two vectors $a = \langle \alpha_1, \cdots, \alpha_n \rangle$ and $b = \langle \beta_1, \cdots, \beta_n \rangle$ are said to be equal, and we write $a = b$ if $\alpha_i = \beta_i$, $i = 1, \cdots, n$. The *sum* $a + b$ of the vectors $a = \langle \alpha_1, \cdots, \alpha_n \rangle$ and $b = \langle \beta_1, \cdots, \beta_n \rangle$ is defined by

$$a + b = \langle \alpha_1 + \beta_1, \cdots, \alpha_n + \beta_n \rangle.$$

The product of the vector a by the real number λ is defined by

$$a = \langle \lambda \alpha_1, \cdots, \lambda \alpha_n \rangle.$$

REMARKS ON THE DEFINITIONS. In elementary physics, for example, vectors are defined as directed line segments, and the operations of addition and multiplication by real numbers are defined geometrically. We briefly interrupt our discussion of the algebraic properties of R_n to show that our definition of the vector space R_n is consistent with the interpretation of vectors used in physics. We shall not make use of this interpretation in this book. The proofs of theorems about the vector space R_n are based on the algebraic properties of the real numbers and do not rest on any results from geometry. Nevertheless, the geometrical way of thinking can often suggest the correct procedure in a purely algebraic problem.

We shall restrict ourselves to vectors in R_3. A vector $a = \langle \alpha_1, \alpha_2, \alpha_3 \rangle$ in R_3 is represented geometrically by the directed line segment $\overrightarrow{op}$ in three-dimensional space from the origin o to the point p with coordinates $\alpha_1, \alpha_2, \alpha_3$. Thus a vector is determined by a length and a direction. In order not to make the definition of a vector depend on the particular choice of the coordinate system in three-dimensional space, it is customary to identify $\overrightarrow{op}$ with all other directed line segments $\overrightarrow{qr}$ such that under a translation of axes which carries the origin into the point q, the point p is carried into the point r. For example, we have $\overrightarrow{op} = \overrightarrow{qr}$, where o is the origin, $p = (3, 1, -2)$, $q = (1, -1, 2)$ and $r = (4, 0, 0)$.

Now let the vectors $a = \langle \alpha_1, \alpha_2, \alpha_3 \rangle$ and $b = \langle \beta_1, \beta_2, \beta_3 \rangle$ in R_3 be represented by $\overrightarrow{op}$ and $\overrightarrow{oq}$ respectively, where o is the origin. If we add $\overrightarrow{op}$ and $\overrightarrow{oq}$, using the parallelogram law (see the accompanying figure), then it can be shown by a geometrical argument that the

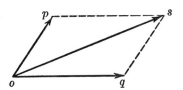

resulting directed line segment $\overrightarrow{os}$ represents the vector $a + b = \langle \alpha_1 + \beta_1, \alpha_2 + \beta_2, \alpha_3 + \beta_3 \rangle$.

Now let λ be a positive real number, and let $a = \langle \alpha_1, \alpha_2, \alpha_3 \rangle$ be represented by the directed line segment $\overrightarrow{op}$, with o the origin and p the point $(\alpha_1, \alpha_2, \alpha_3)$. Let r be the point with coordinates $(\lambda\alpha_1, \lambda\alpha_2, \lambda\alpha_3)$. Then $\overrightarrow{or}$ represents the vector λa. Geometrically r can be located on the ray from o, passing through p, and is such that the distance from the origin to r is λ times the distance from the origin to p. We leave as an exercise the geometrical interpretation of λa, where $a \in R_3$, and λ is a negative real number.

We return now to the algebraic properties of the vector space R_n.

(5.2) **Algebraic Properties of R_n.** *The properties of addition and multiplication in the vector space R_n are:*

$$a + (b + c) = (a + b) + c,$$
$$a + b = b + a, \text{ for all } a, b \in R_n.$$

There is a vector* $0 = \langle 0, \cdots, 0 \rangle$ such that

$$a + 0 = a \quad \text{for all } a \in R_n.$$

---

* For simplicity we use the same notation for the zero vector and the real number zero. The meaning of "0" will always be clear from the context.

For each vector $a = \langle \alpha_1, \cdots, \alpha_n \rangle$ *in* R_n, *there is a vector* $-a = \langle -\alpha_1, \cdots, -\alpha_n \rangle$ *such that*

$$a + (-a) = 0.$$

For all real numbers λ, μ, *etc., and* a *and* $b \in R_n$, *we have*

$$(\lambda + \mu)a = \lambda a + \mu a$$
$$\lambda(a + b) = \lambda a + \lambda b$$
$$\lambda(\mu a) = (\lambda\mu)a$$
$$1a = a.$$

The proofs are all immediate from the properties of the real numbers given in Chapter 1. Note also that these properties are sufficiently close to the axioms for a field given in Chapter 1 such that with care many of the consequences of the axioms for a field can be carried over to vectors in R_n.

There are some consequences of (5.2) which will be needed in the next section. The associative law states that, for a_1, a_2, a_3 in R_n,

$$(a_1 + a_2) + a_3 = a_1 + (a_2 + a_3).$$

If we have four vectors a_1, a_2, a_3, a_4, there are the following possible sums we can form:

$$a_1 + [a_2 + (a_3 + a_4)],$$
$$a_1 + [(a_2 + a_3) + a_4],$$
$$[a_1 + (a_2 + a_3)] + a_4,$$
$$[(a_1 + a_2) + a_3] + a_4.$$

The reader may check that all these expressions represent the same vector. More generally, it can be proved by mathematical induction that all possible ways of adding n vectors $a_1, \cdots, a_n$ together to form a single sum yield a uniquely determined vector which we shall denote by

$$a_1 + \cdots + a_n = \sum_{i=1}^{n} a_i.$$

The commutative law together with this "generalized associative law" imply by a further application of mathematical induction that

$$(a_1 + \cdots + a_n) + (b_1 + \cdots + b_n) = (a_1 + b_1) + \cdots + (a_n + b_n)$$

or, more briefly,

(5.3)
$$\sum_{i=1}^{n} a_i + \sum_{i=1}^{n} b_i = \sum_{i=1}^{n} (a_i + b_i).$$

The other rules can also be generalized to sums of more than two vectors:

$$\left(\sum_{i=1}^{n} \lambda_i\right) a = \sum_{i=1}^{n} \lambda_i a,$$

$$\lambda\left(\sum_{i=1}^{n} a_i\right) = \sum_{i=1}^{n} \lambda a_i,$$

We have also by (5.3):

$$\left(\sum_{i=1}^{n} \lambda_i a_i\right) + \left(\sum_{i=1}^{n} \mu_i a_i\right) = \sum_{i=1}^{n} (\lambda_i + \mu_i) a_i.$$

The main point is that these rules do require proof from the basic rules (5.2), and the reader will find it an interesting exercise in the use of mathematical induction to supply, for example, a proof of (5.3).

EXERCISES

1. Let a and b be vectors in R_n. Prove that there exists a unique vector x such that $a + x = b$. The vector x is called $b - a$. What are the components of x in terms of the components of a and b? If p and q are vectors in R_n, define the vector $\overrightarrow{pq}$ in R_n to be the vector $q - p$. What is the geometrical interpretation of $\overrightarrow{pq}$ in R_3? Show that, if $a = \overrightarrow{pq}$ and $b = \overrightarrow{pr}$, then $\overrightarrow{qr} = \overrightarrow{pr} - \overrightarrow{pq}$ (see Figure 2.1).

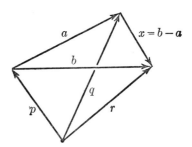

Figure 2.1

2. Let $p = \langle \alpha_1, \cdots, \alpha_n \rangle$, $q = \langle \beta_1, \cdots, \beta_n \rangle$ be two distinct vectors in R_n. Define the *line* $L(p, q)$ containing p and q as the set of all vectors $r = \langle \gamma_1, \cdots, \gamma_n \rangle$ such that for some real number λ, $\overrightarrow{pr} = \lambda \overrightarrow{pq}$ or $r = p + \lambda(q - p)$ (see Figure 2.2).

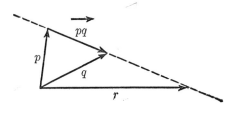

Figure 2.2

a. Show that $r = \langle \gamma_1, \cdots, \gamma_n \rangle$ lies on the line $L(p, q)$ if and only if there exists a fixed real number λ such that

$$\gamma_i = \lambda \beta_i + (1 - \lambda)\alpha_i, \qquad i = 1, 2, \cdots, n.$$

b. Prove that if p' and q' are distinct vectors on the line $L(p, q)$ then the line $L(p', q')$ coincides with the line $L(p, q)$.

c. Determine whether or not the lines $L(p, q)$ and $L(p', q')$ intersect, where

$$\begin{aligned} p &= \langle 3, 0, 2, 0 \rangle, & q &= \langle 3, 2, 2, 2 \rangle \\ p' &= \langle -1, 0, 4, 1 \rangle, & q' &= \langle 11, 3, -2, 1 \rangle. \end{aligned}$$

d. Determine whether or not the vectors

$$\langle -1, 0, 4, 1 \rangle, \qquad \langle 3, 1, 2, 1 \rangle, \qquad \langle 7, 2, 0, 1 \rangle$$

lie on a line $L(p, q)$ for some choice of p and q.

3. Let $p = \langle \alpha_1, \cdots, \alpha_n \rangle$ and $q = \langle \beta_1, \cdots, \beta_n \rangle$ be vectors in R_n. Define the *line segment* $\overline{pq}$ with *endpoints* p and q as the set of all vectors r such that for some real number λ, with $0 \le \lambda \le 1$, we have

$$\overrightarrow{pr} = \lambda \overrightarrow{pq}.$$

Prove that $r = \langle \gamma_1, \cdots, \gamma_n \rangle$ belongs to the line segment $\overline{pq}$ if and only if there exists a real number λ, where $0 \le \lambda \le 1$, such that

$$\gamma_i = \lambda \beta_i + (1 - \lambda)\alpha_i, \qquad 1 \le i \le n.$$

(See Exercise 3 of Section 2 for the motivation in one dimension.)

4. Define a *convex set* in n dimensions as a set of vectors S in R_n with the property that, whenever two vectors p and $q \in S$, then the line segment $\overline{pq} \subset S$. Prove that every line segment is a convex set.

5. Which of the following sets in R_2 are convex? Describe each set geometrically.

   a. All vectors $p = \langle \alpha, \beta \rangle$ such that $|\alpha| + |\beta| \leq 1$.
   b. All vectors $p = \langle \alpha, \beta \rangle$ such that $|\alpha| + |\beta| = 1$.
   c. All vectors $p = \langle \alpha, \beta \rangle$ such that $\alpha^2 + \beta^2 < 1$.

6. A line* L in R_2 has an equation of the form

$$Ax_1 + Bx_2 + C = 0$$

where A, B, C are real numbers, not all zero. Prove that the set of vectors not on L fall into exactly two nonoverlapping convex sets, namely the vectors $\langle \alpha_1, \alpha_2 \rangle$ such that

$$A\alpha_1 + B\alpha_2 + C > 0$$

and the vectors for which

$$A\alpha_1 + B\alpha_2 + C < 0.$$

We call these sets the *half-planes* determined by the line L.

7. Prove that the intersection of two or more convex sets is a convex set.

8. Given three noncollinear† vectors, p, q, r in the plane, the *interior of the triangle pqr* is defined the set of all points common to the following three half-planes: the half-plane determined by $L(p, q)$ containing r, the half-plane determined by $L(q, r)$ containing p, and the half-plane determined by $L(r, p)$ containing q. Prove that the interior of a triangle is a convex set.

9. Let $p_1 = \langle \alpha_{11}, \cdots, \alpha_{1n} \rangle$, $\cdots$, $p_k = \langle \alpha_{k1}, \cdots, \alpha_{kn} \rangle$ be vectors in R_n. Prove that there exists a unique smallest convex set containing $p_1, \cdots, p_k$ which consists of the vectors $x = \langle \xi_1, \cdots, \xi_n \rangle$ such that, for some fixed real numbers $\mu_1, \cdots, \mu_k$ where $\mu_i \geq 0$, $\mu_1 + \cdots + \mu_k = 1$,

$$\xi_i = \mu_1 \alpha_{1i} + \mu_2 \alpha_{2i} + \cdots + \mu_k \alpha_{ki}, \qquad i = 1, 2, \cdots, n.$$

---

* In Section 10 the equivalence of this definition of line in R_2 with the definition in Exercise 2 will be established.

† The vectors p, q, r, $\cdots$, are said to be *collinear* if they all lie on some line.

6. LINEAR DEPENDENCE

Most questions concerning vectors in R_2 or R_3 can be answered by drawing an appropriate diagram, and it is important for the reader to learn to do this. However, pictures of configurations of points and lines and vectors in R_n are less convincing, although still useful. In Sections 6 and 7 we give some basic theorems concerning the vector space R_n. These theorems include all the algebraic results we shall need in studying systems of linear equations and matrices.

These sections will also give the reader an insight into the ways of higher mathematics. We shall give some fundamental and rather complicated definitions (of linear dependence, subspaces, etc.), and prove one theorem concerning them (the Steinitz replacement theorem). This theorem is hard to understand at first, but the effort is worth while because from it follow all of the deeper properties of vectors we require. The reader should not assume that this "master theorem" on vectors was the first result on vectors to be discovered. The ideas in this chapter were familiar to mathematicians all through the nineteenth century, but it was only in the first years of this century that the following efficient and economical way of presenting the subject was found.

For the work of this section the reader will need to know only the definition of the vector space R_n given in (5.1), the properties of addition and multiplication in R_n given in (5.2), and the concept of general sums of vectors $\sum a_i$ discussed at the end of Section 5.

(6.1) Definition. Let $\{a_1, \cdots, a_m\}$ be an arbitrary finite set of vectors in R_n. The set of vectors $\{a_1, \cdots, a_m\}$ is said to be *linearly dependent* if there exist real numbers $\lambda_1, \cdots, \lambda_m$, not all zero, such that

$$\lambda_1 a_1 + \lambda_2 a_2 + \cdots + \lambda_m a_m = 0.$$

Such a formula will be called a *relation of linear dependence*. A set of vectors which is not linearly dependent is said to be *linearly independent*. Thus, the set $\{a_1, \cdots, a_m\}$ is linearly independent if and only if

$$\lambda_1 a_1 + \cdots + \lambda_m a_m = 0$$

where the λ_i are real numbers, implies that $\lambda_1 = \cdots = \lambda_m = 0$.

Before proceeding, let us look at a few simple cases of linear dependence.

First of all, the set consisting of the zero vector $\{0\}$ in R_n always forms a linearly dependent set, since for any $\lambda \neq 0$ in R we have

$$\lambda 0 = 0.$$

But if $a \neq 0$ in R_n then the set $\{a\}$ alone is a linearly independent set. To see this, we have to prove that if

$$\lambda a = 0, \qquad \lambda \in R,$$

then $\lambda = 0$. This statement is equivalent to proving that if the conclusion ($\lambda = 0$) is false then the hypothesis ($\lambda a = 0$, $a \neq 0$) is false also. If $\lambda \neq 0$, then by axiom (A-5) of the real numbers there is a real number λ^{-1} such that $\lambda^{-1}\lambda = 1$. Since $\lambda a = 0$, we obtain

$$\lambda^{-1}(\lambda a) = \lambda^{-1}0 = 0$$

and by the "associative law" for multiplication of vectors by real numbers we have

$$\lambda^{-1}(\lambda a) = (\lambda^{-1}\lambda)a = 0.$$

However, $\lambda^{-1}\lambda = 1$, and hence we have shown that $\lambda a = 0$, where $\lambda \neq 0$, implies $1 \cdot a = a = 0$, contrary to the hypothesis that $a \neq 0$. (The reader will be spared most of these agonizing details in the future, but it does no harm to see what goes into even such a simple statement as the one we have just established.)

Now let $\{a, b\}$ be a set consisting of two vectors in R_n. We shall prove:

(6.2) $\{a, b\}$ *is a linearly dependent set if and only if* $a = \lambda b$ *or* $b = \lambda'a$ *for some* λ *or* λ' *in* R.

Proof.   First suppose $a = \lambda b$, $\lambda \in R$. Then we have

$$a + [-(\lambda b)] = 0.$$

From the properties of the real numbers or from the properties of R_n given in (5.2) it follows that

$$-(\lambda b) = (-\lambda)b$$

and we have

$$1 \cdot a + (-\lambda)b = 0.$$

Since $1 \neq 0$, we have proved that $\{a, b\}$ is a linearly dependent set. Similarly, $b = \lambda'a$ implies that $\{a, b\}$ is a linearly dependent set.

Now suppose that

(6.3) $\alpha a + \beta b = 0, \qquad \alpha, \beta \in R$

where either α or $\beta \neq 0$. If $\alpha \neq 0$, then we have

$$\alpha a = (-\beta)b$$

and

$$a = \alpha^{-1}(\alpha a) = \alpha^{-1}(-\beta)b = (-\alpha^{-1}\beta)b,$$

as we wish to prove. If, on the other hand, $\alpha = 0$ and $\beta \neq 0$, the equation (6.3) becomes $\beta b = 0$, and hence $b = 0$. In that case we have $b = \lambda'a$ for $\lambda' = 0$, and (6.2) is completely proved.

Part of the reason for introducing the concept of linear dependence is that it is the tool needed to discuss clearly the algebraic problems of Section 4. Thus (4.3) is exactly the statement that the three vectors in R_2 are linearly dependent; (4.5) is the assertion that the two vectors $\langle A, B, C \rangle$ and $\langle A', B', C' \rangle$ in R_3 are linearly dependent.

Now we give a few more consequences of the definitions. The first is left as an exercise.

(6.4)★ *The empty set is a linearly independent set.* Any subset of a linearly independent set is linearly independent. Any finite set of vectors containing a linearly dependent set of vectors as a subset is itself linearly dependent.*

(6.5) Definition. Let $\{a_1, \cdots, a_m\}$ be a set of vectors in R_n. A vector $a \in R_n$ is said to be a *linear combination* of $a_1, \cdots, a_m$ if a can be expressed, for some real numbers $\lambda_1, \cdots, \lambda_m$, in the form

$$a = \lambda_1 a_1 + \cdots + \lambda_m a_m.$$

This concept can be used to restate the definition of linear independence. Thus, a set of vectors $\{a_1, \cdots, a_m\}$ is linearly independent if the only linear combination of $a_1, \cdots, a_m$ which is equal to 0 is $0a_1 + \cdots + 0a_m$.

The next theorem is an important generalization of (6.2).

(6.6) Theorem. *A set of vectors $\{a_1, \cdots, a_m\}$ is linearly dependent if and only if there is some a_i, for $1 \leq i \leq m$, that is a linear combination of the remaining vectors a_j, $j \neq i$.*

Proof. First suppose that $\{a_1, \cdots, a_m\}$ is a linearly dependent set. Then for some real numbers $\lambda_1, \cdots, \lambda_m$, not all zero, we have

(6.7) $$\lambda_1 a_1 + \cdots + \lambda_m a_m = 0.$$

---

* This fact is sometimes useful in that it permits results to be stated in a general form without one's having to make exceptions.

By reindexing the a_i's, if necessary, we may assume that $\lambda_1 \neq 0$. Then λ_1^{-1} exists, and we obtain from (6.7)

$$a_1 = \lambda_1^{-1}(\lambda_1 a_1) = \lambda_1^{-1}[(-\lambda_2)a_2 + \cdots + (-\lambda_m)a_m]$$
$$= [\lambda_1^{-1}(-\lambda_2)]a_2 + \cdots + [\lambda_1^{-1}(-\lambda_m)]a_m$$

as we wished to prove. Conversely, if a_1 is a linear combination of $\{a_2, \cdots, a_m\}$, then

$$a_1 = \mu_2 a_2 + \cdots + \mu_m a_m$$

for some real numbers μ_i. Then we have

$$(-1)a_1 + \mu_2 a_2 + \cdots + \mu_m a_m = 0$$

and, since $-1 \neq 0$, the set $\{a_1, \cdots, a_m\}$ is linearly dependent. The same argument applies if any other a_i is a linear combination of the remaining ones.

A sharper version of (6.6) is the following useful result.

(6.8) Lemma. *If $\{a_1, \cdots, a_m\}$ is linearly dependent and if $\{a_1, \cdots, a_{m-1}\}$ is linearly independent, then a_m is a linear combination of $a_1, \cdots, a_{m-1}$.*

Proof. By the hypothesis, we have

$$\lambda_1 a_1 + \cdots + \lambda_m a_m = 0$$

where some $\lambda_i \neq 0$. If $\lambda_m = 0$, then some $\lambda_i \neq 0$ for $1 \leq i \leq m - 1$, and the equation of linear dependence becomes

$$\lambda_1 a_1 + \cdots + \lambda_{m-1} a_{m-1} = 0,$$

contrary to the assumption that $\{a_1, \cdots, a_{m-1}\}$ is linearly independent. Therefore $\lambda_m \neq 0$, and we have

$$a_m = \lambda_m^{-1}[(-\lambda_1)a_1 + \cdots + (-\lambda_{m-1})a_{m-1}]$$
$$= \sum_{i=1}^{m-1} (-\lambda_m^{-1}\lambda_i)a_i$$

as we wished to prove.

Finally, we define the important notion of a subspace of R_n.

(6.9) Definition. A *subspace* S of the vector space R_n is a nonempty set of vectors in R_n such that:

(1) If a and b are in S, then $a + b \in S$.
(2) If $a \in S$ and $\lambda \in R$, then $a\lambda \in S$.

REMARKS.   Clearly, the whole space R_n and the set consisting of the zero vector alone $\{0\}$ are examples of subspaces.

Note that if S is a subspace and if $a \in S$, then $-a = (-1)a \in S$. Therefore $a + (-a) \in S$, and we have shown that every subspace contains the zero vector. More generally, we have the following observation.

(6.10)   *If S is a subspace of R_n containing the vectors $a_1, \cdots, a_m$, then every linear combination of $a_1, \cdots, a_m$ belongs to S.*

Proof.   We prove the result by induction on m. If $m = 1$, the result is true by the definition of a subspace. Suppose that any linear combination of $m - 1$ vectors in S belongs to S, and consider a linear combination

$$a = \lambda_1 a_1 + \cdots + \lambda_m a_m$$

of m vectors belonging to S. Letting $a' = \lambda_2 a_2 + \cdots + \lambda_m a_m$, we have

$$a = \lambda_1 a_1 + a'$$

where $\lambda_1 a_1 \in S$ and $a' \in S$ by the induction hypothesis. By part 1 of the definition of subspace, $a \in S$, and (6.10) is proved.

The process of forming linear combinations leads to a method of constructing subspaces, as follows.

(6.11)   *Let $\{a_1, \cdots, a_m\}$ be a set of vectors in R_n, for $m \geq 1$; then the set of all linear combinations of the vectors $a_1, \cdots, a_m$ forms a subspace $S = S(a_1, \cdots, a_m)$. S is the smallest subspace containing $a_1, \cdots, a_m$ in the sense that if T is any subspace containing $a_1, \cdots, a_m$ then $S \subset T$.*

Proof.   Let $a = \sum\limits_{i=1}^{m} \lambda_i a_i$ and $b = \sum\limits_{i=1}^{m} \mu_i a_i$. Then

$$a + b = \sum_{i=1}^{m} (\lambda_i + \mu_i) a_i$$

is again a linear combination of $a_1, \cdots, a_m$. If $\lambda \in R$, then

$$\lambda a = \lambda \left(\sum_{i=1}^{m} \lambda_i a_i \right) = \sum_{i=1}^{m} \lambda (\lambda_i a_i) = \sum_{i=1}^{m} (\lambda \lambda_i) a_i.$$

These computations prove that S is a subspace, and the fact that it is the smallest one containing the given vectors is immediate by (6.10).

(6.12) Definition. The subspace $S = S(a_1, \cdots, a_m)$ defined in (6.11) is called a subspace *generated by* (or, sometimes, *spanned by*) $a_1, \cdots, a_m$, and $a_1, \cdots, a_m$ are called *generators* of S.

EXERCISES

1. Test the following sets of vectors to determine whether or not they are linearly independent.

   a. $\langle 1, 1 \rangle$, $\langle 2, 1 \rangle$, $\langle 1, 2 \rangle$. [*Hint:* We have to find whether a relation $\lambda \langle 1, 1 \rangle + \mu \langle 2, 1 \rangle + \nu \langle 1, 2 \rangle = 0$ can hold, where λ, μ, ν are not all zero. This equation is equivalent to the following system of equations:
   $$\lambda + 2\mu + \nu = 0$$
   $$\lambda + \mu + 2\nu = 0.$$

   (Why?) Now we have to try to solve this system of equations for λ, μ, ν not all zero. Note that this is the same problem we encountered in Section 4.]

   b. $\langle 1, 1, 2 \rangle$, $\langle 3, 1, 2 \rangle$, $\langle -1, 0, 0 \rangle$.

   c. $\langle 3, -1, 1 \rangle$, $\langle 4, 1, 0 \rangle$, $\langle -2, -3, -2 \rangle$.

2. Prove that any two vectors in R_1 are linearly dependent.

3. Prove that any three vectors in R_2 are linearly dependent. (See Exercise 2 in Section 4.)

4. Determine which of the following subsets of R_n are subspaces.

   a. All vectors $\langle \alpha_1, \cdots, \alpha_n \rangle$ such that $\alpha_1 = 1$.

   b. All vectors $\langle \alpha_1, \cdots, \alpha_n \rangle$ such that $\alpha_1 = 0$.

   c. All vectors $\langle \alpha_1, \cdots, \alpha_n \rangle$ such that $A\alpha_1 + B\alpha_2 = 0$, for some fixed A, B.

   d. All vectors $\langle \alpha_1, \cdots, \alpha_n \rangle$ such that $A\alpha_1 + B\alpha_2 = 1$.

   e. All vectors $\langle \alpha_1, \cdots, \alpha_n \rangle$ such that $\alpha_1^2 = \alpha_2$.

5. Is the intersection of two subspaces always a subspace? Prove your answer.

6. Is the union of two subspaces always a subspace? Explain.

7. Let a in R_n be a linear combination of vectors $b_1, \cdots, b_r$ in R_n, and let each vector b_i, $1 \leq i \leq r$, be a linear combination of vectors $c_1, \cdots, c_s$. Prove that a is a linear combination of $c_1, \cdots, c_s$.

7. THE CONCEPTS OF BASIS AND DIMENSION

We have seen that in R_2 (in Exercise 3 of Section 6) any three vectors are linearly dependent. Let us see what this gives us to say about the possible subspaces of R_2. These are:

$\{0\}$
$S(a)$, a subspace generated by a single vector a
$S(a_1, a_2)$, a subspace generated by two vectors
$S(a_1, a_2, a_3)$, etc.

In fact, we can prove a much sharper result, namely:

(7.1) *The only subspaces in R_2 are $\{0\}$, $S(a)$ for an arbitrary single vector a, and R_2.*

Proof. First of all consider $S = S(a_1, \cdots, a_m) \neq \{0\}$ where no pair $\{a_i, a_j\}$ of the vectors is linearly independent. Then, in particular, since $S \neq 0$ we may assume that $a_1 \neq 0$. For every $i > 1$ the linear dependence of the set $\{a_1, a_i\}$ implies by (6.2) that $a_i = \lambda_i a_1$ for some $\lambda_i \in R$. Therefore, $S \subset S(a_1)$ and, since $S(a_1) \subset S(a_1, \cdots, a_m)$ by (6.10), we have $S(a_1, \cdots, a_m) = S(a_1)$.

Next consider $S(a_1, \cdots, a_m)$ and suppose that some pair of the vectors, say $\{a_1, a_2\}$, forms a linearly independent set. We shall prove that

$$R_2 \subset S(a_1, a_2).$$

Let $b \in R_2$; then, by Exercise 3 of Section 6, $\{a_1, a_2, b\}$ is a linearly dependent set. By lemma (6.8) we have $b \in S(a_1, a_2)$, and hence $R_2 \subset S(a_1, a_2)$. Finally, since $R_2 \subset S(a_1, a_2) \subset S(a_1, a_2, \cdots, a_m)$ we have

$$S(a_1, a_2, \cdots, a_m) = R_2.$$

By the result of Exercise 3 of Section 6, no more than two vectors among the generators of a subspace $S(a_1, \cdots, a_m)$ can be linearly independent, and (7.1) is proved.

The possible subspaces of R_n for $n > 2$ are more numerous. In this section we determine all subspaces of R_n, basing our work on the following theorem on subspaces, which was proved by the German mathematician Ernst Steinitz in the early part of this century.

Throughout the rest of the section, n will denote a fixed positive integer, and we shall be studying subspaces of R_n.

(7.2) Replacement Theorem. *Let* $S = S(a_1, \cdots, a_m)$ *be a subspace of* R_n *generated by an arbitrary set of vectors* $a_1, \cdots, a_m$. *Suppose that* $\{b_1, \cdots, b_q\}$ *is a linearly independent set of vectors contained in the subspace* S. *Then, first,* $q \leq m$ *and, second, there are* $m - q$ *of the vectors* $a_1, \cdots, a_m$ *which we will denote by* $a_{q+1}, \cdots, a_m$ *such that these vectors together with* $b_1, \cdots, b_q$ *generate* S; *in other words,*

$$S = S(b_1, \cdots, b_q, a_{q+1}, \cdots, a_m).$$

REMARK. The possibility that $q = m$ is not excluded; in such a case it is understood that the set $\{a_{q+1}, \cdots, a_m\}$ is empty, and the conclusion then reads $S = S(b_1, \cdots, b_q)$. Also, it should be clear to the reader why the theorem is called the "replacement theorem": it says that a set of linearly independent vectors in a subspace can always be used to replace some of the generators in a given set of generators of the subspace.

Proof. This theorem will be proved by mathematical induction. Among the several possible positive integers appearing in the statement of the theorem, namely n, m, and q, it will be convenient to make the induction on $q + 1$. In other words, we are to think of m as fixed and to think of q as taking on the values 0, 1, 2, $\cdots$. The theorem is obviously true if $q = 0$ and the set $\{b_1, \cdots, b_q\}$ is empty.* As our induction hypothesis, we assume that the conclusion of the theorem holds for any linearly independent set of $q - 1$ vectors in S, where $q - 1 \geq 0$, and we have to prove that the statement holds when we are given a set of q linearly independent vectors, $\{b_1, \cdots, b_q\}$. Applying the induction hypothesis to the subset $\{b_1, \cdots, b_{q-1}\}$, we obtain $q - 1 \leq m$, and

$$S = S(b_1, \cdots, b_{q-1}, a_q, \cdots, a_m).$$

Now consider b_q. Since $b_q \in S$, we have

(7.3) $b_q = \lambda_1 b_1 + \cdots + \lambda_{q-1} b_{q-1} + \mu_q a_q + \cdots + \mu_m a_m$

for some real numbers $\lambda_1, \cdots, \lambda_{q-1}$ and $\mu_q, \cdots, \mu_m$. At this point we see that $q \leq m$, for if $q > m$ then $q - 1 \geq m$ and, since $q - 1 \leq m$ by the induction hypothesis, we have $q - 1 = m$. Thus if $q > m$ we have $S = S(b_1, \cdots, b_{q-1})$. Then (7.3) becomes $b_q = \lambda_1 b_1 + \cdots + \lambda_{q-1} b_{q-1}$, which contradicts the assumption that $\{b_1, \cdots, b_q\}$ is a linearly independent set.

---

* We have pointed out in (6.4) that the empty set is a linearly independent set.

Returning to (7.3), we prove next that some $\mu_i \neq 0$. Otherwise, $\mu_q = \cdots = \mu_n = 0$, which again contradicts the hypothesis that $b_1, \cdots, b_{q-1}$ are linearly independent. Therefore, some $\mu_i \neq 0$, and by renaming the a_i's, we may assume that $\mu_q \neq 0$. Then we can solve the equation (7.3) for a_q as follows:

(7.4) $a_q = \mu_q^{-1}[(-\lambda_1)b_1 + \cdots + (-\lambda_{q-1})b_{q-1} + b_q + (-\mu_{q+1})a_{q+1} + \cdots + (-\mu_m)a_m]$.

In other words, we have shown that:

(7.5) $a_q \in S(b_1, \cdots, b_{q-1}, b_q, a_{q+1}, \cdots, a_m)$.

Obviously, $b_1, \cdots, b_{q-1}$ and $a_{q+1}, \cdots, a_m \in S(b_1, \cdots, b_q, a_{q+1}, \cdots, a_m)$, and this fact combined with (7.5) and the induction hypothesis yields

$$S = S(b_1, \cdots, b_{q-1}, a_q, \cdots, a_m) \subset S(b_1, \cdots, b_q, a_{q+1}, \cdots, a_m).$$

Since the other inclusion,

$$S(b_1, \cdots, b_q, a_{q+1}, \cdots, a_m) \subset S,$$

is clear, we have

$$S = S(b_1, \cdots, b_q, a_{q+1}, \cdots, a_m),$$

and the theorem is proved.

The replacement theorem has many important consequences, and the rest of this section will be devoted to them.

(7.6) **Theorem.** *Let S be a subspace of R_n generated by m vectors: $S = S(a_1, \cdots, a_m)$; then any set of $m + 1$ vectors in S is linearly dependent.*

Proof. If the result is false, we contradict the first statement ($q \leq m$) of the replacement theorem.

The next result has already been anticipated in some special cases [for example, in Exercise 3 of Section 6, which was used to derive (7.1)].

(7.7) **Corollary.** *Any set of $n + 1$ vectors in R_n is a linearly dependent set.*

Proof. By (7.6), it is sufficient to prove that R_n is generated by some set of n vectors. Let:

(7.8) $e_1 = \langle 1, 0, 0, \cdots, 0 \rangle$, $e_2 = \langle 0, 1, 0, \cdots, 0 \rangle$, $\cdots$, $e_n = \langle 0, \cdots, 0, 1 \rangle$.

The vectors e_i will be called the *unit vectors* in R_n. We prove that:

(7.9) $R_n = S(e_1, \cdots, e_n)$.

Let $a = \langle \alpha_1, \cdots, \alpha_n \rangle \in R_n$. Then we have

$$a = \alpha_1 e_1 + \cdots + \alpha_n e_n$$

by an easy computation, and (7.9) is established. As we have observed, (7.9) and (7.6) imply (7.7).

(7.10)   Definition.   Let S be a subspace of R_n. A *basis* for S is a set of linearly independent vectors, $\{b_1, \cdots, b_m\}$, such that $S = S(b_1, \cdots, b_m)$.

(7.11)   Theorem.   *Every subspace S of R_n has a basis.*

Proof.   If $S = 0$, we agree that the empty set $\varnothing$ spans S, and $\varnothing$ is a basis for S. Now let $S \neq 0$ be a subspace of R_n. Since any set of $n + 1$ vectors in R_n is linearly dependent and since a set consisting of a single nonzero vector is linearly independent, it follows that, for some integer $m \geq 1$, S contains linearly independent vectors $b_1, \cdots, b_m$ such that any set of $m + 1$ vectors in S is linearly dependent. We prove that $\{b_1, \cdots, b_m\}$ is a basis for S, and for this it is sufficient to show, for any vector $b \in S$, that $b \in S(b_1, \cdots, b_m)$. Because of the properties of the set $\{b_1, \cdots, b_m\}$, $\{b_1, \cdots, b_m, b\}$ is a linearly dependent set. Since $\{b_1, \cdots, b_m\}$ is linearly independent, (6.8) implies that $b \in S(b_1, \cdots, b_m)$, and the theorem is proved.

(7.12)   Theorem.   *Any two bases of a subspace S contain the same number of vectors.*

Proof.   The result is obvious if $S = 0$. Let $S \neq 0$ and let $\{b_1, \cdots, b_r\}$ and $\{b_1', \cdots, b_s'\}$ be bases of S. Applying the replacement theorem to $S = S(b_1, \cdots, b_r)$ and the linearly independent set $\{b_1', \cdots, b_s'\}$ in S, we obtain $s \leq r$. Reversing the argument, we have $r \leq s$. Combining our results, we have (7.12).

(7.13)   Definition.   Let S be a subspace of R_n. The uniquely determined number of vectors in a basis for S is called the *dimension* of S (notation, dim S). In particular, the subspace $\{0\}$ has dimension 0.

One more basic result is the following.

(7.14) Theorem.   *If $S = S(a_1, \cdots, a_m)$ is a subspace of R_n, then a basis for S can be selected from among the vectors $a_1, \cdots, a_m$.* (In other words, a set of generators always contains a basis.)

Proof.   The result is clear if $S = 0$. Now let $S \neq 0$. For some index r, where $1 \leq r \leq m$, we may assume, for a suitable ordering of $a_1, \cdots, a_m$, that $\{a_1, \cdots, a_r\}$ is linearly independent and that any larger set of the a_i's is linearly dependent. Then by (6.8) it follows that $a_{r+1}, \cdots, a_m$ all belong to $S(a_1, \cdots, a_r)$. Therefore $S(a_1, \cdots, a_m)$ $= S(a_1, \cdots, a_r)$ and, since $\{a_1, \cdots, a_r\}$ is linearly independent, we conclude that it is a basis of S.

The last of our general theorems on vector spaces is the following result.

(7.15) Theorem.   *Let $\{b_1, \cdots, b_q\}$ be a linearly independent set of vectors in a subspace S of R_n; then there exist other vectors $b_{q+1}, \cdots, b_m$ in S such that $\{b_1, \cdots, b_m\}$ is a basis of S.*

Proof.   By theorem (7.11), S has a basis $\{a_1, \cdots, a_m\}$ where $m = \dim S$. By the replacement theorem we have $q \leq m$, and

(7.16) $$S = S(b_1, \cdots, b_q, a_{q+1}, \cdots, a_m)$$

for suitably chosen vectors $a_{q+1}, \cdots, a_m$ from the original basis. Then $\{b_1, \cdots, b_q, a_{q+1}, \cdots, a_m\}$ is the required basis of S if we can show that these vectors are linearly independent. If, on the contrary, they are linearly dependent, then (7.16) together with theorem (7.14) implies that S has a basis of fewer than m vectors. This is impossible by theorem (7.12). Therefore $\{b_1, \cdots, b_q, a_{q+1}, \cdots, a_m\}$ forms a basis for S, and (7.15) is proved.

The thoughtful reader should not have been so overwhelmed with the relentless sequence of theorems that he failed to notice an important gap in the whole development, namely, that the theorems given so far are purely descriptive in nature and give no computational procedure, or algorithm, for testing sets of vectors for linear dependence or for explicitly finding bases of subspaces with given sets of generators. This gap is filled in the exercises at the end of this section, where we give a computational procedure for testing for linear dependence of sets of vectors which can be used to handle many of the numerical problems in the book.

It is not too much to say that theorems (7.2), (7.6), (7.11), (7.12), (7.14), and (7.15) constitute "what everyone should know about vector spaces" and that with their help virtually any problem concerning bases or dimension in vector spaces can be settled. As an illustration of this last point, we shall conclude the section with an application of these theorems to the interesting problem of determining the dimension of the intersection $S \cap T$ of two subspaces S and T of R_n.

We first consider certain operations on subspaces of R_n that lead to new subspaces. If S, T are subspaces of R_n it follows at once, from the definition, that $S \cup T$ is not always a subspace, as the following example in R_2 shows (see Exercise 6 of Section 6):

$$S = \{\langle 0, \beta \rangle, \quad \beta \in R\}, \qquad T = \{\langle \alpha, 0 \rangle, \quad \alpha \in R\}.$$

Because of this example, we define, for subspaces S and T of R_n,

$$S + T = \{s + t; \quad s \in S, t \in T\}.$$

It is easy to show that $S + T$ is a subspace and is, in fact, the smallest subspace containing $S \cup T$. On the other hand, if S and T are subspaces, $S \cap T$ is always a subspace. It is natural to ask for the dimensions of $S \cap T$ and $S + T$, given the dimensions of S and T. The answer is provided by the following result, suggested by a counting procedure for finite sets: if A and B are finite sets, then the number of objects in $A \cup B$ is the sum of the numbers of objects in A and B, less the number of objects in the overlap $A \cap B$.

(7.17) $\dim (S + T) + \dim (S \cap T) = \dim S + \dim T.$

Proof.   We shall give a sketch of the proof, leaving some of the details to the reader. Although it is not actually necessary, we consider first the special case $S \cap T = \{0\}$. Let $\{s_1, \cdots, s_d\}$ be a basis of S and $\{t_1, \cdots, t_e\}$ be a basis of T. Then it is easily checked that the vectors $s_1, \cdots, s_d, t_1, \cdots, t_e$ generate $S + T$, and (7.17) will follow in this case if we can show that these vectors are linearly independent. Suppose we have

$$\alpha_1 s_1 + \cdots + \alpha_d s_d + \beta_1 t_1 + \cdots + \beta_e t_e = 0.$$

Then

$$\alpha_1 s_1 + \cdots + \alpha_d s_d = -\beta_1 t - \cdots - \beta_e t_e \in S \cap T = \{0\}.$$

Since the s's and t's are linearly independent, we have $\alpha_1 = \cdots = \alpha_d = 0$ and $\beta_1 = \cdots = \beta_e = 0$.

Now suppose that $S \cap T \neq 0$. By theorem (7.11), $S \cap T$ has a basis $\{u_1, \cdots, u_c\}$ where $c = \dim S \cap T$. By theorem (7.15) we can find sets of vectors $\{v_1, \cdots, v_d\}$ and $\{w_1, \cdots, w_e\}$ such that

$$\{u_1, \cdots, u_c, v_1, \cdots, v_d\} \text{ is a basis for } S,$$

$$\{u_1, \cdots, u_c, w_1, \cdots, w_e\} \text{ is a basis for } T.$$

Then $S + T = S(u_1, \cdots, u_c, v_1, \cdots, v_d, w_1, \cdots, w_e)$, and theorem (7.17) will be proved if we can show that these vectors are linearly independent. Suppose we have

$$(7.18) \quad \xi_1 u_1 + \cdots + \xi_c u_c + \lambda_1 v_1 + \cdots + \lambda_d v_d + \mu_1 w_1 + \cdots + \mu_e w_e = 0.$$

Then

$$\lambda_1 v_1 + \cdots + \lambda_d v_d = -\left(\sum \xi_i u_i\right) - \left(\sum \mu_i w_i\right) \in S \cap T$$

and hence there exist real numbers $\zeta_1, \cdots, \zeta_c$ such that

$$\lambda_1 v_1 + \cdots + \lambda_d v_d = \zeta_1 u_1 + \cdots + \zeta_c u_c.$$

Since $\{v_1, \cdots, v_d, u_1, \cdots, u_c\}$ are linearly independent, we have $\lambda_1 = \cdots = \lambda_d = 0$. Then from (7.18) we have $\xi_1 = \cdots = \xi_c = \mu_1 = \cdots = \mu_e = 0$, and the proof is completed.

EXERCISES

1. Prove that $\dim R_n = n$. (*Hint:* Prove that a basis for R_n is given by the *unit vectors* $e_1 = \langle 1, 0, \cdots, 0 \rangle$, $e_2 = \langle 0, 1, 0, \cdots, 0 \rangle$, $\cdots$, $e_n = \langle 0, \cdots, 0, 1 \rangle$, where e_i has its ith component equal to 1 and all other components equal to zero.)

2. Prove that if S and T are subspaces, and $S \subset T$, then $\dim S \leq \dim T$. Prove that if $S \subset T$ and $\dim S = \dim T$ then $S = T$. Does $\dim S = \dim T$ imply $S = T$ without the additional condition $S \subset T$?

Note. The next exercise gives the theoretical basis for most of the numerical work we shall do with vectors. A thorough knowledge of the statements and methods contained in this exercise will be essential for subsequent work.

3. a. Let $a_1, \cdots, a_p$ be vectors in R_n. Prove that $S(a_1 + \lambda a_i, a_2, \cdots, a_p) = S(a_1, \cdots, a_p)$ for any $\lambda \in R$ and $i \neq 1$.

b. Prove that $S(a_1, \cdots, a_p) = S(\lambda a_1, a_2, \cdots, a_p)$ for $\lambda \neq 0$.

c. An ordered collection of vectors $\{a_1, \cdots, a_p\}$ in R_n is said to be in *echelon form* if each $a_i \neq 0$ and if the index of the first nonzero entry in a_i is less than the index of the first nonzero entry in a_{i+1}, for $i = 1, 2, \cdots, p - 1$. For example,

$$\langle 1, 0, -2, 3 \rangle, \qquad \langle 0, 1, 2, 0 \rangle, \qquad \langle 0, 0, 0, 1 \rangle$$

are in echelon form. Prove that a set of vectors in echelon form is always a linearly independent set. (*Hint:* Try mathematical induction.)

d. We say that two sets of vectors $\{a_1, \cdots, a_p\}$ and $\{b_1, \cdots, b_q\}$ are *equivalent* if $S(a_1, \cdots, a_p) = S(b_1, \cdots, b_q)$. Prove that every finite set of nonzero vectors $\{a_1, \cdots, a_p\}$ in R_n is equivalent to a set of vectors in echelon form. (*Hint:* Try mathematical induction, using parts **a** and **b** of this exercise. See also Exercise 4 for an illustration of the general method.)

e. Let $S = S(a_1, \cdots, a_p)$ and suppose that $\{a_1, \cdots, a_p\}$ is equivalent to the set $\{b_1, \cdots, b_q\}$ where $b_1, \cdots, b_q$ are in echelon form. Prove that dim $S = q$ and that $\{b_1, \cdots, b_q\}$ is a basis for S.

4. Test the following vectors for linear dependence:

$$a = \langle -3, 2, 1, 4 \rangle, \quad b = \langle 4, 1, 0, 2 \rangle, \quad c = \langle -10, 3, 2, 6 \rangle.$$

Solution. By theorem (7.14) the vectors a, b, and c are linearly independent or dependent, according to whether the dimension of the subspace $S(a, b, c)$ is 3 or less than 3. We can test the dimension of $S(a, b, c)$ by Exercise 3. We pick a vector with a nonzero entry as far to the left as possible. In our example, any one of the vectors can be chosen. But if we had $\langle 0, 1 \rangle, \langle 2, 3 \rangle$ we would start from $\langle 2, 3 \rangle$. Let us start with a.

The next step is to apply **a** and **b** of Exercise 3 to express

$$S = S(a, b, c) = S(a, b', c')$$

where $b' = \lambda a + b$ and $c' = \mu a + c$ are determined so that the first components of b' and c' are zero. Thus we will have a start on putting the vectors in echelon form. Then we repeat the process with $\{b', c'\}$, etc. Specifically, we have

$$b' = \tfrac{4}{3}a + b = \langle 0, \tfrac{11}{3}, \tfrac{4}{3}, \tfrac{22}{3} \rangle,$$
$$c' = -\tfrac{10}{3}a + c = \langle 0, -\tfrac{11}{3}, -\tfrac{4}{3}, -\tfrac{22}{3} \rangle.$$

Since $b' = -c'$, we see that

$$S(a, b, c) = S(a, b')$$

and a and b' are in echelon form. Therefore $\{a, b, c\}$ is linearly dependent. Notice that the method also gives a basis for $S(a, b, c)$, namely $\{a, b'\}$, and the relation of linear dependence connecting a, b, and c which we obtain from $b' = -c'$. Thus we have

$$\tfrac{4}{3}a + b = +\tfrac{10}{3}a - c,$$

or

$$2a - b - c = 0.$$

5. Test the following vectors for linear dependence:

$$a_1 = \langle 0, 1, 1, 2 \rangle \qquad a_3 = \langle -2, 1, 0, 1 \rangle$$
$$a_2 = \langle 3, 1, 5, 2 \rangle \qquad a_4 = \langle 1, 0, 3, -1 \rangle$$

6. Determine whether $\langle 1, 1, 1 \rangle$ belongs to the subspace of R_3 generated by $\langle 1, 3, 4 \rangle$, $\langle 4, 0, 1 \rangle$, $\langle 3, 1, 2 \rangle$. Explain your reasoning. (*Hint:* Use Exercises 2 and 3.)

7. Determine whether $\langle 13, 11, -3, 5 \rangle$ belongs to the subspace of R_4 generated by $\langle 11, 8, -2, 3 \rangle$, $\langle 1, -10, 4, -9 \rangle$, $\langle 7, -1, 1, -3 \rangle$.

8. Find a basis for the subspace of R_5 generated by $\langle 1, 1, 0, 0, 1 \rangle$, $\langle -1, 1, 1, 0, 0 \rangle$, $\langle 2, 1, 0, 1, 1 \rangle$, $\langle 0, -1, -1, -1, 0 \rangle$.

9. Let

$$a_1 = \langle 2, 1, 0, -1 \rangle \qquad a_3 = \langle 1, -3, 2, 0 \rangle \qquad a_5 = \langle -2, 0, 6, 1 \rangle$$
$$a_2 = \langle 4, 8, -4, -3 \rangle \qquad a_4 = \langle 1, 10, -6, -2 \rangle \qquad a_6 = \langle 3, -1, 2, 4 \rangle$$

and let

$$S = S(a_1, a_2, a_3, a_4), \qquad T = S(a_4, a_5, a_6).$$

Find dim S, dim T, dim $(S + T)$ and, using theorem (7.17), find dim $(S \cap T)$.

8. SYSTEMS OF LINEAR EQUATIONS

As an application of the results and computational procedures of the previous section and exercises, we shall give in this section both the theory and a method for solution of systems of linear equations.

We shall describe *a system* of *m linear equations* in *n unknowns* by the notation

$$\alpha_{11}x_1 + \alpha_{12}x_2 + \cdots + \alpha_{1n}x_n = \beta_1$$
$$\alpha_{21}x_1 + \alpha_{22}x_2 + \cdots + \alpha_{2n}x_n = \beta_2$$

(8.1)

$$\cdots\cdots\cdots\cdots\cdots\cdots\cdots\cdots\cdots\cdots\cdots$$
$$\cdots\cdots\cdots\cdots\cdots\cdots\cdots\cdots\cdots\cdots\cdots$$
$$\cdots\cdots\cdots\cdots\cdots\cdots\cdots\cdots\cdots\cdots\cdots$$

$$\alpha_{m1}x_1 + \alpha_{m2}x_2 + \cdots + \alpha_{mn}x_n = \beta_m$$

where the α_{ij} and β_i are fixed real numbers and the $x_1, \cdots, x_n$ are the *unknowns*. The indexing is chosen such that for $1 \le i \le m$, the ith equation is

$$\alpha_{i1}x_1 + \cdots + \alpha_{im}x_n = \beta_i$$

where the first index appearing with α_{ij} stands for the equation in which α_{ij} appears and the second index j denotes the unknown x_j of which α_{ij} is the coefficient. Thus α_{21} is the coefficient of x_1 in the second equation, etc. The function or rule that assigns the real number α_{ij} to each pair (i, j), for $1 \le i \le m$ and $1 \le j \le n$, is called the *coefficient matrix* of the system (8.1). In general, an "*m-by-n*" (or $m \times n$) matrix is any rule which assigns to each ordered pair of natural numbers (i, j), where $1 \le i \le m$ and $1 \le j \le n$, a real number α_{ij}. An m-by-n matrix will be denoted by (α_{ij}) or simply by A. With any m-by-n matrix (α_{ij}) we can associate two sets of vectors in the vector spaces R_m and R_n respectively, viz., the *row vectors*

$$\{r_1, \cdots, r_m\} \subset R_n$$

where the ith row vector is

$$r_i = \langle \alpha_{i1}, \cdots, \alpha_{im} \rangle, \qquad 1 \le i \le m$$

and the *column vectors*

$$\{c_1, \cdots, c_n\} \subset R_m$$

where the jth column vector is

$$c_j = \langle \alpha_{1j}, \alpha_{2j}, \cdots, \alpha_{nj} \rangle.$$

Sometimes it is convenient also to write column vectors in the form

$$c_j = \begin{bmatrix} \alpha_{1j} \\ \alpha_{2j} \\ \cdot \\ \cdot \\ \cdot \\ \alpha_{mj} \end{bmatrix}$$

The *row subspace* of the m-by-n matrix (α_{ij}) is the subspace $S(r_1, \cdots, r_m)$ of R_n, and the *column subspace* is the subspace $S(c_1, \cdots, c_n)$ of R_m.

A *solution* of the system (8.1) is an n-tuple of real numbers $\{\lambda_1, \cdots, \lambda_n\}$ such that

$$\alpha_{11}\lambda_1 + \cdots + \alpha_{1n}\lambda_n = \beta_1$$
$$\cdots\cdots\cdots\cdots\cdots\cdots\cdots\cdots$$
$$\cdots\cdots\cdots\cdots\cdots\cdots\cdots\cdots$$
$$\cdots\cdots\cdots\cdots\cdots\cdots\cdots\cdots$$
$$\alpha_{m1}\lambda_1 + \cdots + \alpha_{mn}\lambda_n = \beta_m.$$

In other words, the numbers $\{\lambda_i\}$ in the solution satisfy the equations (8.1) upon being substituted for the unknowns. We may identify a solution with a vector in R_n and may therefore speak of a *solution vector* of the system (8.1). Recalling the definition of the column vectors, we see that $x = \langle \lambda_1, \cdots, \lambda_n \rangle$ is a solution of the system (8.1) if and only if

(8.2) $$\lambda_1 c_1 + \lambda_2 c_2 + \cdots + \lambda_n c_n = b$$

where $b = \langle \beta_1, \cdots, \beta_n \rangle$, and we may describe the original system of equations by the more economical notation:

(8.3) $$x_1 c_1 + \cdots + x_n c_n = b.$$

A system of *homogeneous equations*, or a homogeneous system, is a system (8.3) in which the vector $b = 0$; if we allow the possibility $b \neq 0$, we speak of a *nonhomogeneous system*. If we have a homogeneous system,

(8.4) $$x_1 c_1 + \cdots + x_n c_n = 0,$$

then the zero vector $\langle 0, \cdots, 0 \rangle$ is always a solution vector, called the *trivial solution*. A solution different from $\langle 0, \cdots, 0 \rangle$ is called a *nontrivial solution*.

By this time the reader should be beside himself in a wish to apply the results of the preceding section to systems of equations. Rather than give any more definitions, we dispose of some theoretical points of fundamental importance.

(8.5) **Theorem.** *A nonhomogeneous system $x_1 c_1 + \cdots + x_n c_n = b$ has a solution if and only if either of the following conditions is satisfied:*

(1) *b belongs to the column space $S(c_1, \cdots, c_n)$.*
(2) $\dim S(c_1, \cdots, c_n) = \dim S(c_1, \cdots, c_n, b)$.

Proof. The fact that the first statement is equivalent to the existence of a solution is immediate from (8.2). To prove that condition 2 is equivalent to condition 1, we proceed as follows. If $b \in S(c_1, \cdots, c_n)$, then clearly $S(c_1, \cdots, c_n, b) = S(c_1, \cdots, c_n)$ and condition 2 holds. Conversely, if condition 2 holds, then since

$$S(c_1, \cdots, c_n) \subset S(c_1, \cdots, c_n, b)$$

we have by Exercise 2 of Section 7

$$S(c_1, \cdots, c_n) = S(c_1, \cdots, c_n, b)$$

and $b \in S(c_1, \cdots, c_n)$. This completes the proof.

REMARK.   Since we have in Exercise 3 of Section 7 a computational procedure for finding $\dim S(a_1, \cdots, a_m)$ for any set of vectors $\{a_1, \cdots, a_m\}$, part (2) of (8.5) gives us a practical method of testing nonhomogeneous systems for existence of solutions. The equation (8.2) tells us that to find an actual solution we have to express b as a linear combination of the column vectors; this can be done by putting $\{c_1, \cdots, c_n, b\}$ in echelon form and keeping track of the results.

EXAMPLE.   We use the example given in Exercise 4 of Section 7 to illustrate this procedure. Letting the vectors a, b, c be column vectors, we consider the system

$$
\begin{aligned}
-3x_1 + 4x_2 &= -10 \\
2x_1 + x_2 &= 3 \\
x_1 + 0x_2 &= 2 \\
4x_1 + 2x_2 &= 6
\end{aligned}
$$

with column vectors c_1 and c_2, where $b = \langle -10, 3, 2, 6 \rangle$. From the results of Exercise 4 of Section 7, we have

$$S(c_1, c_2) = S(c_1, c_2, b)$$

and hence the system has a solution. In that exercise we also obtained the relation of linear dependence

$$2c_1 - c_2 - b = 0$$

which asserts that $\langle 2, -1 \rangle$ is a solution of the system.

The result of theorem (8.4) can be restated in a convenient way by using the following concepts.

(8.6)   **Definition.**   Let (α_{ij}) be an m-by-n matrix with column vectors $\{c_1, \cdots, c_n\}$. The *rank* of the matrix is defined as the dimension of the column space $S(c_1, \cdots, c_n)$.

(8.7)   **Definition.**   If $x_1c_1 + \cdots + x_nc_n = b$ is a nonhomogeneous system whose coefficient matrix has columns $c_1, \cdots, c_n$, then the

m-by-$(n + 1)$ matrix with columns $\{c_1, \cdots, c_n, b\}$ is called the *augmented matrix* of the system.

The next result is immediate from our definitions and theorem (8.5).

(8.8) Theorem. *A nonhomogeneous system has a solution if and only if the rank of its coefficient matrix is equal to the rank of the augmented matrix.*

We have now settled the question of whether a nonhomogeneous system has a solution or not. If it does possess a solution, then we should ask to determine *all* solutions of the system. The key to this problem is furnished by the next theorem.

(8.9) Theorem. *Suppose that a nonhomogeneous system*

(8.10) $$x_1c_1 + \cdots + x_nc_n = b$$

has a solution x_0; then for all solutions x of the homogeneous system

(8.11) $$x_1c_1 + \cdots + x_nc_n = 0,$$

$x_0 + x$ is a solution of (8.10) and all solutions of (8.10) can be expressed in this form.

Proof. Suppose first that $x = \langle \alpha_1, \cdots, \alpha_n \rangle$ is a solution of the homogeneous system and that $x_0 = \langle \alpha_1^{(0)}, \cdots, \alpha_n^{(0)} \rangle$ is a solution of (8.10). Then we have:

(8.12) $$\alpha_1^{(0)}c_1 + \cdots + \alpha_n^{(0)}c_n = b$$
and
$$\alpha_1c_1 + \cdots + \alpha_nc_n = 0.$$

Adding these equations, we obtain

$$(\alpha_1^{(0)} + \alpha_1)c_1 + \cdots + (\alpha_n^{(0)} + \alpha_n)c_n = b,$$

which asserts that $x_0 + x$ is a solution of (8.10).

Now let $y = \langle \beta_1, \cdots, \beta_n \rangle$ be an arbitrary solution of (8.10), so that we have

(8.13) $$\beta_1c_1 + \cdots + \beta_nc_n = b.$$

Subtracting (8.12) from (8.13), we obtain

$$(\beta_1 - \alpha_1^{(0)})c_1 + \cdots + (\beta_n - \alpha_n^{(0)})c_n = 0.$$

This asserts that $u = y - x_0$ is a solution of the homogeneous system, and we have

$$y = x_0 + u$$

as required. This completes the proof.

Thus the problem of finding all solutions of a nonhomogeneous system comes down to finding one solution of the nonhomogeneous system, and solving a homogeneous system. We shall show how to solve homogeneous systems in the next section, and content ourselves here with a few preliminary remarks.

(8.14)   Theorem.   *The set S of all solution vectors of a homogeneous system $x_1c_1 + \cdots + x_nc_n = 0$ forms a subspace of R_n.*

Proof.   Let $a = \langle \lambda_1, \cdots, \lambda_n \rangle$ and $b = \langle \mu_1, \cdots, \mu_n \rangle$ belong to S. Then we have

$$\lambda_1c_1 + \cdots + \lambda_nc_n = 0, \qquad \mu_1c_1 + \cdots + \mu_nc_n = 0.$$

Adding these equations, we obtain

$$(\lambda_1 + \mu_1)c_1 + \cdots + (\lambda_n + \mu_n)c_n = 0,$$

which shows that $a + b \in S$. If $\lambda \in R$, then we have also

$$\lambda(\lambda_1c_1 + \cdots + \lambda_nc_n) = (\lambda\lambda_1)c_1 + \cdots + (\lambda\lambda_n)c_n = 0$$

and $\lambda a \in S$. This completes the proof.

From this theorem and the results of the preceding sections, we will know all solutions of a homogeneous system as soon as we find a basis for the *solution space,* that is, the set of solutions of the system.

EXERCISES

1. Test for solvability of the following systems of equations, and if solvable, find a solution:

a. $x_1 + x_2 + x_3 = 8.$
$x_1 + x_2 + x_4 = 1.$
$x_1 + x_3 + x_4 = 14.$
$x_2 + x_3 + x_4 = 14.$

b. $x_1 + x_2 - x_3 = 3.$
$x_1 - 3x_2 + 2x_3 = 1.$
$2x_1 - 2x_2 + x_3 = 4.$

c. $3x_1 + 4x_2 = -1.$
$-x_1 - x_2 = 1.$
$x_1 - 2x_2 = 0.$
$2x_1 + 3x_2 = 0.$

2. For what values of α does the following system of equations have a solution?

$$3x_1 - x_2 + \alpha x_3 = 1$$
$$3x_1 - x_2 + x_3 = 5$$

3. Prove that a system of m homogeneous equations in $n > m$ unknowns always has a nontrivial solution.

4. Prove that a system of homogeneous equations $x_1 c_1 + \cdots + x_n c_n$ in n unknowns has a nontrivial solution if and only if the rank of the coefficient matrix is less than n.

9. SYSTEMS OF HOMOGENEOUS EQUATIONS

In Section 8 we showed that the problem of solving a nonhomogeneous system was reduced to solving a homogeneous system and that the set of solutions of a homogeneous system of m equations in n unknowns is a subspace of R_n. The system will be solved if we give a method of finding a basis of the solution space, for then the set of all solutions will be precisely the set of linear combinations of the basis vectors. The whole question is settled by the following theorem.

(9.1) Theorem. *Let*

$$\alpha_{11}x_1 + \cdots + \alpha_{1n}x_n = 0$$
$$\cdots\cdots\cdots\cdots\cdots\cdots\cdots\cdots$$
$$\cdots\cdots\cdots\cdots\cdots\cdots\cdots\cdots$$
$$\cdots\cdots\cdots\cdots\cdots\cdots\cdots\cdots$$
$$\alpha_{m1}x_1 + \cdots + \alpha_{mn}x_n = 0$$

be a homogeneous system of m equations in n unknowns, with column vectors $c_1, \cdots, c_n$ arranged such that, for some r, $\{c_1, \cdots, c_r\}$ is a basis for the subspace $S(c_1, \cdots, c_n)$. Then for each i, if $r + 1 \leq i \leq n$, there exists a relation of linear dependence

$$\lambda_1^{(i)} c_1 + \cdots + \lambda_r^{(i)} c_r - c_i = 0, \qquad \lambda_j^{(i)} \in R.$$

Then for $r + 1 \leq i \leq n$

$$u_i = \underbrace{\langle \lambda_1^{(i)}, \cdots, \lambda_r^{(i)}, 0, \cdots, 0, -1, 0, \cdots, 0 \rangle}_{i}$$

(where it is to be understood that the -1 appears in the ith position in u_i) is a solution of the system, and $\{u_{r+1}, \cdots, u_n\}$ is a basis for the solution space of the system.

Proof. By theorem (7.14) it is indeed possible to select a basis for $S(c_1, \cdots, c_n)$ from among the vectors $c_1, \cdots, c_n$ themselves. Rearranging the indices so that these vectors occupy the $1, \cdots, r$th positions changes the solution space only in that a corresponding change of position has been made in the components of the solution vectors.

Since $\{c_1, \cdots, c_r\}$ forms a basis for $S(c_1, \cdots, c_n)$, each vector c_i where $r + 1 \leq i \leq n$ is a linear combination of the basis vectors, and we have a relation of linear dependence

$$\lambda_1^{(i)} c_1 + \cdots + \lambda_r^{(i)} c_r - c_i = 0, \qquad \lambda_j^{(i)} \in R, \quad r + 1 \leq i \leq n,$$

as in the statement of the theorem.

As we saw in formula (8.4), the vectors

$$u_i = \langle \lambda_1^{(i)}, \cdots, \lambda_r^{(i)}, \cdots, -1, \cdots, 0 \rangle, \qquad r + 1 \leq i \leq n$$

with the -1 in the ith position of u_i are solutions of the system. It remains to show that the $\{u_i\}$ are linearly independent, and that they generate the solution space.

To show that they are linearly independent, suppose we have a possible relation of linear dependence:

(9.2) $\mu_{r+1} u_{r+1} + \cdots + \mu_n u_n = 0, \quad \text{for } \mu_i \in R.$

The left side is a vector in R_n all of whose components are zero. For $r + 1 \leq i \leq n$, the ith component of (9.2) is $-\mu_i$ (Why?), and it follows that $\mu_{r+1} = \cdots = \mu_n = 0$. Now let $x = \langle \alpha_1, \cdots, \alpha_n \rangle$ be an arbitrary solution of the original system. From the definition of $u_{r+1}, \cdots, u_n$, we have

$$x + \sum_{k=r+1}^{m} \alpha_k u_k = \langle \xi_1, \cdots, \xi_r, 0, \cdots, 0 \rangle$$

where $\xi_1, \cdots, \xi_r$ are some elements of R. Since the set of solutions is a subspace of R_n, the vector $y = \langle \xi_1, \cdots, \xi_r, 0, \cdots, 0 \rangle$ is a solution of the original system and we have, by (8.4),

$$\xi_1 c_1 + \cdots + \xi_r c_r + 0 c_{r+1} + \cdots + 0 c_n = 0.$$

Since $c_1, \cdots, c_r$ are linearly independent, we have $\xi_1 = \cdots = \xi_r = 0$ and hence

$$x = \sum_{k=r+1}^{m} (-\alpha_k) u_k \in S(u_{r+1}, \cdots, u_n).$$

This completes the proof of the theorem.

(9.3) Corollary. *The dimension of the solution space of a homoge-*

neous system in n unknowns is $n - r$, where r is the rank of the coefficient matrix.

This result is immediate from our definition of the rank as the dimension of the column space of the coefficient matrix.

REMARKS AND EXAMPLE. We wish to emphasize that theorem (9.1) is a good theorem in the sense that each step in the proof can be carried out in a particular case by the computational procedures developed earlier in this chapter. Specifically, we have a method of finding the dimension of the space $S(c_1, \cdots, c_n)$—that of putting $c_1, \cdots, c_n$ in echelon form; and when we have found the dimension of the column space we can find by trial and error a subset of $\{c_1, \cdots, c_n\}$ containing the correct number of linearly independent vectors. We know that these form a basis for $S(c_1, \cdots, c_n)$ (Why?). Finally, the problem of finding the solution vector u_i is solved by putting $c_1, \cdots, c_r, c_i$ in echelon form and keeping track of the result. For example, let us solve the system

$$3x_1 - 2x_2 + x_3 - x_4 = 0$$
$$x_1 + x_2 + x_3 + x_4 = 0$$

with column vectors

$$c_1 = \begin{pmatrix} 3 \\ 1 \end{pmatrix}, \quad c_2 = \begin{pmatrix} -2 \\ 1 \end{pmatrix}, \quad c_3 = \begin{pmatrix} 1 \\ 1 \end{pmatrix}, \quad c_4 = \begin{pmatrix} -1 \\ 1 \end{pmatrix}.$$

Since $S(c_1, c_2, c_3, c_4) \subset R_2$, and since c_1 and c_2 are linearly independent, $\{c_1, c_2\}$ forms a basis for the column space (Why?). Putting c_1, c_2, c_3 in echelon form we obtain

$$2c_1 + 3c_2 = \begin{pmatrix} 0 \\ 5 \end{pmatrix},$$

$$c_1 - 3c_3 = \begin{pmatrix} 0 \\ -2 \end{pmatrix},$$

$$2(2c_1 + 3c_2) = -5(c_1 - 3c_3),$$

which gives us

$$-9c_1 - 6c_2 + 15c_3 = 0.$$

Thus one solution is

$$u_3 = \langle -9, -6, 15, 0 \rangle,$$

which could be normalized in the form of the u_i in theorem (9.1) by multiplying by $-1/15$. Putting c_1, c_2, c_4 in echelon form, we obtain

$$c_1 + 3c_4 = \begin{pmatrix} 0 \\ 4 \end{pmatrix}$$

and

$$5(c_1 + 3c_4) = 4(2c_1 + 3c_2).$$

This gives us, for the second solution,

$$u_4 = \langle -3, -12, 0, 15 \rangle.$$

By theorem (9.1), $\{u_3, u_4\}$ is a basis for the solution space.

We shall now apply our result to derive a useful and unexpected result about the rank of a matrix

$$A = \begin{pmatrix} \alpha_{11} & \cdots & \alpha_{1n} \\ & \cdots & \\ & \cdots & \\ & \cdots & \\ \alpha_{m1} & \cdots & \alpha_{mn} \end{pmatrix}$$

with columns $c_1, \cdots, c_n$ and rows $r_1, \cdots, r_m$. Let us define the *row rank* of A as the dimension of the row space $S(r_1, \cdots, r_m)$. Some writers call the rank as we have defined it the "column rank" but, as the next theorem shows, the row rank and the column rank are always equal.

(9.4)   Theorem.   *The row rank of an m-by-n matrix A is equal to the rank of A.*

Proof.   With the matrix A, let us consider the homogeneous system

$$\alpha_{11}x_1 + \cdots + \alpha_{1n}x_n = 0$$

(9.5)

$$\alpha_{m1}x_1 + \cdots + \alpha_{mn}x_n = 0$$

It is convenient for this proof and for some arguments in the next section to use the notation

$$r_i \cdot x = \alpha_{i1}x_1 + \cdots + \alpha_{in}x_n$$

for the two vectors r_i and x, so that the system (9.5) can be described also by the system of equations

$$r_1 \cdot x = 0$$

(9.6)

$$r_m \cdot x = 0$$

The "scalar multiplication" $r \cdot x$ has the property that

(9.7) $(\lambda r + \mu s) \cdot x = \lambda(r \cdot x) + \mu(s \cdot x),$ for λ and $\mu \in R,$

and for r and $s \in R_n.$

Now, without changing the column rank we may assume that $\{r_1, \cdots, r_t\}$ forms a basis for the row space of A, where t is the row rank of A. Then from (9.7) it follows easily that the system of equations

(9.8)

$$r_1 \cdot x = 0$$
$$\cdots\cdots$$
$$\cdots\cdots$$
$$\cdots\cdots$$
$$r_t \cdot x = 0$$

has the same solution space as (9.6). To see this, it is sufficient to prove that any solution x of (9.8) is a solution of (9.6). For $t + 1 \leq i \leq m$, we have

$$r_i = \xi_1 r_1 + \cdots + \xi_t r_t, \qquad \xi_j \in R.$$

Then, by (9.7),

$$r_i \cdot x = \sum_{k=1}^{t} \xi_k (r_k \cdot x) = 0$$

since x is a solution of (9.8), and our assertion is proved.

The columns of the matrix A' whose rows are $r_1, \cdots, r_t$ are in R_t; hence

$$\text{rank } A' \leq t$$

and

$$n - \text{rank } A' \geq n - t.$$

Since (9.6) and (9.8) have the same solution space, we have by corollary (9.3)

$$n - \text{rank } A = n - \text{rank } A' \geq n - t,$$

and hence rank $A \leq t$. Interchanging the rows and columns of A, we obtain an n-by-m matrix A^*; repeating the argument with A^*, we have rank $A^* \leq$ row rank of A^*. But rank $A^* = t$ and row rank $A^* = $ rank A. Combining our results, we have

$$\text{rank } A = \text{row rank } A$$

and theorem (9.4) is proved.

EXERCISES

1. Find a basis for the solution space of the system

$$3x_1 - x_2 \qquad + x_4 = 0$$
$$x_1 + x_2 + x_3 + x_4 = 0.$$

2. Find bases for the solution spaces of the homogeneous systems associated with the systems given in Exercise 1 of Section 8.

3. Describe all solutions of the system

$$-x_1 + 2x_2 + x_3 + 4x_4 = 0$$
$$2x_1 + x_2 - x_3 + x_4 = 1.$$

4. Let $\langle \alpha_1, \alpha_2 \rangle$, $\langle \beta_1, \beta_2 \rangle$ be distinct vectors in R_2, and let A, B, C and A', B', C' be real numbers such that

$$A \langle \alpha_1, \alpha_2 \rangle + B \langle \beta_1, \beta_2 \rangle + C \langle 1, 1 \rangle = 0,$$
$$A' \langle \alpha_1, \alpha_2 \rangle + B' \langle \beta_1, \beta_2 \rangle + C' \langle 1, 1 \rangle = 0.$$

Prove that vectors $\langle A, B, C \rangle$ and $\langle A', B', C' \rangle$ are linearly dependent. [*Note:* This settles in an efficient way the question in (4.5) of uniqueness of the line passing through two distinct points.]

10. LINEAR MANIFOLDS*

In this section we shall apply the results of Sections 7 to 9 to a discussion of the generalizations in R_n of lines and planes in two and three dimensions.

In the exercises of Section 5 we defined a *line* in R_n as a one-dimensional subspace $S(a)$ or, more generally, a translate $b + S(a)$ of a one-dimensional subspace by some fixed vector b. Thus a vector p belongs to the line $b + S(a)$ if, for some $\lambda \in R$ (see Figure 2.3),

$$p = b + \lambda a.$$

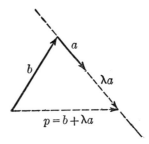

Figure 2.3

---

* This section is optional.

By analogy we might then define a *plane* in R_n as a two-dimensional subspace $S \subset R_n$ or, more generally, a translate $b + S$ of a two-dimensional space S by a fixed vector b. If $\{a_1, a_2\}$ is a basis of S, then $p \in b + S$ if and only if (see Figure 2.4).

$$p = b + \lambda_1 a_1 + \lambda_2 a_2, \qquad \lambda_i \in R.$$

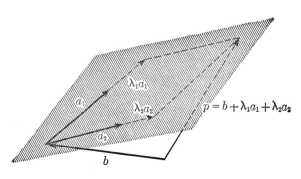

Figure 2.4

The general concept we are looking for is the following generalization of the concept of subspace.

(10.1) Definition. A *linear manifold* V in R_n is the set of all vectors in $b + S$, where b is a fixed vector and S is a fixed subspace of R_n. Thus $p \in V$ if and only if $p = b + a$ for some $a \in S$. The subspace S is called the *directing space* of V. The *dimension* of V is the dimension of the subspace S.

(10.2) Theorem. *Let* $V = b + S$ *be a linear manifold in* R_n; *then the directing space of* V *is the set of all vectors* $p - q$ *where* $p, q \in V$.

Proof. Let $p, q \in V$; then there exist vectors $a, a' \in S$ such that

$$p = b + a, \qquad q = b + a'.$$

Then

$$p - q = (b + a) - (b + a') = a - a' \in S.$$

On the other hand, if $a \in S$, then $a = b - (b - a)$, so that $a = p - q$ where $p = b$ and $q = b - a$ both belong to V. This completes the proof.

This theorem shows that the directing space of $V = b + S$ is determined independently of the vector b.

We know that lines and planes in R_2 and R_3 are also described as the sets of solutions of certain linear equations. The definition of a linear manifold $V = b + S$ suggests that a linear manifold can be described by equations in the general case. From Section 8 we know that vectors in $b + S$ have the form we obtained for the solutions of a nonhomogeneous system of linear equations, where b is the particular solution and S is the solution space of the associated homogeneous system.

In working out this idea we begin by indicating how to describe a subspace S by a system of linear equations.

(10.3) Lemma. *Let S be an r-dimensional subspace of R_n; then there exists a set of $n - r$ homogeneous linear equations in n unknowns whose solution space is exactly S.*

REMARK. No set of less than $n - r$ equations can have S as solution space. Why?

Proof of Lemma (10.3). Let $\{b_1, \cdots, b_r\}$ be a basis for S. The only system of equations which are possibly relevant to the problem is [in the notation of (9.6)]:

(10.4)
$$\begin{aligned} b_1 \cdot x &= 0 \\ &\cdots \\ b_r \cdot x &= 0 \end{aligned}$$

But these obviously do not solve the problem, since it may happen (and usually does) that, say, $b_1 \cdot b_1 \neq 0$, so that b_1 is not, in general, a solution vector of (10.4). Let S^* be the solution space of (10.4). By (9.4) the rank of the matrix whose rows are $b_1, \cdots, b_r$ is r; hence S^* has dimension $n - r$, by (9.3). Let $\{c_1, \cdots, c_{n-r}\}$ be a basis for S^* and consider the system of equations

(10.5)
$$\begin{aligned} c_1 \cdot x &= 0 \\ &\cdots \\ c_{n-r} \cdot x &= 0 \end{aligned}$$

By the same reasoning, the solution space S^{**} of this system has dimension r and, clearly, $S \subset S^{**}$ (Why?). Since $\dim S = r$, we have by Exercise 2 of Section 7 the result that $S = S^{**}$, and the lemma is proved.

REMARK.   Note that our computational procedures in Sections 7 to 9 can be applied to carrying out each of the steps in the proof of lemma (10.3).

(10.6) Theorem. *A necessary and sufficient condition for a set of vectors $V \subset R_n$ to form a linear manifold of dimension r is that V be the set of all solutions of a system of $n - r$ nonhomogeneous equations in n unknowns whose coefficient matrix has rank $n - r$.*

Proof.   First let

$$x_1 c_1 + \cdots + x_n c_n = b, \qquad c_i \in R_{n-r}$$

be a system of $n - r$ equations in n unknowns whose coefficient matrix has rank $n - r$. By theorem (8.9) the set V of all solutions is a linear manifold $x_0 + S$ where S is the solution space of the homogeneous system $x_1 c_1 + \cdots + x_n c_n = 0$. By corollary (9.3), dim $S = n - (n - r)$ and hence dim $V = r$.

To prove the converse, let $V = y + S$ be a linear manifold of dimension r. By lemma (10.3) there exists a system of $n - r$ equations whose solution space is S:

$$x_1 c_1 + \cdots + x_n c_n = 0.$$

If $y = \langle \eta_1, \cdots, \eta_n \rangle$, let

$$b = \eta_1 c_1 + \cdots + \eta_n c_n.$$

Then the nonhomogeneous system $x_1 c_1 + \cdots + x_n c_n = b$ has for its solutions exactly the set $y + S = V$. This completes the proof of the theorem.

EXERCISES

1. Find a set of homogeneous linear equations whose solution space is generated by the vectors $\langle 2, 1, -3 \rangle$, $\langle 1, -1, 0 \rangle$, $\langle 1, 3, -4 \rangle$.

2. Find a set of homogeneous equations whose solution space S is generated by the vectors $\langle 3, -1, 1, 2 \rangle$, $\langle 4, -1, -2, 3 \rangle$, $\langle 10, -3, 0, 7 \rangle$, $\langle -1, 1, -7, 0 \rangle$. Find a system of nonhomogeneous equations whose set of solutions is the linear manifold with directing space S and which passes through $\langle 1, 1, 1, 1 \rangle$.

3. A *hyperplane* is a linear manifold of dimension $n - 1$ in R_n. Prove that a linear manifold is a hyperplane if and only if it is the set of solutions of a single linear equation $\alpha_1 x_1 + \cdots + \alpha_n x_n = \beta$. Prove that a linear manifold of dimension r is the intersection of exactly $n - r$ hyperplanes.

   Remarks. A *line* is defined as a one-dimensional linear manifold in R_n; this definition is consistent with the definition given in the exercises at the end of Section 5. By Exercise 3, a line in R_2 is the intersection of $2 - 1 = 1$ hyperplanes, which explains why a line in R_2, and in no other dimension, is the set of solutions of a single linear equation.

4. By Exercise 3, a line in R_n is the intersection of $n - 1$ hyperplanes. Find a system of linear equations whose set of solutions is the line passing through $\langle 1, -1, 0, 2 \rangle$ and $\langle 2, 0, 1, 1 \rangle$.

5. Prove that, if p and q are vectors belonging to a linear manifold V, then the line through p and q is contained in V.

6. Let H be the hyperplane defined by the equation

$$\alpha_1 x_1 + \alpha_2 x_2 + \cdots + \alpha_n x_n = \beta, \qquad \alpha_i, \beta \in R.$$

   Prove that the vectors not on H fall into exactly two nonempty convex sets. (*Hint:* See Exercises 4 and 6 in Section 5.)

7. Let S and T be subspaces of R_n, which are represented as the solution spaces of homogeneous systems

$$a_1 \cdot x = 0, \cdots, a_r \cdot x = 0$$

   and

$$b_1 \cdot x = 0, \cdots, b_s \cdot x = 0$$

   respectively. Prove that $S \cap T$ is the solution space of the system

$$a_1 \cdot x = 0, \cdots, a_r \cdot x = 0, \qquad b_1 \cdot x = 0, \cdots, b_s \cdot x = 0.$$

   Use this remark to find a basis for $S \cap T$, where S and T are as in Exercise 9 of Section 7.

CHAPTER 3

DETERMINANTS

In Chapter 2 we have given an effective method of testing sets of vectors for linear dependence. For theoretical purposes it is convenient to have a formula which assigns to a set of vectors $a_1, \cdots, a_n$ from R_n a number in such a way that the vectors are linearly independent if and only if that number is different from zero. The determinant gives us such a function and, as we shall see, it has several other useful properties. Among them is its connection with the concepts of area and volume, which we shall use to motivate the definition.

11. DEFINITION OF DETERMINANTS

Let us begin with a study of the function $A(a_1, a_2)$ which assigns to each pair of vectors $a_1, a_2 \in R_2$ the area of the parallelogram with edges a_1 and a_2 (Figure 3.1). Instead of working out a formula for this function in terms of the components of a_1 and a_2, let us see what

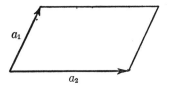

Figure 3.1

are some of the general properties of the function A. We have, first of all,

(11.1) $A(e_1, e_2) = 1$,   if $e_1 = \langle 1, 0 \rangle$, $e_2 = \langle 0, 1 \rangle$.

Second, if we multiply one of the vectors by a positive real number λ, we multiply A by λ, since the area of a parallelogram is the product of the lengths of the base and height (see Figure 3.2) and the length of λa_1 is λ times the length of a_1.*

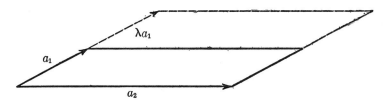

Figure 3.2

In terms of the function A we have:

(11.2) $A(\lambda a_1, a_2) = A(a_1, \lambda a_2) = \lambda A(a_1, a_2)$,   for $\lambda > 0$.

Finally, the base and height of the parallelogram with edges a_1, a_2 are the same as those of the parallelogram with edges $a_1 + a_2$ and a_2 (see Figure 3.3), and hence we have:

(11.3) $A(a_1 + a_2, a_2) = A(a_1, a_2) = A(a_1, a_2 + a_1)$.

---

   * The concept of length will be studied more fully in Chapter 6. For the present discussion, we define the length of $a = \langle \alpha_1, \alpha_2 \rangle$ as $\sqrt{\alpha_1^2 + \alpha_2^2}$.

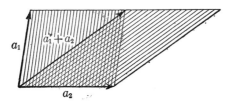

Figure 3.3

Now stop! One would think that we have not yet described all the essential properties of the area function. We are going to prove, however, that there is one and only one function which assigns to each pair of vectors in R_2 a nonnegative real number satisfying conditions (11.1), (11.2), and (11.3). Note also that the function A has a further property, mentioned in the introduction:

(11.4) $A(a_1, a_2) \neq 0$ *if and only if a_1 and a_2 are linearly independent.*

It will be convenient to begin by defining a function on sets of vectors from R_n which satisfy axioms (11.1), (11.2), and (11.3) for arbitrary λ (positive or negative). We shall derive consequences of these axioms in this section and postpone to the next section the task of proving that such a function really does exist. The reader will note that there is nothing logically wrong with this procedure; it is, for example, what we do in Euclidean geometry, namely, to derive consequences of certain axioms before we have a construction of certain objects that satisfy the axioms. We return to the connection with areas and volumes in Section 14.

(11.5) Definition.   A *determinant* is a function which assigns to each n-tuple $\{a_1, \cdots, a_n\}$ of vectors in R_n a real number $D = D(a_1, \cdots, a_n)$ such that the following conditions are satisfied.

(1) $D(a_1, \cdots, a_{i-1}, a_i + a_j, a_{i+1}, \cdots, a_n) = D(a_1, \cdots, a_n)$,   for $1 \leq i \leq n$ and $j \neq i$.

(2) $D(a_1, \cdots, a_{i-1}, \lambda a_i, a_{i+1}, \cdots, a_n) = \lambda D(a_1, \cdots, a_n)$,   for all real numbers λ.

(3) $D(e_1, \cdots, e_n) = 1$,   if e_i is the ith unit vector

$$\langle 0, \cdots, 0, 1, 0, \cdots, 0 \rangle$$

with a 1 in the ith position and zeros elsewhere.

Now we shall derive some consequences of the definition.

(11.6)   Theorem.   *Let D be a determinant function on R_n; then the following statements are valid.*

(A) $D(a_1, \cdots, a_n)$ *is multiplied by -1 if two of the vectors a_i and a_j are interchanged (where $i \neq j$).*

(B) $D(a_1, \cdots, a_n) = 0$ *if two of the vectors a_i and a_j are equal.*

(C)   *D is unchanged if a_i is replaced by $a_i + \sum_{j \neq i} \lambda_j a_j$, for arbitrary real numbers λ_j.*

(D) $D(a_1, \cdots, a_n) = 0$, *if $\{a_1, \cdots, a_n\}$ is linearly dependent.*

(E) $D(a_1, \cdots, a_{i-1}, \lambda a_i + \mu a_i', a_{i+1}, \cdots, a_n)$
$$= \lambda D(a_1, \cdots, a_i, \cdots, a_n) + \mu D(a_1, \cdots, a_i', \cdots, a_n)$$

for $1 \leq i \leq n$, for arbitrary real numbers λ and μ, and for vectors a_i and $a_i' \in R_n$.

Proof.   **A.**   We shall use the notation
$$D(\cdots, \underset{i}{a}, \cdots, \underset{j}{b}, \cdots)$$

to indicate that the ith argument of the function D is a and the jth is b, etc. Then we have, for arbitrary i and j,

$$D(\cdots, \underset{i}{a_i}, \cdots, \underset{j}{a_j}, \cdots) = -D(\cdots, \underset{i}{-a_i}, \cdots, \underset{j}{a_j}, \cdots) \quad \text{by property 2}$$

$$= -D(\cdots, \underset{i}{-a_i}, \cdots, \underset{j}{-a_i + a_j}, \cdots) \quad \text{by property 1}$$

$$= \quad D(\cdots, \underset{i}{-a_i}, \cdots, \underset{j}{+a_i - a_j}, \cdots) \quad \text{by property 2}$$

$$= \quad D(\cdots, \underset{i}{-a_j}, \cdots, \underset{j}{a_i - a_j}, \cdots) \quad \begin{array}{l} \text{by property 1,} \\ \text{since } -a_i \\ + (a_i - a_j) \\ = -a_j \end{array}$$

$$= -D(\cdots, \underset{i}{-a_j}, \cdots, \underset{j}{-a_i + a_j}, \cdots) \quad \text{by property 2}$$

$$= -D(\cdots, \underset{i}{-a_j}, \cdots, \underset{j}{-a_i}, \cdots) \quad \begin{array}{l} \text{by properties} \\ \text{1 and 2.} \end{array}$$

$$= -D(\cdots, \underset{i}{a_j}, \cdots, \underset{j}{a_i}, \cdots)$$

B.   If $a_i = a_j$, $i \neq j$, then by statement A we have
$$D(a_1, \cdots, a_n) = D(\cdots, \underset{i}{a_j}, \cdots, \underset{j}{a_i}, \cdots) = -D(a_1, \cdots, a_n)$$

and hence
$$2D(a_1, \cdots, a_n) = 0.$$

This implies that $D(a_1, \cdots, a_n) = 0$, and statement B is proved.

C. Let $j \neq i$, and $\lambda \in R$. We may assume $\lambda \neq 0$. Then

$$D(\cdots, \underset{i}{a_i}, \cdots, \underset{j}{a_j}, \cdots) = \lambda^{-1}D(\cdots, \underset{i}{a_i}, \cdots, \underset{j}{\lambda a_j}, \cdots) \quad \text{by property 2}$$

$$= \lambda^{-1}D(\cdots, \underset{i}{a_i + \lambda a_j}, \cdots, \underset{j}{\lambda a_j}, \cdots) \quad \text{by property 1}$$

$$= D(\cdots, a_i + \lambda a_j, \cdots, a_j, \cdots).$$

Repeating this argument, we obtain statement C.

D. If $a_1, \cdots, a_n$ are linearly dependent, then some a_i can be expressed as a linear combination of the remaining vectors:

$$a_i = \sum_{j \neq i} \lambda_j a_j.$$

By proposition C we have

$$D(a_1, \cdots, a_n) = D(\cdots, \underset{i}{a_i - \sum_{j \neq i} \lambda_j a_j}, \cdots)$$

$$= D(\cdots, \underset{i}{0}, \cdots)$$

$$= 0D(\cdots, \underset{i}{0}, \cdots) \quad \text{by property 2}$$

$$= 0.$$

E. Because of property 2 it is sufficient to prove, for example, that

$$\textbf{(11.7)} \quad D(a_1 + a_1', a_2, \cdots, a_n)$$
$$= D(a_1, a_2, \cdots, a_n) + D(a_1', a_2, \cdots, a_2).$$

We may assume that $\{a_2, \cdots, a_n\}$ are linearly independent [otherwise, by statement D both sides of (11.7) are zero and there is nothing to prove]. By (7.15) the set $\{a_2, \cdots, a_n\}$ can be completed to a basis

$$\{\bar{a}_1, a_2, \cdots, a_n\}$$

of R_n. Then by statement C and axiom 2 we have:

$$\textbf{(11.8)} \quad D(\lambda_1 \bar{a}_1 + \sum_{i>1} \lambda_i a_i, a_2, \cdots, a_n) = \lambda_1 D(\bar{a}_1, a_2, \cdots, a_n), \quad \text{for all}$$

choices of $\lambda_1, \cdots, \lambda_n$.

Now let

$$a_1 = \lambda_1 \bar{a}_1 + \lambda_2 a_2 + \cdots + \lambda_n a_n,$$
$$a_1' = \mu_1 \bar{a}_1 + \mu_2 a_2 + \cdots + \mu_n a_n.$$

Then

$$a_1 + a_1' = (\lambda_1 + \mu_1)\bar{a}_1 + (\lambda_2 + \mu_2)a_2 + \cdots + (\lambda_n + \mu_n)a_n.$$

By (11.8) we have

$$D(a_1 + a_1', a_2, \cdots, a_n) = (\lambda_1 + \mu_1)D(\bar{a}_1, a_2, \cdots, a_n),$$
$$D(a_1, a_2, \cdots, a_n) = \lambda_1 D(\bar{a}_1, a_2, \cdots, a_n),$$
$$D(a_1', a_2, \cdots, a_n) = \mu_1 D(\bar{a}_1, a_2, \cdots, a_n).$$

By the distributive law in R we obtain (11.7), and the proof of the theorem is completed.

REMARK.   Many authors use statements E and A instead of axiom 1 in the definition of determinant. The point of our definition (using axiom 1) is that we are assuming much less and can still prove the fundamental rule E by using the fairly deep result (7.15) concerning sets of linearly independent vectors in R_n.

EXERCISES

Note.   In these exercises D always denotes a fixed determinant function on R_n.

1. Prove that if $a_1 = \langle \xi, \eta \rangle$, $a_2 = \langle \lambda, \mu \rangle$ in R_2, then

$$D(a_1, a_2) = \xi\mu - \eta\lambda.$$

Show that the system of equations

$$\xi x_1 + \lambda x_2 = \beta_1$$
$$\eta x_1 + \mu x_2 = \beta_2$$

has the solutions

$$x_1 = \frac{D(b, a_2)}{D(a_1, a_2)}, \qquad x_2 = \frac{D(a_1, b)}{D(a_1, a_2)},$$

where $b = \langle \beta_1, \beta_2 \rangle$ and $D(a_1, a_2) \neq 0$.

2. Prove that if $a = \langle \alpha_1, \alpha_2, \alpha_3 \rangle$, $b = \langle \beta_1, \beta_2, \beta_3 \rangle$, $c = \langle \gamma_1, \gamma_2, \gamma_3 \rangle$, then

$$D(a, b, c) = \alpha_1(\beta_2\gamma_3 - \gamma_2\beta_3) - \alpha_2(\beta_1\gamma_3 - \beta_3\gamma_1) + \alpha_3(\beta_1\gamma_2 - \beta_2\gamma_1).$$

Remark.   These problems suggest that definition (11.5) and theorem (11.6) can be used to calculate determinants in particular cases, even though we have not as yet proved in general the existence of determinant functions. The next problem gives what is probably the most efficient method of calculating determinants; it is based on the fundamental Exercise 3 in Section 7, on reducing sets of vectors to echelon form.

3. a. Let $a_1, \cdots, a_n$ be vectors in R_n. Prove either that $a_1, \cdots, a_n$ are linearly dependent [and hence $D(a_1, \cdots, a_n) = 0$] or that

$$D(a_1, \cdots, a_n) = D(b_1, \cdots, b_n),$$

where $b_1, \cdots, b_n$ are in echelon form. (*Hint:* Use theorem (11.6) and the method of Exercise 3, Section 7; also, see Exercise 4, below.)

b. Suppose $b_1, \cdots, b_n$ are in echelon form and that $\beta_1, \cdots, \beta_n$ are the first nonzero entries of $b_1, \cdots, b_n$, respectively. Prove that

$$D(b_1, \cdots, b_n) = \beta_1 \cdots \beta_n.$$

c. Prove that if $a_1, \cdots, a_n$ are linearly independent then $D(a_1, \cdots, a_n) \neq 0$.

4. Calculate the following determinants.

a. $D(a_1, a_2, a_3, a_4)$, where $a_1 = \langle -1, 0, 1, 1 \rangle$, $a_2 = \langle 2, -1, 0, 2 \rangle$, $a_3 = \langle 1, 2, 1, -1 \rangle$, $a_4 = \langle -1, -1, 1, 0 \rangle$.

Solution. By theorem (11.6) we have

$$D(a_1, a_2, a_3, a_4) = D(a_1, a_2', a_3', a_4')$$

where

$$a_2' = a_2 + 2a_1 = \langle 0, -1, 2, 4 \rangle,$$
$$a_3' = a_3 + a_1 = \langle 0, 2, 2, 0 \rangle,$$
$$a_4' = a_4 - a_1 = \langle 0, -1, 0, -1 \rangle.$$

Again by theorem (11.6), we have

$$D(a_1, a_2', a_3', a_4') = D(a_1, a_2', a_3'', a_4'')$$

where

$$a_3'' = a_3' + 2a_2' = \langle 0, 0, 6, 8 \rangle,$$
$$a_4'' = a_4' - a_2' = \langle 0, 0, -2, -5 \rangle.$$

Finally,

$$D(a_1, a_2, a_3, a_4) = D(a_1, a_2', a_3'', a_4''')$$

where

$$a_4''' = a_4'' + \tfrac{1}{3}a_3'' = \langle 0, 0, 0, -\tfrac{7}{3} \rangle.$$

The vectors a_1, a_2', a_3'', a_4''' are in echelon form, so by part **b** of Exercise 3 we have

$$D(a_1, a_2, a_3, a_4) = (-1)(-1)(6)(-\tfrac{7}{3}) = -14.$$

Note that this whole procedure is easy to check for arithmetical errors.

b. $D(a_1, a_2, a_3)$, where $a_1 = \langle 1, 2, 4 \rangle$, $a_2 = \langle 1, 1, 1 \rangle$, $a_3 = \langle 1, 3, 9 \rangle$.

c. $D(a_1, a_2, a_3, a_4, a_5)$, where $a_1 = \langle 0, 1, 3, 0, 2 \rangle$, $a_2 = \langle 1, -1, 0, 2, 1 \rangle$, $a_3 = \langle 2, 3, -1, 0, 0 \rangle$, $a_4 = \langle 3, 0, 0, -1, 2 \rangle$, $a_5 = \langle 0, -1, 2, 1, 5 \rangle$.

d. $D(a_1, a_2, a_3, a_4)$, where $a_1 = \langle 1, 2, -1, 0 \rangle$, $a_2 = \langle 2, 0, 0, 1 \rangle$, $a_3 = \langle 1, 1, -1, 2 \rangle$, $a_4 = \langle 0, 1, 2, -1 \rangle$.

5. Let $D^*(a_1, \cdots, a_n)$ be a function on vectors $a_1, \cdots, a_n$ in R_n to R such that, for all a_j, a_i', a_{ij}'' in R_n,

(1) $D^*(e_1, \cdots, e_n) = 1$, where the e_i are the unit vectors.

(2) $D^*(a_1, \cdots, \lambda a_i, \cdots, a_n) = \lambda D^*(a_1, \cdots, a_n)$,   for $\lambda \in R$.

(3) $D^*(a_1, \cdots, a_i' + a_i'', \cdots, a_n) = D^*(a_1, \cdots, a_i', \cdots, a_n)$
$$\qquad\qquad\qquad\qquad + D^*(a_1, \cdots, a_i'', \cdots, a_n).$$

(4) $D^*(a_1, \cdots, a_n) = 0$ if $a_i = a_j$ for $i \neq j$.

Prove that D^* is a determinant function on R_n.

12. EXISTENCE AND UNIQUENESS OF DETERMINANTS

It is time to remove all doubts about whether a function D satisfying the conditions of definition (11.5) exists or not. In this section we shall prove, first, that at most one such function can exist, and then we shall give a construction of such a function. In the course of the discussion we shall obtain some other useful properties of determinants.

(12.1)   Theorem. *Let D and D' be two functions satisfying conditions 1, 2, and 3 of definition* (11.5); *then, for all $a_1, \cdots, a_n$ in R_n,*

$$D(a_1, \cdots, a_n) = D'(a_1, \cdots, a_n).$$

Proof. Consider the function Δ defined by

$$\Delta(a_1, \cdots, a_n) = D(a_1, \cdots, a_n) - D'(a_1, \cdots, a_n).$$

Then, because both the functions D and D' satisfy the conditions of (11.5) as well as of (11.6), Δ has the following properties.

(12.2) $\Delta(e_1, \cdots, e_n) = 0.$

(12.3) $\Delta(a_1, \cdots, a_n)$ changes sign if two of the vectors a_i and a_j are interchanged, and $\Delta(a_1, \cdots, a_n) = 0$,   if $a_i = a_j$ for $i \neq j$.

(12.4) $\Delta(\cdots, \lambda a_i, \cdots) = \lambda \Delta(\cdots, a_i, \cdots)$,   for $\lambda \in R$.

(12.5) $\Delta(\cdots, a_i + a_i', \cdots) = \Delta(\cdots, a_i, \cdots) + \Delta(\cdots, a_i', \cdots)$.

Now let $a_1, \cdots, a_n$ be arbitrary vectors in R_n. It is sufficient to prove that $\Delta(a_1, \cdots, a_n) = 0$, and we shall show that this is a consequence of the properties (12.2) to (12.5). Because $e_1, \cdots, e_n$ is a basis of R_n we can express

$$a_i = \lambda_{i1}e_1 + \cdots + \lambda_{in}e_n = \sum_{j=1}^{n} \lambda_{ij}e_j.$$

Using (12.4) and (12.5) applied to the first position, then to the second position, etc., we have

$$\Delta(a_1, \cdots, a_n) = \Delta\left(\sum_{j=1}^{n} \lambda_{1j}e_j, a_2, \cdots, a_n\right)$$

$$= \sum_{j=1}^{n} \lambda_{1j}\Delta(e_j, a_2, \cdots, a_n)$$

$$= \sum_{j_1=1}^{n} \lambda_{1j_1}\Delta\left(e_{j_1}, \sum_{j_2=1}^{n} \lambda_{2j_2}e_{j_2}, a_3, \cdots, a_n\right)$$

$$= \sum_{j_1=1}^{n} \sum_{j_2=1}^{n} \lambda_{1j_1}\lambda_{2j_2}\Delta(e_{j_1}, e_{j_2}, a_3, \cdots, a_n)$$

$$= \cdots = \sum_{j_1=1}^{n} \sum_{j_2=1}^{n} \cdots \sum_{j_n=1}^{n} \lambda_{1j_1}\lambda_{2j_2} \cdots \lambda_{nj_n}\Delta(e_{j_1}, \cdots, e_{j_n})$$

$$= \sum_{j_1, \cdots, j_n=1}^{n} \lambda_{1j_1} \cdots \lambda_{nj_n}\Delta(e_{j_1}, \cdots, e_{j_n})$$

where the last sum consists of n^n terms, and is obtained by letting $j_1, \cdots, j_n$ range independently between 1 and n inclusive. By (12.2) and (12.3) it follows easily by induction* that for all choices of $j_1, \cdots, j_n$, $\Delta(e_{j_1}, \cdots, e_{j_n}) = 0$. Therefore $\Delta(a_1, \cdots, a_n) = 0$, and the uniqueness theorem is proved.

Now we come to the proof of existence of determinants.

---

* What has to be proved by induction is that either $\Delta(e_{j_1}, \cdots, e_{j_n}) = 0$ (if two of the j's are equal) or $\Delta(e_{j_1}, \cdots, e_{j_n}) = \pm\Delta(e_1, \cdots, e_n)$ (if the j's are distinct).

(12.6) Theorem. *There exists a function* $D(a_1, \cdots, a_n)$ *satisfying the conditions of definition* (11.5).

Proof. We use induction on n. For $n = 1$, the function $D(\alpha) = \alpha$, $\alpha \in R$, satisfies the requirements. Now suppose that D is a function on R_{n-1} that satisfies the conditions in definition (11.5). Fix an index j, $1 \leq j \leq n$, and let the vectors $a_1, \cdots, a_n$ in R_n be given by

$$a_i = (\alpha_{i1}, \cdots, \alpha_{in}), \qquad \alpha_{ik} \in R, \quad 1 \leq i \leq n.$$

Then *define:*

(12.7) $D(a_1, \cdots, a_n) = (-1)^{1+i}\alpha_{1j}D_{1j} + \cdots + (-1)^{n+i}\alpha_{nj}D_{nj}$

where, for $1 \leq i \leq n$, D_{ij} is the determinant of the vectors $a_1^{(i)}, \cdots, a_{n-1}^{(i)}$ in R_{n-1} obtained from the $n - 1$ vectors $a_1, \cdots, a_{i-1}$, $a_{i+1}, \cdots, a_n$ by deleting the jth component in each case.

We shall prove that the function D defined by (12.7) satisfies the axioms for a determinant. By the uniqueness theorem (12.1) it will then follow that all the expansions (12.7) for different j are equal, which is an important result in its own right.

Let us look more closely at (12.7). It says that $D(a_1, \cdots, a_n)$ is obtained by taking the coefficients of the jth column of the matrix A with rows $a_1, \cdots, a_n$ and multiplying each of them by a power of (-1) times the determinant of certain vectors, which form the rows of a matrix obtained from A, by deleting the jth column and one of the rows.

First let $e_1, \cdots, e_n$ be the unit vectors in R_n; then the matrix A is given by

$$A = \begin{pmatrix} 1 & & & & 0 \\ & 1 & & & \\ & & \ddots & & \\ & & & \ddots & \\ 0 & & & & 1 \end{pmatrix}$$

where zeros fill all the vacant spaces. Then there is only one nonzero entry in the jth column, namely $\alpha_{jj} = 1$. The matrix from whose rows D_{jj} is computed is the $(n - 1)$-by-$(n - 1)$ matrix

$$\begin{pmatrix} 1 & & & 0 \\ & 1 & & \\ & & \ddots & \\ 0 & & & 1 \end{pmatrix}$$

Hence (12.7) becomes
$$D(e_1, \cdots, e_n) = (-1)^{i+i}\alpha_{jj}D_{jj} = 1$$
since $\alpha_{jj} = 1$, and since $D_{jj} = 1$ by the determinant axioms for R_{n-1}.

Next let us consider replacing a_i by λa_i for some $\lambda \in R$. Then the matrix A' whose rows are $a_1, \cdots, a_{i-1}, \lambda a_i, a_{i+1}, \cdots, a_n$ is

$$A' = \begin{pmatrix} \alpha_{11} & \cdots & \alpha_{1j} & \cdots & \alpha_{1n} \\ \cdots\cdots\cdots\cdots\cdots\cdots\cdots \\ \alpha_{i-1,1} & \cdots & \alpha_{i-1,j} & \cdots & \alpha_{i-1,n} \\ \lambda\alpha_{i1} & \cdots & \lambda\alpha_{ij} & \cdots & \lambda\alpha_{in} \\ \cdots\cdots\cdots\cdots\cdots\cdots\cdots \\ \alpha_{n1} & \cdots & \alpha_{nj} & \cdots & \alpha_{nn} \end{pmatrix}.$$

Then (12.7) becomes

$$(12.8) \quad \begin{aligned} D(\cdots, \lambda a_i, \cdots) &= (-1)^{1+i}\alpha_{1j}D'_{1j} + \cdots + (-1)^{i+i}\lambda\alpha_{ij}D'_{ij} \\ &\quad + \cdots + (-1)^{n+i}\alpha_{nj}D'_{nj} \end{aligned}$$

where D'_{ij} is defined for A' as D_{ij} is defined for A. From this definition and the properties of D on R_{n-1} we have $D'_{kj} = \lambda D_{kj}$, for $k \neq i$, and $D'_{ij} = D_{ij}$. Then (12.8) yields the result that

$$D(\cdots, \lambda a_i, \cdots) = \lambda D(a_1, \cdots, a_n).$$

Finally, let $i \neq k$, and consider the determinant of the vectors

$$a_1, \cdots, \underbrace{a_i + a_k}_{i}, \cdots, a_k, \cdots, a_n.$$

Then the matrix A'' whose rows are these vectors is

$$A'' = \begin{matrix} \\ i \\ \\ k \\ \\ \\ \end{matrix} \begin{pmatrix} \alpha_{11} & \cdots & \alpha_{1n} \\ \cdots\cdots\cdots\cdots\cdots \\ \alpha_{i1} + \alpha_{k1} & \cdots & \alpha_{in} + \alpha_{kn} \\ \cdots\cdots\cdots\cdots\cdots \\ \alpha_{k1} & \cdots & \alpha_{kn} \\ \cdots\cdots\cdots\cdots\cdots \\ \alpha_{n1} & \cdots & \alpha_{nn} \end{pmatrix}.$$

Then (12.7) becomes

$$(12.9) \quad \begin{aligned} D'' &= D(\cdots, \underset{i}{a_i + a_k}, \cdots, \underset{k}{a_k}, \cdots, a_n) \\ &= (-1)^{1+i}\alpha_{1j}D''_{1j} + \cdots + (-1)^{i+i}(\alpha_{ij} + \alpha_{kj})D''_{ij} \\ &\quad + \cdots + (-1)^{k+i}\alpha_{kj}D''_{kj} + \cdots + (-1)^{n+i}\alpha_{nj}D''_{nj} \end{aligned}$$

where the D''_{ij} are defined as in (12.7) from the vectors which constitute the rows of A''. From the induction hypothesis that

$$D(\cdots, \underset{i}{a'_i + a'_s}, \cdots) = D(a'_1, \cdots, a'_{n-1}), \qquad i \neq s \text{ in } R_{n-1}$$

we have now:

(12.10) $D''_{sj} = D_{sj}$,   for $1 \leq s \leq n$ and $s \neq i, k$.

Inspection of A'' yields also

$$D''_{ij} = D_{ij}.$$

But D''_{kj} is not so easy. The vectors contributing to D''_{kj} are obtained from A'' by deleting the kth row and jth column. Since the ith row of A'' is a sum $a_i + a_j$, we can apply statement E of (11.6) to express D''_{kj} as a sum of two determinants, of which the first is D_{kj} and the second $\pm D_{ij}$, where the $\pm$ sign is determined by statement A of (11.6) and by an inductive argument is equal to $(-1)^{|k-i|+1}$. Thus we have

$$D''_{kj} = D_{kj} + (-1)^{|k-i|+1}D_{ij}.$$

We shall also need the facts that $(-1)^{|a|} = (-1)^a$ and $(-1)^{a+2b} = (-1)^a$ for all integers a, b. Substituting in (12.9), we obtain

$$
\begin{aligned}
D'' &= (-1)^{1+i}\alpha_{1j}D_{1j} + \cdots + (-1)^{i+i}(\alpha_{ij} + \alpha_{kj})D_{ij} \\
&\quad + \cdots + (-1)^{k+i}\alpha_{kj}[D_{kj} + (-1)^{|k-i|+1}D_{ij}] \\
&\quad + \cdots + (-1)^{n+i}\alpha_{nj}D_{nj} \\
&= D(a_1, \cdots, a_n) + [(-1)^{i+i} + (-1)^{k+j+|k-i|+1}]\alpha_{kj}D_{ij}.
\end{aligned}
$$

We are finished if we can show that the coefficient of $\alpha_{kj}D_{ij}$ is zero. We have

$$
\begin{aligned}
(-1)^{i+i} + (-1)^{k+j+|k-i|+1} &= (-1)^{i+i} + (-1)^{k+i}(-1)^{k-i}(-1) \\
&= (-1)^{i+i} + (-1)^{j-i+1} = (-1)^{i+i} + (-1)^{j+i+1} = 0.
\end{aligned}
$$

This completes the proof of the theorem.

In this section we have proved the existence of a determinant function $D(a_1, \cdots, a_n)$ of n vectors $a_1, \cdots, a_n$ in R_n. If these vectors are given by

$$
\begin{aligned}
a_1 &= \alpha_{11}e_1 + \cdots + \alpha_{1n}e_n \\
&\quad \cdots\cdots\cdots\cdots\cdots \\
a_n &= \alpha_{n1}e_1 + \cdots + \alpha_{nn}e_n
\end{aligned}
$$

that is, if we think of them as the rows of the matrix

$$
A = \begin{pmatrix} \alpha_{11} \cdots \alpha_{1n} \\ \cdots\cdots \\ \cdots\cdots \\ \cdots\cdots \\ \alpha_{n1} \cdots \alpha_{nn} \end{pmatrix},
$$

then in the proof of theorem (12.1) we have shown that

(12.11) $\quad D(a_1, \cdots, a_n) = \sum_{j_1=1}^{n} \cdots \sum_{j_n=1}^{n} \alpha_{1j_1} \cdots \alpha_{nj_n} D(e_{j_1}, \cdots, e_{j_n})$

where the sum is taken over the n^n possible choices of $(j_1, \cdots, j_n)$. Since $D(e_{j_1}, \cdots, e_{j_n}) = 0$ when two of the entries are the same, we can rewrite (12.11) in the form

(12.12) $\quad D(a_1, \cdots, a_n) = \sum_{j_1, \cdots, j_n} \alpha_{1j_1} \cdots \alpha_{nj_n} D(e_{j_1}, \cdots, e_{j_n})$

where it is understood that the sum is taken over the $n! = n(n-1)(n-2) \cdots 3 \cdot 2 \cdot 1$ possible choices of $\{j_1, \cdots, j_n\}$ in which all the j_i's are distinct. The formula (12.12) is called the *complete expansion* of the determinant. If we view the determinant $D(a_1, \cdots, a_n)$ as a function $D(A)$ of the matrix whose rows are $a_1, \cdots, a_n$, then the complete expansion shows that, since the $D(e_{j_1}, \cdots, e_{j_n})$ are ± 1, the determinant is a sum (with coefficients ± 1) of products of the coefficients of the matrix A. If the matrix A is viewed as a point in the n^2-dimensional space, then (12.12) shows that $D(A)$ is a continuous function of A.

The idea of viewing the determinant $D(a_1, \cdots, a_n)$ as a function of a matrix A with rows $a_1, \cdots, a_n$ at once raises another problem. Let $c_1, \cdots, c_n$ be the columns of A. Then we can form $D(c_1, \cdots, c_n)$ and ask what is the relation of this function to $D(a_1, \cdots, a_n)$.

(12.13) **Theorem.** *Let A be an n-by-n matrix with rows $a_1, \cdots, a_n$ and columns $c_1, \cdots, c_n$; then $D(a_1, \cdots, a_n) = D(c_1, \cdots, c_n)$.*

Proof. Let us use the complete expansion (12.12) and view (12.12) as defining a new function:

(12.14) $\quad D^*(c_1, \cdots, c_n) = \sum_{j_1, \cdots, j_n} \alpha_{1j_1} \cdots \alpha_{nj_n} D(e_{j_1}, \cdots, e_{j_n})$

$$= D(a_1, \cdots, a_n).$$

We shall prove that $D^*(c_1, \cdots, c_n)$ satisfies the axioms for a determinant function; then theorem (12.1) will imply that $D^*(c_1, \cdots, c_n) = D(c_1, \cdots, c_n)$.

First suppose that $c_1, \cdots, c_n$ are the unit vectors $e_1, \cdots, e_n$. Then the row vectors $a_1, \cdots, a_n$ are also the unit vectors and we have

$$D^*(e_1, \cdots, e_n) = D(e_1, \cdots, e_n) = 1.$$

From (12.14) it is clear, since each term in the sum has exactly one entry from a given column, that

$$D^*(\cdots, \lambda c_i, \cdots) = \lambda D^*(\cdots, c_i, \cdots).$$

Finally, let us consider

$$D^*(\cdots, c_i + c_k, \cdots), \qquad k \neq i.$$

That means that, for $1 \leq r \leq n$, α_{ri} is replaced by $\alpha_{ri} + \alpha_{rk}$. Making this substitution in (12.14), we can split up $D^*(\cdots, c_i + c_k, \cdots)$ as a sum $D^*(\cdots, c_i + c_k, \cdots) = D^*(\cdots, c_i, \cdots) + D^*(\cdots, c_k, \cdots)$, and we shall be finished if we can show that $D^*(c_1, \cdots, c_n) = 0$ if two of the vectors, c_r and c_s, are equal, for $r \neq s$. In (12.14), consider a term

$$\alpha_{1j_1} \cdots \alpha_{kj_k} \cdots \alpha_{lj_l} \cdots \alpha_{nj_n} D(e_{j_1}, \cdots, e_{j_k}, \cdots, e_{j_l}, \cdots, e_{j_n})$$

such that $j_k = r$, $j_l = s$. There will also be a term in (12.14) of the form

$$\alpha_{1j_1} \cdots \alpha_{kj_l} \cdots \alpha_{lj_k} \cdots \alpha_{nj_n} D(e_{j_1}, \cdots, e_{j_l}, \cdots, e_{j_k}, \cdots, e_{j_n})$$

and the sum of these two terms will be zero, since $c_r = c_s$ and

$$D(\cdots, e_{j_k}, \cdots, e_{j_l}, \cdots) = -D(\cdots, e_{j_l}, \cdots, e_{j_k}, \cdots).$$

Thus each term of $D^*(c_1, \cdots, c_n)$ is canceled by another, and we have shown that $D^*(c_1, \cdots, c_n) = 0$ if $c_r = c_s$, for $r \neq s$. We have proved that D^* satisfies the axioms for a determinant function. By theorem (12.1) we conclude that $D(a_1, \cdots, a_n) = D(c_1, \cdots, c_n)$, and theorem (12.13) is proved.

We can now speak unambiguously of $D(A)$ for any n-by-n matrix A and know that $D(A)$ satisfies the axioms of a determinant function when viewed as a function either of rows or of columns. When

$$A = \begin{pmatrix} \alpha_{11} & \cdots & \alpha_{1n} \\ \cdots\cdots\cdots \\ \cdots\cdots\cdots \\ \cdots\cdots\cdots \\ \alpha_{n1} & \cdots & \alpha_{nn} \end{pmatrix}$$

we shall frequently use the notation

$$D(A) = \begin{vmatrix} \alpha_{11} & \cdots & \alpha_{1n} \\ \cdots\cdots\cdots \\ \cdots\cdots\cdots \\ \cdots\cdots\cdots \\ \alpha_{n1} & \cdots & \alpha_{nn} \end{vmatrix}.$$

Theorem (12.13) can be restated in the form

(12.15) $$D(A) = D({}^t A)$$

where ${}^tA$ is called the *transpose* of A and is obtained from A by interchanging rows and columns. Thus, if α_{ij} is the (i,j) entry of A, α_{ji} is the (i,j) entry of ${}^tA$.

13. THE MULTIPLICATION THEOREM FOR DETERMINANTS

We consider next what is perhaps the most important property of determinants and one that we shall use frequently in the later parts of the book. The definition we have given for determinants was chosen partly because it leads to a simple proof of this theorem. To motivate the theorem we shall begin with a discussion of the concept of a linear transformation as it arises from our study of systems of linear equations. In Chapter 5 we shall have a more abstract discussion of linear transformations.

A system of linear equations,

$$(13.1) \qquad \sum_{j=1}^{n} \alpha_{ij}x_j = y_i, \qquad i = 1, \cdots, m,$$

can be viewed in two ways. As in Section 8, we may think of $y_1, \cdots, y_m$ as given and try to find $x_1, \cdots, x_n$ such that the equations are satisfied. Or we may think of the equations (13.1) as defining a function or transformation which assigns to a given vector $x = \langle x_1, \cdots, x_n \rangle$ in R_n another vector $y = \langle y_1, \cdots, y_m \rangle$ in R_m. This transformation is simply a generalization of the linear function $y = ax$.

(13.2) Definition. Let (α_{ij}) be a fixed m-by-n matrix. The *linear transformation* T *with matrix* (α_{ij}) is the rule which assigns to each vector $x = \langle x_1, \cdots, x_n \rangle$ in R_n the vector $\langle y_1, \cdots, y_m \rangle$ in R_m whose components are given by (13.1), and we shall write $T(x) = y$.

From (13.1) it is clear that we have the important relations

$$(13.3) \qquad T(x_1 + x_2) = T(x_1) + T(x_2), \qquad x_1, x_2 \in R_n,$$
$$T(\alpha x) = \alpha T(x), \qquad \alpha \in R, x \in R_n.$$

(13.4) Theorem. *Let T be a linear transformation of R_n into R_m with matrix (α_{ij}) and let U be a linear transformation of R_m into R_q with matrix (β_{ij}); then the mapping UT of R_n into R_q defined by*

(13.5) $$(UT)x = U(T(x))$$

is a linear transformation with a q-by-n matrix (γ_{ij}) defined by

(13.6) $$\gamma_{ik} = \sum_{j=1}^{m} \beta_{ij}\alpha_{jk}, \qquad 1 \leq i \leq q, \quad 1 \leq k \leq n.$$

Proof. Let $T(x) = y$ where

$$y_i = \sum_{j=1}^{n} \alpha_{ij}x_j, \qquad 1 \leq i \leq m$$

and let $U(y) = z$ where

$$z_i = \sum_{j=1}^{m} \beta_{ij}y_j, \qquad 1 \leq i \leq q.$$

Then, for $1 \leq i \leq q$,

$$z_i = \sum_{j=1}^{m} \beta_{ij}y_j = \sum_{j=1}^{m} \beta_{ij}\left(\sum_{k=1}^{n} \alpha_{jk}x_k\right)$$

$$= \sum_{k=1}^{n}\left(\sum_{j=1}^{m} \beta_{ij}\alpha_{jk}\right)x_k$$

and the theorem is proved.

The linear transformation UT defined by (13.5) is called the product of the transformations U and T, and the matrix (γ_{ij}) is by definition the *product* of the matrices (α_{ij}) and (β_{ij}). The rule (13.5) is the same as the definition of composite function,* or "function of a function" in calculus. Theorem (13.4) says that the matrix of a product of two transformations is the product of their matrices.

Let us examine (13.6) more closely. It gives a rule for multiplying a matrix with q rows and m columns by a matrix with m rows and n columns to obtain a matrix with q rows and n columns. To obtain the element of the ith row and jth column of $(\beta_{ij})(\alpha_{ij})$ we take the ith row

$$(\beta_{i1}, \cdots, \beta_{im})$$

of (β_{ij}) and the jth column

$$\begin{pmatrix} \alpha_{1j} \\ \cdot \\ \cdot \\ \cdot \\ \alpha_{mj} \end{pmatrix}$$

---

* See Exercise 3 of Section 3.

of (α_{ij}), multiply corresponding elements, and add. For example,

$$\begin{pmatrix} 2 & -1 & 3 \\ 0 & 1 & 1 \end{pmatrix} \begin{pmatrix} -1 & 0 & 1 \\ 1 & 2 & 1 \\ 3 & -1 & 0 \end{pmatrix} = \begin{pmatrix} 6 & -5 & 1 \\ 4 & 1 & 1 \end{pmatrix}.$$

A natural question to ask is the following. Suppose that $A = (\alpha_{ij})$ and $B = (\beta_{ij})$ are n-by-n matrices; then AB is an n-by-n matrix. Is there any relation between $D(AB)$ and $D(A)$ and $D(B)$?

The first step is the following preliminary result.*

(13.7) Lemma. *Let $F(a_1, \cdots, a_n)$ be a function of n-tuples of vectors $a_i \in R_n$ to the real numbers which satisfies axioms 1 and 2 in the definition (11.5) of the determinant function; then for all $a_1, \cdots, a_n$ in R_n we have*

$$F(a_1, \cdots, a_n) = D(a_1, \cdots, a_n)F(e_1, \cdots, e_n)$$

where the e_i are the unit vectors and D is the determinant function on R_n.

Proof. If $F(e_1, \cdots, e_n) = 1$, then $F = D$ by theorem (12.1), and the lemma is proved.

Now suppose $F(e_1, \cdots, e_n) \neq 1$ and consider the function

(13.8) $\qquad D'(a_1, \cdots, a_n) = \dfrac{D(a_1, \cdots, a_n) - F(a_1, \cdots, a_n)}{1 - F(e_1, \cdots, e_n)}.$

It is clear that D' satisfies the axioms 1, 2, and 3 of (11.5). Hence, by theorem (12.1), $D' = D$, and solving for $F(a_1, \cdots, a_n)$ in (13.8) we obtain the conclusion of the lemma.

(13.9) Theorem. *Let A and B be n-by-n matrices; then $D(AB) = D(A)D(B)$.*

Proof. Let $A = (\alpha_{ij})$, $B = (\beta_{ij})$ and let U be the linear transformation whose matrix is β_{ij}. Define a function F by

$$F(a_1, \cdots, a_n) = D[U(a_1), \cdots, U(a_n)], \qquad a_i \in R_n.$$

By axioms 1 and 2 of (11.5) for D and by (13.3) it is clear that F satisfies axioms 1 and 2. By lemma (13.7) we have $F(a_1, \cdots, a_n) = D(a_1, \cdots, a_n)F(e_1, \cdots, e_n)$ and, hence,

---

* The idea of using this lemma as a key to the multiplication theorem comes from Schreier and Sperner (see Bibliography).

(13.10) $D[U(a_1), \cdots, U(a_n)] = D(a_1, \cdots, a_n)D[U(e_1), \cdots, U(e_n)].$

Now let $a_1, \cdots, a_n$ be the columns of the matrix A. Then for $1 \le i \le n$ we compute $U(a_i)$.

Since $a_i = \langle \alpha_{1i}, \cdots, \alpha_{ni} \rangle$, $U(a_i)$ is the vector

$$\left\langle \sum_{k=1}^{n} \beta_{1k}\alpha_{ki}, \cdots, \sum_{k=1}^{n} \beta_{nk}\alpha_{ki} \right\rangle$$

which is the ith column of the matrix BA. Similarly,

$$U(e_i) = \langle \beta_{1i}, \beta_{2i}, \cdots, \beta_{ni} \rangle$$

which is the ith column of the matrix B. Then equation (13.10) yields

$$D(BA) = D(A)D(B)$$

and, since $D(A)D(B) = D(B)D(A)$, the theorem is proved.

As a first application of the multiplication theorem, we prove:

(13.11)   Theorem.   *Let A be an n-by-n matrix; then A has rank n if and only if $D(A) \ne 0$.*

Proof.   Part D of theorem (11.6) shows that if A has rank less than n then $D(A) = 0$. It remains to prove that if A has rank n then $D(A) \ne 0$. (For another proof see exercise 3 of Section 11.) Let $\{a_1, \cdots, a_n\}$ be the row vectors of A. Since A has rank n, $\{a_1, \cdots, a_n\}$ is a basis for R_n; therefore for each i, $1 \le i \le n$, we can express the ith unit vector e_i as a linear combination of $\{a_1, \cdots, a_n\}$:

(13.12) $\qquad\qquad e_i = \beta_{i1}a_1 + \cdots + \beta_{in}a_n.$

Let B be the matrix (β_{ij}); then (13.12) implies that the matrix whose rows are $\{e_1, \cdots, e_n\}$ is the product matrix BA. Since $D(e_1, \cdots, e_n) = 1$, we have by theorem (13.9)

$$1 = D(BA) = D(B)D(A)$$

and $D(A) \ne 0$ as required.

We conclude this section with an application of theorem (13.11) to give a useful criterion for a linear transformation T to be one-to-one. Our discussion is based on (13.11) and on the theory of systems of linear equations. The same topic will be discussed from a more abstract point of view in Chapter 5.

(13.13)   Theorem.   *Let $T:R_n \to R_n$ be a linear transformation with matrix A. Then the following statements are equivalent:*

(1) T *is a one-to-one transformation.*
(2) T *maps* R_n *onto* R_n [i.e., for every $y \in R_n$, *there exists a vector* $x \in R_n$ *such that* $T(x) = y$].
(3) $D(A) \neq 0$.

Proof. First assume statement (1). Since T is one-to-one, the system of equations

$$(13.14) \qquad \sum_{j=1}^{n} \alpha_{ij}x_j = y_i, \qquad i = 1, 2, \cdots, n,$$

defining T has a unique solution x for each y in R_n for which the system is solvable. Therefore, by theorem (8.9), the homogeneous system associated with (13.14) has only the trivial solution. By corollary (9.3) the matrix $A = (\alpha_{ij})$ has rank n. It then follows from theorem (8.5) that for every vector y the system (13.14) has a solution. Thus the mapping T is onto, and we have shown that statement (1) implies statement (2).

Now assume statement (2). The vectors y defined by the right-hand side of (13.14) are linear combinations of the column vectors of A. Since T is onto, the column vectors of A generate all of R_n. Therefore A has rank n, and by (13.11) $D(A) \neq 0$. Thus statement (2) implies statement (3).

Finally assume statement (3). By (13.11) A has rank n. By theorems (9.3) and (8.9) the system (13.14) has a unique solution for each y. Therefore T is one-to-one. This completes the proof of the theorem.

Another application of the multiplication theorem to permutations is given in the following exercises.

EXERCISES

1. Compute $D(AB)$ by multiplying out the matrices and also by theorem (13.9) where

$$A = \begin{pmatrix} 1 & 1 & -2 & 1 \\ 0 & -1 & 3 & 1 \\ 0 & 0 & 3 & 2 \\ 0 & 0 & 0 & -2 \end{pmatrix}, \qquad B = \begin{pmatrix} 3 & 0 & 0 & 0 \\ -1 & 1 & 0 & 0 \\ 0 & 1 & -2 & 0 \\ 3 & 2 & 1 & 1 \end{pmatrix}.$$

2. Show that if A, B, C are n-by-n matrices such that $AB = C$, where $D(C) \neq 0$, then $D(A) \neq 0$.

3. Let A be an n-by-n matrix such that ${}^t A \cdot A = I$, where ${}^t A$ is the transpose of A and I is the identity matrix whose rows are the unit vectors $e_1, \cdots, e_n$. Prove that $D(A) = \pm 1$.

4. **Definitions.** If $X = \{1, 2, \cdots, n\}$. A *permutation* of X is a one-to-one mapping σ of X onto X. The set of all permutations of X will be denoted by $P(X)$. A permutation σ can be described by the notation

$$\sigma = \begin{pmatrix} 1 & 2 & \cdots & n \\ j_1 & j_2 & \cdots & j_n \end{pmatrix}$$

where $\sigma(1) = j_1$, $\sigma(2) = j_2$, $\cdots$, $\sigma(n) = j_n$. If σ, $\tau \in P(X)$, define their product $\sigma\tau$ by the rule

$$(\sigma\tau)(x) = \sigma[\tau(x)], \qquad x \in X.$$

Prove that $\sigma\tau \in P(X)$. For example,

$$\begin{pmatrix} 1 & 2 & 3 & 4 \\ 2 & 3 & 1 & 4 \end{pmatrix} \begin{pmatrix} 1 & 2 & 3 & 4 \\ 1 & 3 & 4 & 2 \end{pmatrix} = \begin{pmatrix} 1 & 2 & 3 & 4 \\ 2 & 1 & 4 & 3 \end{pmatrix}.$$

a. Define a *transposition* $\sigma = (ij)$ to be a permutation such that $\sigma(i) = j$ and $\sigma(j) = i$ for $i \neq j$ and such that $\sigma(x) = x$ for all x different from i or j. Prove by induction that every permutation $\sigma \in P(X)$ is a product of transpositions.

b. Define for each $\sigma \in P(X)$ the *signature* $\epsilon(\sigma)$ by

$$\epsilon(\sigma) = D(e_{\sigma(1)}, \cdots, e_{\sigma(n)})$$

where $e_1, \cdots, e_n$ are the unit vectors. Prove that $\epsilon(\sigma) = \pm 1$ and that $\epsilon(\sigma\tau) = \epsilon(\sigma)\epsilon(\tau)$ for all σ, $\tau \in P(X)$. [*Hint:* For the last assertion use theorem (13.9).]

c. Define a permutation $\sigma \in P(X)$ as *even* if $\epsilon(\sigma) = 1$ and *odd* if $\epsilon(\sigma) = -1$. Prove that σ is even if and only if σ can be factored in at least one way as a product of an even number of transpositions. Prove that even and odd permutations multiply in the following way:

$$\begin{aligned} \text{(even)(even)} &= \text{even} \\ \text{(even)(odd)} = \text{(odd)(even)} &= \text{odd} \\ \text{(odd)(odd)} &= \text{even}. \end{aligned}$$

d. Prove that the complete expansion of the determinant $D(A)$ of a matrix $A = (\alpha_{ij})$ (see Section 12) can be given in the form

$$D(A) = \sum_{\sigma \in P(X)} \epsilon(\sigma) \alpha_{1\sigma(1)} \cdots \alpha_{n\sigma(n)}.$$

[This formula is sometimes used as the definition of $D(A)$.]

14. FURTHER PROPERTIES OF DETERMINANTS*

In this section we take up a few of the many special topics one can study in the theory of determinants.

ROW AND COLUMN EXPANSIONS, AND INVERTIBLE MATRICES

Let $A = (\alpha_{ij})$ be an n-by-n matrix. Define the (i, j) *cofactor* A_{ij} as $A_{ij} = (-1)^{i+j}D_{ij}$ where D_{ij} is the determinant of the $n - 1$ by $n - 1$ matrix, obtained by deleting the ith row and jth column of A. Then the formulas (12.7) can be stated in the form

$$(14.1) \qquad D(A) = \sum_{k=1}^{n} \alpha_{kj}A_{kj}, \qquad j = 1, 2, \cdots, n.$$

We shall refer to this formula as the *expansion of $D(A)$ along the jth column*. A related formula is

$$(14.2) \qquad \sum_{k=1}^{n} \alpha_{kj}A_{kl} = 0, \qquad j \neq l.$$

This is easily obtained from (14.1) as follows. Consider the matrix A' obtained from A by replacing the lth column of A by the jth column, for $j \neq l$; then A' has two equal columns and hence $D(A') = 0$, since the determinant function satisfies the conditions 1, 2, and 3 of (11.5) when considered as a function of either the row or the column

---

* This section is optional.

vectors, according to the proof of theorem (12.13). Taking the expansion of $D(A')$ along the lth column, we obtain (14.2).

Let ^tA be the transpose of A; then the column expansions of $D(^tA)$ yield the following *row expansions* of $D(A)$, since $D(A) = D(^tA)$ by (12.15).

(14.3) $$\sum_{k=1}^{n} \alpha_{jk}A_{jk} = D(A), \qquad j = 1, 2, \cdots, n.$$

(14.4) $$\sum_{k=1}^{n} \alpha_{jk}A_{lk} = 0, \qquad j \neq l.$$

These formulas become especially interesting if we interpret them from the point of view of matrix multiplication. Let A^* be the matrix with A_{ji} in the (i, j) position and let I be the matrix whose ith row is the ith unit vector e_i (I is called the *identity matrix*). For any matrix $A = (\alpha_{ij})$, let λA be the matrix whose (i, j) entry is $\lambda\alpha_{ij}$. Then the formulas (14.1) and (14.2) become

(14.5) $$A^*A = D(A)I$$

while (14.3) and (14.4) become

(14.6) $$AA^* = D(A)I.$$

We note that the matrix I plays the same role as 1 in the real number system:
$$AI = IA = A$$
for all matrices A. We consider now the problem of deciding when a matrix $A \neq 0$ has a multiplicative inverse A^{-1} such that $A^{-1}A = AA^{-1} = I$. Let us make the following definition.

(14.7) **Definition.** An n-by-n matrix A is *invertible* if there exists an n-by-n matrix A^{-1}, called an *inverse* of A, such that
$$AA^{-1} = A^{-1}A = I.$$

(14.8) **Theorem.** *An n-by-n matrix A is invertible if and only if $D(A) \neq 0$. If $D(A) \neq 0$, then an inverse A^{-1} is given by*
$$D(A)^{-1}A^*$$
where A^* is the matrix whose (j, i) entry is $A_{ij} = (-1)^{i+j}D_{ij}$.

Proof. If $AA^{-1} = I$, then $D(A) \neq 0$ by the multiplication theorem. If $D(A) \neq 0$, then setting $A^{-1} = D(A)^{-1}A^*$ we have $A^{-1}A = AA^{-1} = I$ by formulas (14.5) and (14.6). This completes the proof.

We remark that it can be shown that matrix multiplication is associative:

$$A(BC) = (AB)C$$

for all n-by-n matrices A, B, and C (this fact will be proved in Chapter 5, and can be easily verified by direct computation). We can then show that the inverse A^{-1} of an invertible matrix A is uniquely determined. Indeed, if A is invertible and B a matrix such that

$$AB = I$$

then multiplying on the left by A^{-1} we obtain

$$A^{-1}(AB) = A^{-1}I = A^{-1}$$

and, by the associative law,

$$A^{-1}(AB) = (A^{-1}A)B = IB = B.$$

Then $B = A^{-1}$. Similarly, if $CA = I$, then $C = A^{-1}$.

DETERMINANTS AND SYSTEMS OF EQUATIONS

We shall now combine our results to relate determinants to some of the questions studied in Chapter 2 concerning systems of linear equations and the rank of a matrix. The first relation gives an explicit formula for the solution of a system of n nonhomogeneous equations in n unknowns, one that is useful for theoretical purposes. It is less efficient than the methods developed in Chapter 2 for actually computing a solution of a particular system of equations, and cannot be applied to systems with a nonsquare coefficient matrix.

(14.9) Theorem (Cramer's Rule). *A nonhomogeneous system of n linear equations in n unknowns*

$$\alpha_{11}x_1 + \cdots + \alpha_{1n}x_n = \beta_1$$

(14.10)

$$\vdots$$

$$\alpha_{n1}x_1 + \cdots + \alpha_{nn}x_n = \beta_n$$

has a unique solution if and only if the determinant of the coefficient matrix $D(A) \neq 0$. If $D(A) \neq 0$, the solution is given by

$$x_i = \frac{D(c_1, \cdots, c_{i-1}, b, c_i, \cdots, c_n)}{D(A)}, \qquad 1 \leq i \leq n$$

where $c_1, \cdots, c_n$ are the columns of A and $b = \langle \beta_1, \cdots, \beta_n \rangle$.

Proof. By (13.11), $D(A) \neq 0$ if and only if the columns $c_1, \cdots, c_n$ are linearly independent, and thus the statement about the existence of a unique solution follows from the theorems in Sections 8 and 9 (Why?). Finally, let $D(A) \neq 0$, and let $\langle x_1, \cdots, x_n \rangle$ be a solution. As in the first part of this section, let

$$A_{ij} = (-1)^{i+j} D_{ij}, \qquad 1 \leq i, j \leq n.$$

For a fixed i, multiply the kth equation in (14.10) by A_{ki}, obtaining

$$A_{ki}\alpha_{k1}x_1 + \cdots + A_{ki}\alpha_{ki}x_i + \cdots + A_{ki}\alpha_{kn}x_n = A_{ki}\beta_k.$$

Adding these expressions together, we obtain

$$\left(\sum_{k=1}^{n} A_{ki}\alpha_{k1} \right) x_1 + \cdots + \left(\sum_{k=1}^{n} A_{ki}\alpha_{ki} \right) x_i$$

$$+ \cdots + \left(\sum_{k=1}^{n} A_{ki}\alpha_{kn} \right) x_n = \sum_{k=1}^{n} A_{ki}\beta_k.$$

By (14.1) and (14.2) we have

$$D(A)x_i = \sum_{k=1}^{n} A_{ki}\beta_k = D(c_1, \cdots, c_{i-1}, b, c_{i+1}, \cdots, c_n)$$

which is the required formula.

One important consequence of these formulas is that when $D(A) \neq 0$ the solution $\langle x_1, \cdots, x_n \rangle$ of a system (14.10) depends continuously on the coefficient matrix A.

In Sections 8 and 9 we defined the rank of an m-by-n matrix and proved that the row rank and column rank are the same. In (13.11) we showed that for an n-by-n matrix A, the rank is n if and only if $D(A) \neq 0$. By using this result it is possible to prove a connection between determinants and rank for arbitrary matrices. We first define an *r-rowed minor determinant* of A as the determinant of an r-by-r matrix obtained from A by deleting rows and columns. For example, the two-rowed minors of

$$\begin{pmatrix} 1 & -1 & 0 \\ 2 & 3 & 1 \end{pmatrix}$$

are

$$\begin{vmatrix} 1 & -1 \\ 2 & 3 \end{vmatrix}, \quad \begin{vmatrix} 1 & 0 \\ 2 & 1 \end{vmatrix}, \quad \begin{vmatrix} -1 & 0 \\ 3 & 1 \end{vmatrix}.$$

(14.11) **Theorem.** *The rank of an m-by-n matrix A is s if and only if there exists a nonzero s-rowed minor and all $(s + k)$-rowed minors are zero for $k = 1, 2, \cdots$.*

Proof. Let us call the number s defined in the statement of the theorem det rank A. We prove first that rank $A = r$ implies det rank $A \geq r$. From Section 9, rank $A = r$ implies that there exists an r-by-r matrix of rank r obtained by deleting rows and columns from A. Then (13.11) implies det rank $A \geq r$.

Conversely, det rank $= s$ implies that there exist s linearly independent rows of A; hence rank $A \geq s$. Combining the inequalities, we have det rank $A = $ rank A, and the theorem is proved.

DETERMINANTS AND VOLUMES

We conclude the chapter with the n-dimensional interpretation of the determinant as a volume function. A *volume function* V in R_n is a function which assigns to each n-tuple of vectors $\{a_1, \cdots, a_n\}$ in R_n a real number $V(a_1, \cdots, a_n)$ such that

$$V(a_1, \cdots, a_n) \geq 0,$$
$$V(\cdots, a_i + a_k, \cdots) = V(a_1, \cdots, a_n), \qquad i \neq k,$$
$$V(\cdots, \lambda a_i, \cdots) = |\lambda| V(a_1, \cdots, a_n), \qquad \lambda \in R,$$
$$V(e_1, \cdots, e_n) = 1, \qquad e_i = \text{unit vectors}.$$

Such a function can be interpreted as the volume of the n-dimensional parallelopiped, with edges $a_1, \cdots, a_n$, which consists of all vectors $x = \sum \lambda_i a_i$, for $0 \leq \lambda_i \leq 1$. The connection between volume functions and determinants is given in the following theorem.

(14.12) **Theorem.** *There is one and only one volume function $V(a_1, \cdots, a_n)$ on R_n, which is given by*
$$V(a_1, \cdots, a_n) = |D(a_1, \cdots, a_n)|.$$

Proof. Clearly, $|D(a_1, \cdots, a_n)|$ is a volume function. Now let V be a volume function, and define

$$V^*(a_1, \cdots, a_n) = \begin{cases} \dfrac{V(a_1, \cdots, a_n) D(a_1, \cdots, a_n)}{|D(a_1, \cdots, a_n)|}, & D \neq 0 \\ \\ 0, & \text{if } D(a_1, \cdots, a_n) = 0. \end{cases}$$

Then one verifies easily that V^* satisfies the axioms for a determinant function and hence that

$$V^*(a_1, \cdots, a_n) = D(a_1, \cdots, a_n)$$

for all $a_1, \cdots, a_n$ in R_n. It then follows from the definition of V^* that $V(a_1, \cdots, a_n) = |D(a_1, \cdots, a_n)|$, and the theorem is proved.

An inductive definition of the k-dimensional volume of a k-dimensional parallelopiped in R_n, based on the fact that the area of a parallelogram is the product of the base and the height, is given in Section 3, Chapter X, of Birkoff and MacLane (see the Bibliography). They show, by an interesting argument, that the k-dimensional volume in R_n is given by a certain determinant.

EXERCISES

1. Test the following matrices to see whether or not they are invertible; if they are invertible, find an inverse.

$$\begin{pmatrix} 2 & -1 \\ -2 & 1 \end{pmatrix}, \quad \begin{pmatrix} 2 & 1 \\ 1 & 1 \end{pmatrix}, \quad \begin{pmatrix} 3 & 1 & 0 \\ 1 & 2 & 1 \\ 0 & -1 & 2 \end{pmatrix}.$$

2. Find a solution of the system

$$\begin{array}{rcl} 3x_1 + x_2 & = & 1 \\ x_1 + 2x_2 + x_3 & = & 2 \\ - x_2 + 2x_3 & = & -1 \end{array}$$

both by Cramer's rule and by the methods of Chapter 2.

3. Find the ranks of the following matrices using determinants:

$$\begin{pmatrix} 1 & 2 & 3 & 4 \\ -1 & 2 & 1 & 0 \end{pmatrix}, \quad \begin{pmatrix} -1 & 0 & 1 & 2 \\ 1 & 1 & 3 & 0 \\ -1 & 2 & 4 & 1 \end{pmatrix}.$$

4. Prove that the equation of the line through the distinct points (α, β), (γ, δ) in the plane is given by

$$\begin{vmatrix} x_1 & x_2 & 1 \\ \alpha & \beta & 1 \\ \gamma & \delta & 1 \end{vmatrix} = 0.$$

5. Prove that the following is the equation of the hyperplane in R_3 containing the distinct vectors $\langle \alpha_1, \alpha_2, \alpha_3 \rangle$, $\langle \beta_1, \beta_2, \beta_3 \rangle$, $\langle \gamma_1, \gamma_2, \gamma_3 \rangle$.

$$\begin{vmatrix} x_1 & x_2 & x_3 & 1 \\ \alpha_1 & \alpha_2 & \alpha_3 & 1 \\ \beta_1 & \beta_2 & \beta_3 & 1 \\ \gamma_1 & \gamma_2 & \gamma_3 & 1 \end{vmatrix} = 0.$$

6. Show that the linear transformation $T : a \to T(a)$ of $R_2 \to R_2$, which takes $a = \langle x_1, x_2 \rangle$ onto $T(a) = \langle y_1, y_2 \rangle$ where

$$\begin{aligned} y_1 &= 3x_1 - x_2 \\ y_2 &= x_1 + 2x_2, \end{aligned}$$

carries the square consisting of all points p such that $\vec{op} = \lambda e_1 + \mu e_2$, for $0 \le \lambda$ and $\mu \le 1$, onto a parallelogram. Show that the area of this parallelogram is the absolute value of the determinant of the matrix of the transformation T,

$$\begin{pmatrix} 3 & -1 \\ 1 & 2 \end{pmatrix}.$$

7. Show that the area of the triangle in the plane with the vertices (α_1, α_2), (β_1, β_2), (γ_1, γ_2) is given by the absolute value of

$$\frac{1}{2} \begin{vmatrix} \alpha_1 & \alpha_2 & 1 \\ \beta_1 & \beta_2 & 1 \\ \gamma_1 & \gamma_2 & 1 \end{vmatrix}.$$

8. Show that the volume of the tetrahedron with vertices $(\alpha_1, \alpha_2, \alpha_3)$, $(\beta_1, \beta_2, \beta_3)$, $(\gamma_1, \gamma_2, \gamma_3)$, $(\delta_1, \delta_2, \delta_3)$ is given by the absolute value of

$$\frac{1}{6} \begin{vmatrix} \alpha_1 & \alpha_2 & \alpha_3 & 1 \\ \beta_1 & \beta_2 & \beta_3 & 1 \\ \gamma_1 & \gamma_2 & \gamma_3 & 1 \\ \delta_1 & \delta_2 & \delta_3 & 1 \end{vmatrix}.$$

9. Let $p_1, \cdots, p_n$ be vectors in R_n and let

$$p_i = \langle \alpha_{i1}, \cdots, \alpha_{in} \rangle, \qquad 1 \le i \le n.$$

Prove that $p_1, \cdots, p_n$ lie on a linear manifold of dimension $< n - 1$ if and only if

$$\begin{vmatrix} x_1 & \cdots & x_n & 1 \\ \alpha_{11} & \cdots & \alpha_{1n} & 1 \\ \cdots & \cdots & \cdots & \cdots \\ \alpha_{n1} & \cdots & \alpha_{nn} & 1 \end{vmatrix} = 0$$

for all $x_1, \cdots, x_n$ in R. Prove that, if $p_1, \cdots, p_n$ do not lie on a linear manifold of dimension of $< n - 1$, then $p_1, \cdots, p_n$ lie on a unique hyperplane whose equation is given by the above formula.

10. Prove the following formula for the *van der Monde determinant:*

$$\begin{vmatrix} 1 & \xi_1 & \xi_1^2 & \cdots & \xi_1^{n-1} \\ 1 & \xi_2 & \xi_2^2 & \cdots & \xi_2^{n-1} \\ \cdots & \cdots & \cdots & \cdots & \cdots \\ 1 & \xi_n & \xi_n^2 & \cdots & \xi_n^{n-1} \end{vmatrix} = \pm \prod_{i > j} (\xi_i - \xi_j).$$

(*Hint:* Let $c_1, c_2, \cdots, c_n$ be the columns of the van der Monde matrix. Show that

$$D(c_1, \cdots, c_n) = D(c_1, c_2 - \xi_1 c_1, \cdots, c_{n-1} - \xi_1 c_{n-2}, c_n - \xi_1 c_{n-1})$$

$$= \begin{vmatrix} 1 & 0 & 0 & \cdots & 0 \\ 1 & \xi_2 - \xi_1 & \xi_2^2 - \xi_1 \xi_2 & \cdots & \xi_2^{n-1} - \xi_1 \xi_2^{n-2} \\ \cdots & \cdots & \cdots & \cdots & \cdots \\ 1 & \xi_n - \xi_1 & \xi_n^2 - \xi_1 \xi_n & \cdots & \xi_n^{n-1} - \xi_1 \xi_n^{n-2} \end{vmatrix}.$$

Then take the row expansion along the first row, factor out appropriate factors from the result, and use induction.)

11. Let I be the n-by-n identity matrix, that is, the matrix whose rows are the unit vectors in R_n. Define an *elementary matrix* as any one of the matrices $P_{ij}, B_{ij}(\lambda), D_i(\mu)$ for all $i, j = 1, \cdots, n$, and $\lambda, \mu \in R$. These matrices are defined as follows.

(A) P_{ij} is obtained from I by interchanging the ith and jth rows.

(B) $B_{ij}(\lambda)$ is obtained from I by adding λ times the jth row of I to the ith row.

(C) $D_i(\mu)$ is obtained from I by multiplying the ith row of I by μ.

For example, in the set of 2-by-2 matrices we have

$$P_{12} = \begin{pmatrix} 0 & 1 \\ 1 & 0 \end{pmatrix}, \qquad B_{12}(\lambda) = \begin{pmatrix} 1 & \lambda \\ 0 & 1 \end{pmatrix}, \qquad D_2(\mu) = \begin{pmatrix} 1 & 0 \\ 0 & \mu \end{pmatrix}.$$

Now let A be an arbitrary n-by-n matrix. Prove that:

a. $P_{ij}A$ is obtained from A by interchanging the ith and jth rows of A.

b. $B_{ij}(\lambda)A$ is obtained from A by adding λ times the jth row of A to the ith row.

c. $D_i(\mu)A$ is obtained from A by multiplying the ith row of A by μ.

The operations on A described in **a**, **b**, and **c** are called *elementary operations* and may be referred to as types 1, 2, and 3, respectively.

12. (Continuation of Exercise 11.)   Let A be an arbitrary n-by-n matrix. Prove by methods similar to those used in Exercises 3 of Section 7 and 3 of Section 11, etc., that there exists a sequence of elementary operation of types 1, 2, or 3 which reduces A to a matrix of the form

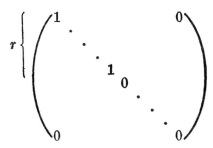

where r is the rank of A. In particular, if A is invertible, Exercise 11 implies that there exist elementary matrices $E_1, \cdots, E_s$ of types A, B, C such that

$$E_s E_{s-1} \cdots E_1 A = I.$$

Prove that

$$A^{-1} = E_s E_{s-1} \cdots E_1 I,$$

so that if the elementary operations given by $E_1, \cdots, E_s$ reduce A to I, the same sequence of elementary operations applied to I will yield A^{-1}. Apply this construction of A^{-1} to the matrices given in Exercise 1 above, which are invertible. Check your results.

13. (Continuation of Exercise 12.)   Prove that every invertible n-by-n matrix A is a product of elementary matrices of type A, B, or C.

CHAPTER 4

POLYNOMIALS
and COMPLEX NUMBERS

This chapter begins with the observation that although some of the results of the preceding chapters (such as the material on convex sets) used the order properties of the real numbers, most of the theorems, and the proofs we have given, are valid if we interpret our basic number system, from which the components of vectors are taken, as an arbitrary field, that is, any system which satisfies the algebra axioms in Section 2. Perhaps the concepts of vectors, matrices, and determinants should have been introduced in their full generality from the beginning; if we had done this, however, the geometrical motivation for much of our work would have been far less convincing and we would have had less reason to introduce, for example, the important idea of convex set. Our approach illustrates one way mathematics is discovered: by first studying deeply some special problems and later attempting to formulate the unifying principles which govern the special problems. We shall continue this process of abstraction in Chapter 5, where we study an axiomatic approach to vector spaces and linear transformations.

The remainder of this chapter contains the theory of prime factorization of polynomials and the construction and properties of the field of complex numbers.

15. VECTORS AND MATRICES DEFINED OVER AN ARBITRARY FIELD

We recall first the definition of a field, which is a repetition of the algebra axioms of the real numbers:

(15.1) Definition. A *field* is a mathematical system F consisting of a nonempty set F together with two operations, addition and multiplication, which assign to each pair of elements $\alpha, \beta \in F$ uniquely determined elements $\alpha + \beta$ and $\alpha\beta$ of F, such that the following conditions are satisfied for $\alpha, \beta, \gamma \in F$.

1. $\alpha + \beta = \beta + \alpha$, $\alpha\beta = \beta\alpha$ (commutative laws).
2. $\alpha + (\beta + \gamma) = (\alpha + \beta) + \gamma$, $(\alpha\beta)\gamma = \alpha(\beta\gamma)$ (associative laws).
3. $\alpha(\beta + \gamma) = \alpha\beta + \alpha\gamma$ (distributive law).
4. There exists an element 0 such that $\alpha + 0 = \alpha$ for all $\alpha \in F$.
5. For each element $\alpha \in F$ there exists an element $-\alpha$ such that $\alpha + (-\alpha) = 0$.
6. There exists an element $1 \in F$ such that $1 \neq 0$ and such that $\alpha \cdot 1 = \alpha$ for all $\alpha \in F$.
7. For each nonzero $\alpha \in F$ there exists an element $\alpha^{-1} \in F$ such that $\alpha\alpha^{-1} = 1$.

Examples of fields are, of course, the set of all real numbers and the set of all rational numbers. Other examples are given in the exercises at the end of this section and more will be constructed in the course of this chapter.

(15.2) Definition. Let F be an arbitrary field. The *vector space F_n* is the set of all vectors $\langle \alpha_1, \cdots, \alpha_n \rangle$ with *components* $\alpha_i \in F$. If $a = \langle \alpha_1, \cdots, \alpha_n \rangle$, $b = \langle \beta_1, \cdots, \beta_n \rangle$, then we define

$$a = b, \quad \text{if and only if } \alpha_1 = \beta_1, \cdots, \alpha_n = \beta_n,$$
$$a + b = \langle \alpha_1 + \beta_1, \cdots, \alpha_n + \beta_n \rangle,$$
$$\alpha \cdot a = \langle \alpha\alpha_1, \cdots, \alpha\alpha_n \rangle, \qquad \alpha \in F, \quad a \in F_n.$$

Then (as in Section 5) we have for all a, b, $c \in F_n$*

$$a + b = b + a$$
$$a + (b + c) = (a + b) + c$$
$$a + 0 = a, \quad \text{if } 0 = \langle 0, \cdots, 0 \rangle$$
$$a + (-a) = 0, \quad \text{if } -a = \langle -\alpha_1, \cdots, -\alpha_n \rangle$$
$$(\lambda + \mu)a = \lambda a + \mu a, \quad \lambda, \mu \in F$$
$$\lambda(a + b) = \lambda a + \lambda b, \quad \lambda \in F$$
$$(\lambda\mu)a = \lambda(\mu a), \quad \lambda, \mu \in F$$
$$1a = a.$$

The concepts of linear dependence, subspaces, basis, and dimension in the vector space F_n may now be defined as in Sections 6 and 7. *We assert that the replacement theorem and all of the numbered theorems concerning subspaces of F_n and their applications to systems of linear equations with coefficients in F are valid, and the proofs we have given apply unchanged to the more general situation.*

To verify this assertion the reader must review Sections 5 to 9 and check that the only properties of the real numbers used in the proofs are the algebra axioms.

A similar general assertion can be made concerning determinants. Specifically, we can assert that there exists a uniquely determined function that assigns, to each n-by-n matrix with coefficients in F, an element of F which satisfies the axioms (11.5) when viewed as a function of its row vectors and for which are valid theorem (11.6), the uniqueness and existence theorems of Section 12, the theorems on the complete expansion, the fact that $D(A) = D({}^tA)$, the row and column expansions, the applications to rank and systems of linear equations (but of course not the interpretation as a volume), and the multiplication theorem of Section 13, and that the proofs we have given carry over without any changes at all.†

The point of what has been done is that the theorems of Chapters 2 and 3, which may have seemed rather complicated in view of the single application we had in mind to analytic geometry, have now had their scope enormously extended.

---

* We shall use the same symbol for the zero vector and the zero element of the field, since it is always clear from the context which is being used.

† There is one exception! In the exercises in Section 15 an example is given of a field F such that $2\alpha = \alpha + \alpha = 0$ for all $\alpha \in F$. The proof of part B of theorem (11.6) should be modified, to take account of this possibility, as follows:

$$D(\cdots, a_i, \cdots, a_i, \cdots) = D(\cdots, 2a_i, \cdots, a_i, \cdots)$$
$$= -2D(\cdots, -a_i, \cdots, a_i, \cdots) = -2D(\cdots, 0, \cdots, a_i, \cdots) = 0.$$

EXERCISES

1. Show that the following systems are examples of fields.

   a. The set $Q(\sqrt{2})$ of all real numbers of the form $\alpha + \beta\sqrt{2}$, where α and β belong to the field of rational numbers Q. Addition and multiplication in $Q(\sqrt{2})$ are the operations already defined for the field of real numbers. Note in this case it must be checked that if $a, b \in Q(\sqrt{2})$ then $a \pm b$, ab, and a/b, for $b \neq 0$, also belong to $Q(\sqrt{2})$, in other words, that $Q(\sqrt{2})$ is a *subfield* of R.

   b. Let q be a rational number > 0 such that the equation $x^2 - q = 0$ has no rational solutions. Show that the set $Q(\sqrt{q})$ of all real numbers $\alpha + \beta\sqrt{q}$, for $\alpha, \beta, \in Q$, forms a field, the operations being as given in **a**. In particular, what is the formula for $(\alpha + \beta\sqrt{q})^{-1}$? Note that, since $\sqrt{q} \notin Q$, $Q(\sqrt{q})$ does not coincide with the field of rational numbers.

   c. Let F be the system consisting of two elements $\{0, 1\}$, with the operations defined by the tables

+	0 1
0	0 1
1	1 0

·	0 1
0	0 0
1	0 1

   Show that F is a field, with the property $2\alpha = \alpha + \alpha = 0$ for all $\alpha \in F$.

2. Consider the vector space F_n, when F is the field defined in Exercise 1c. Show that F_n contains exactly 2^n distinct vectors. How many distinct bases does F_n have?

3. Let Z be the system of all integers, which is not a field (Why?). Let Z_n be the set of all n-tuples

$$\langle \alpha_1, \cdots, \alpha_n \rangle, \qquad \alpha_i \in Z,$$

with the operations of addition and scalar multiplication by elements of Z as defined for the vector space R_n. Define linear dependence, subspace, etc., as for R_n. Which of the theorems and lemmas in Sections 6 and 7 hold for Z_n? In particular, is the replacement theorem valid for Z_n?

16. POLYNOMIALS

Everyone is familiar with the concept of a polynomial $\alpha_0 + \alpha_1 x + \alpha_2 x^2 + \cdots + \alpha_n x^n$ where the α_i are real numbers. However, there are some questions which should be answered: Is a polynomial a function or, if not, what is it? What is x? Is it a variable, or an indeterminate, or a number?

In this section we give one approach to polynomials which answers these questions, and we prove the basic theorem on prime factorization of polynomials in preparation for the theory of linear transformations, to come in the next chapter.

We begin with a definition. Let F be an arbitrary field. A *polynomial* with coefficients in F is by definition a sequence

$$f = \{\alpha_0, \alpha_1, \alpha_2, \cdots\}, \qquad \alpha_i \in F,$$

such that for some positive integer M depending on f, $\alpha_M = \alpha_{M+1} = \cdots = 0$. We make the following definitions. If

$$g = \{\beta_0, \beta_1, \beta_2, \cdots\},$$

then $f = g$ if and only if $\alpha_0 = \beta_0$, $\alpha_1 = \beta_1$, $\alpha_2 = \beta_2$, $\cdots$. We define addition as for vectors:

$$f + g = \{\alpha_0 + \beta_0, \alpha_1 + \beta_1, \cdots\}$$

and multiplication by the rule

$$fg = \{\gamma_0, \gamma_1, \gamma_2, \cdots\}$$

where, for each k,

(16.1) $$\gamma_k = \sum_{i+j=k} \alpha_i \beta_j = \alpha_0 \beta_k + \alpha_1 \beta_{k-1} + \cdots + \alpha_k \beta_0.$$

It is clear that both $f + g$ and fg are polynomials; that is, $\alpha_M + \beta_M$ and γ_M are zero for sufficiently large M.

(16.2) **Theorem.** *The polynomials with coefficients in F satisfy all the axioms for a field [definition (15.1)] except the axiom concerning the existence of α^{-1} for $\alpha \neq 0$ such that $\alpha \alpha^{-1} = 1$.*

Proof. Since addition of polynomials is defined as vector addition, it is clear that all the axioms concerning addition alone are satisfied.

The commutative law for multiplication is clear by (16.1). For the associative law, let

$$h = \{\delta_0, \delta_1, \delta_2, \cdots\}.$$

Then the kth coefficient of $(fg)h$ is

$$\sum_{r+s=k}\left(\sum_{i+j=r}\alpha_i\beta_j\right)\delta_s = \sum_{i+j+s=k}(\alpha_i\beta_j)\delta_s$$

while the kth coefficient of $f(gh)$ is

$$\sum_{i+t=k}\alpha_i\left(\sum_{j+s=t}\beta_j\delta_s\right) = \sum_{i+j+s=k}\alpha_i(\beta_j\delta_s)$$

and both expressions are equal because of the associative law in F. Finally, we check the distributive law for multiplication. The kth coefficient of $f(g + h)$ is

$$\sum_{i+j=k}\alpha_i(\beta_j + \delta_j)$$

while the kth coefficient of $fg + fh$ is

$$\sum_{i+j=k}\alpha_i\beta_j + \sum_{i+j=k}\alpha_i\delta_j$$

and these expressions are equal because of the distributive law in F. This completes the proof.

REMARK. A system which satisfies the axioms for a field except, possibly, the one concerning the existence of solutions of the equations $\alpha x = 1$ is called a *commutative ring*. Thus, the polynomials form a commutative ring. We shall see that the polynomials do not form a field. Another important example of a commutative ring that is not a field is the system of integers defined in Section 3.

It is clear that the mapping

$$\alpha \to \{\alpha, 0, 0, \cdots\} = \alpha'$$

is a one-to-one mapping of F into the polynomials such that

$$(\alpha + \beta)' = \alpha' + \beta', \qquad (\alpha\beta)' = \alpha'\beta'.$$

If we let F' be the set of all polynomials α' obtained in this way, then F' is a field that is *isomorphic* with F, and we shall identify the elements of F with the polynomials that correspond to them; that is, we shall write

$$\alpha = \{\alpha, 0, 0, \cdots\}.$$

Now let x be the polynomial defined by the sequence

$$x = \{0, 1, 0, \cdots\}.$$

Then

$$x^2 = \{0, 0, 1, 0, \cdots\}$$

and (remembering that we index the coefficients starting from 0), in general,

$$x^i = \{0, 0, \cdots, \underset{i}{1}, \cdots\}.$$

Moreover, it is easily checked that we have

$$\alpha x^i = \{\alpha, 0, \cdots\}\{0, \cdots, \underset{i}{1}, \cdots\} = \{0, \cdots, \underset{i}{\alpha}, \cdots\} = x^i\alpha,$$

$$\alpha \in F, \quad i = 1, 2, \cdots.$$

Therefore an arbitrary polynomial

$$f = \{\alpha_0, \alpha_1, \alpha_2, \cdots\}$$

can be expressed uniquely in the form

(16.3) $$f = \alpha_0 + \alpha_1 x + \alpha_2 x^2 + \cdots + \alpha_r x^r.$$

We shall use the notation $F[x]$ for the set of polynomials with coefficients in F.

(16.4) Definition. Let $f = \alpha_0 + \alpha_1 x + \alpha_2 x^2 + \cdots$ be a polynomial in $F[x]$. We say that the *degree* of f is r, and write $\deg f = r$, if $\alpha_r \neq 0$ and $\alpha_{r+1} = \alpha_{r+2} = \cdots = 0$. We say that the polynomial $0 = 0 + 0x + 0x^2 + \cdots$ does not have a degree.

(16.5) Theorem. *Let f, g be nonzero polynomials in $F[x]$; then:*

$$\deg (f + g) \leq \max \{\deg f, \deg g\}, \qquad if f + g \neq 0,$$
$$\deg fg = \deg f + \deg g.$$

Proof. Let

$$f = \alpha_0 + \alpha_1 x + \cdots + \alpha_r x^r, \qquad \alpha_r \neq 0,$$
$$g = \beta_0 + \beta_1 x + \cdots + \beta_s x^s, \qquad \beta_s \neq 0.$$

Then

$$f + g = (\alpha_0 + \beta_0) + (\alpha_1 + \beta_1)x + \cdots + (\alpha_t + \beta_t)x^t,$$

where $t = \max \{r, s\}$, proving the first statement. For the second statement of the theorem, we observe that fg has no nonzero terms $\gamma_i x^i$ for $i > r + s$ and that the coefficient of x^{r+s} is exactly $\alpha_r\beta_s$, which is nonzero since the product of two nonzero elements of a field is different from zero (Why?). This completes the proof.

(16.6) Corollary. If $f, g \in F[x]$, then $fg = 0$ implies that $f = 0$ or $g = 0$. If $fg = hg$, $g \neq 0$, then $f = h$.

Proof. If both $f \neq 0$ and $g \neq 0$ then, by (16.5), $\deg fg \geq 0$ and hence $fg \neq 0$. For the proof of the second part let $fg = hg$. Then $(f - h)g = 0$ and, since $g \neq 0$, $f - h = 0$ by the first part of the proof.

(16.7) Corollary. Let $f \neq 0$ be a polynomial in $F[x]$; then there exists a polynomial $g \in F[x]$ such that $fg = 1$ if and only if $\deg f = 0$. Consequently, $F[x]$ is definitely not a field.

Proof. If $\deg f = 0$, then $f = \alpha \in F$ and we have $\alpha\alpha^{-1} = 1$ by the axioms for a field. Conversely, if $fg = 1$ for some $g \in F[x]$, then by (16.5) we have

$$\deg f + \deg g = \deg 1 = 0.$$

Since $\deg f$ is a nonnegative integer, this equation implies that $\deg f = 0$, and (16.7) is proved.

(16.8) Theorem (Division Process). Let f, g be polynomials in $F[x]$ such that $g \neq 0$; then there exist the uniquely determined polynomials Q, R called the quotient and the remainder, respectively, such that

$$f = Qg + R$$

where either $R = 0$ or $\deg R < \deg g$.

Proof. If $f = 0$, then we may take $Q = R = 0$. Now let

(16.9)
$$\begin{aligned} f &= \alpha_0 + \alpha_1 x + \cdots + \alpha_r x^r, & \alpha_r \neq 0, \quad r \geq 0, \\ g &= \beta_0 + \beta_1 x + \cdots + \beta_s x^s, & \beta_s \neq 0, \quad s \geq 0. \end{aligned}$$

We use induction on r to prove the existence of Q and R. First let $r = 0$. If $s > 0$, then

$$f = 0 \cdot g + f$$

satisfies our requirements while, if $s = 0$, then by (16.7) we have $gg^{-1} = 1$ and can write

$$f = (fg^{-1})g + 0.$$

Now assume that $r > 0$ and that the existence of Q and R has been proved for polynomials of degree $\leq r - 1$. Consider f and g as in (16.9). If $s > r$, then $f = 0 \cdot g + f$ satisfies the requirements and there is nothing to prove. Finally, let $s \leq r$. Then, using the distributive law in $F[x]$, we obtain

$$\alpha_r \beta_s^{-1} x^{r-s} g = \beta_0' + \beta_1' x + \cdots + \alpha_r x^r + 0 x^{r+1} + \cdots$$

with coefficients $\beta_i' \in F$ where $\beta_r' = \alpha_r$. The polynomial

(16.10) $$f_1 = f - \alpha_r \beta_s^{-1} x^{r-s} g$$

has degree $\leq r - 1$, since the coefficients of x^r are canceled out. By the induction hypothesis there exist polynomials Q and R with either $R = 0$ or deg $R <$ deg g such that

$$f_1 = Qg + R.$$

Substituting (16.10) in this formula, we obtain

$$f = (Q + \alpha_r \beta_s^{-1} x^{r-s}) g + R,$$

and the existence part of the theorem is proved.

For the uniqueness, let

$$f = Qg + R = Q'g + R'$$

where both R and R' satisfy the requirements of the theorem. We show first that $R = R'$. Otherwise, $R - R' \neq 0$ and we have

$$R - R' = (Q' - Q)g,$$

where deg $(R - R') <$ deg g by (16.5), while $(Q' - Q)g =$ deg $(Q' - Q) +$ deg $g \geq$ deg g. This is a contradiction, and so we must have $R = R'$. Then we obtain

$$(Q - Q')g = 0, \qquad g \neq 0$$

and by (16.6) we have $Q - Q' = 0$. This completes the proof of the theorem.

Now we come to the important concept of polynomial function.

(16.11)   Definition.   Let $f = \sum \alpha_i x^i \in F[x]$ and let $\xi \in F$. We define an element $f(\xi) \in F$ by

$$f(\xi) = \sum \alpha_i \xi^i$$

and call $f(\xi)$ the *value of the polynomial f when ξ is substituted for x*. For a fixed polynomial $f \in F[x]$ the *polynomial function $f(x)$* is the rule which assigns to each $\xi \in F$ the element $f(\xi) \in F$.* A *zero* of a polynomial f is an element $\xi \in F$ such that $f(\xi) = 0$; a zero of f will also be called a *solution* or *root* of the polynomial equation $f(x) = 0$.

---

* The notation $f(x)$ is sometimes used for a polynomial f; this notation suppresses the distinction between polynomials (which are sequences) and polynomial functions.

The next two results govern the connection between finding the zeros of a polynomial and factoring the polynomial. First we require an important lemma.

(16.12) Lemma. Let $f, g \in F[x]$ and let $\xi \in F$; then $(f \pm g)(\xi) = f(\xi) \pm g(\xi)$ and $(fg)(\xi) = f(\xi)g(\xi)$.

Proof. Let $f = \alpha_0 + \alpha_1 x + \cdots + \alpha_r x^r$ and $g = \beta_0 + \beta_1 x + \cdots + \beta_s x^s$. Then

$$(f + g)(\xi) = (\alpha_0 + \beta_0) + (\alpha_1 + \beta_1)\xi + (\alpha_2 + \beta_2)\xi^2 + \cdots$$
$$= (\alpha_0 + \alpha_1\xi + \alpha_2\xi^2 + \cdots) + (\beta_0 + \beta_1\xi + \beta_2\xi^2 + \cdots)$$
$$= f(\xi) + g(\xi).$$

Similarly, $(f - g)(\xi) = f(\xi) - g(\xi)$. Next we have

$$(fg)(\xi) = \alpha_0\beta_0 + (\alpha_0\beta_1 + \alpha_1\beta_0)\xi + (\alpha_0\beta_2 + \alpha_1\beta_1 + \alpha_2\beta_0)\xi^2 + \cdots$$
$$= (\alpha_0 + \alpha_1\xi + \alpha_2\xi^2 + \cdots)(\beta_0 + \beta_1\xi + \beta_2\xi^2 + \cdots)$$
$$= f(\xi)g(\xi).$$

This completes the proof of the lemma.

(16.13) Remainder Theorem. Let $f \in F[x]$ and let $\xi \in F$; then the remainder obtained upon dividing f by $x - \xi$ is equal to $f(\xi)$:

$$f = Q(x - \xi) + f(\xi).$$

Proof. By the division process we have

$$f = Q(x - \xi) + r$$

where r is either 0 or an element of F. Substituting ξ for x, we obtain by (16.12) the desired result: $r = f(\xi)$.

(16.14) Factor Theorem. Let $f \in F[x]$ and let $\xi \in F$; then

$$f = (x - \xi)Q$$

for some $Q \in F[x]$ if and only if $f(\xi) = 0$.

The proof is immediate by the remainder theorem.

Now let A be a commutative ring (actually, we have in mind the particular ring $A = F[x]$). If $r, s \in A$, then we say that $r \mid s$ (read "r divides s" or "r is a *factor* of s" or "s is a *multiple* of r") if $s = rt$ for some $t \in A$. An element u of A is called a *unit* if $u \mid 1$. An element is, clearly, a unit if and only if it is a factor of every element of A and hence is uninteresting from the point of view of factorization. Since every nonzero element of a field is a unit, it is of no interest to study questions of factorization in a field. An element $p \in A$ is called a *prime** when p is neither 0 nor a unit and when $p = ab$ implies that either a or b is a unit. Two distinct elements are *relatively prime* if their only common divisors are units. Let $r_1, \cdots, r_k \in A$. An element $d \in A$ is called a *greatest common divisor* of $r_1, r_2, \cdots, r_k \in A$ if $d \mid r_i$, for $1 \leq i \leq k$, and if d' is such that $d' \mid r_i$, $1 \leq i \leq k$, then $d' \mid d$.

We are now going to study these concepts for the ring of polynomials $F[x]$. An almost identical discussion holds for the ring of integers Z, and the reader will find it worth while to write out this application for himself.

We require first of all some preliminary results concerning the system of natural numbers N (see Section 3). The reader may, if he wishes, skip (16.15), and assume (16.16) as an axiom. It is interesting, however, that (16.16) is a consequence of the principle of mathematical induction.

(16.15)   Lemma.   Let $r \in N$; *then there is no natural number x such that $r < x < r + 1$.*

Proof.   First suppose that $r = 1$ and that $1 < x < 2$ for some $x \in N$. Let $N' = N - \{x\}$. Then it is easily checked, by using (3.2), that N' satisfies conditions 1 and 2 of theorem (3.1), and this contradicts the definition of N as the smallest set of real numbers satisfying conditions 1 and 2. Thus there is no integer x such that $1 < x < 2$. If r and x are elements of N such that $r < x < r + 1$, then by (3.12) we have $1 < x - r + 1 < 2$ and $x - r + 1 \in N$. By what has been proved this is impossible, and (16.15) is proved in all cases.

Now we establish another theorem.

(16.16)   Theorem (Well-Ordering Principle for Sets of Natural Numbers).   *Let M be a nonempty set of natural numbers; then M has a least element.*

Proof.   Suppose M is a set of natural numbers that has no least element. We shall prove that M is empty. Since 1 is the least natural number, $1 \notin M$. Suppose as an induction hypothesis that, for all natural numbers x such that $1 \leq x \leq r$, $x \notin M$. Now let y be a natural number such that $1 \leq y \leq r + 1$. By (16.15), either $1 \leq y \leq r$ and $y \notin M$ or, if $y \in M$, then $y = r + 1$. By (16.15), $y = r + 1$ must, then, be the least element of M, contrary to as-

---

* The primes in $F[x]$, where F is a field, are sometimes called *irreducible polynomials*.

sumption. Therefore no integer y such that $1 \leq y \leq r + 1$ is in M, and by the principle of mathematical induction we conclude that M is empty. This completes the proof of the theorem.*

Returning to the polynomial ring $F[x]$, we note first that the set of units in $F[x]$ coincides with the "constant" polynomials $\alpha \in F$ where $\alpha \neq 0$, that is, the polynomials of degree zero.

(16.17)   Theorem. *Let $f_1, \cdots, f_k$ be arbitrary nonzero polynomials in $F[x]$; then:*

(1) *The elements $f_1, \cdots, f_k$ possess at least one greatest common divisor d.*
(2) *The greatest common divisor d is uniquely determined up to a unit factor and can be expressed in the form*

$$d = h_1 f_1 + \cdots + h_k f_k$$

for some polynomials $\{h_i\}$ in $F[x]$.

Proof.   Consider the set S of all polynomials of the form

$$\sum_{i=1}^{k} g_i f_i.$$

Then S contains the set of polynomials $\{f_1, \cdots, f_k\}$ and has the property that, if $p \in S$ and $h \in F[x]$, then $ph \in S$. Since the degrees of nonzero elements of S are in $N \cup \{0\}$, by the well-ordering principle (16.16) we can find a nonzero polynomial

$$d = h_1 f_1 + \cdots + h_k f_k \in S$$

such that $\deg d \leq \deg d'$ for all nonzero $d' \in S$.

We prove first that $d \mid f_i$ for $1 \leq i \leq k$. By the division process we have, for $1 \leq i \leq k$,

$$f_i = dq_i + r_i$$

where either $r_i = 0$, or $\deg r_i < \deg d$ and

$$r_i = f_i - dq_i \in S.$$

Because of the choice of d as a polynomial of least degree in S we have $r_i = 0$ and, hence, d divides each f_i for $1 \leq i \leq k$.

Now let d' be another common divisor of $f_1, \cdots, f_k$. Then there are polynomials g_i such that $f_i = d'g_i$, $1 \leq i \leq k$, and

$$d = \sum h_i f_i = \sum h_i d' g_i = d' \left(\sum h_i g_i \right).$$

---

* The reader will find it interesting to prove that the Well-Ordering Principle implies the Principle of Mathematical Induction.

Therefore $d' \mid d$, and d is a greatest common divisor of $\{f_1, \cdots, f_k\}$.

Finally, let e be another greatest common divisor of $\{f_1, \cdots, f_k\}$. Then $d \mid e$ and $e \mid d$. Therefore there exist polynomials u and v such that $e = du$, $d = ev$. Then $e = euv$ and $e(1 - uv) = 0$. By (16.6) we have $1 - uv = 0$, so that u and v are units. This completes the proof of the theorem.

(16.18)   Corollary. *Let $r_1, \cdots, r_k$ be elements of $F[x]$ that have no common factors other than units; then there exist elements $x_1, \cdots, x_k$ in A such that*

$$x_1 r_1 + \cdots + x_k r_k = 1.$$

(16.19)   Corollary. *Let p be a prime in $F[x]$ and let $p|ab$; then either $p \mid a$ or $p \mid b$.*

Proof. Suppose p does not divide a. Then a and p are relatively prime, and by (16.18) we have

$$au + pv = 1$$

for some $u, v \in F[x]$. Then

$$abu + pvb = b$$

and, since $p \mid ab$, we have $p \mid b$ by the distributive law in $F[x]$.

(16.20)   Unique Factorization Theorem. *Let $a \neq 0$ be an element of $F[x]$; then either a is a unit or*

$$a = p_1 \cdots p_s, \qquad s \geq 1,$$

where $p_1, \cdots, p_s$ are primes. Moreover,

(16.21) $$p_1 \cdots p_s = q_1 \cdots q_t,$$

where the $\{p_i\}$ and $\{q_j\}$ are primes, implies that $s = t$, and for a suitable indexing of the p's and q's we have

$$p_1 = \epsilon_1 q_1, \cdots, p_s = \epsilon_t q_t$$

where the ϵ_i are units.

Proof. The existence of at least one factorization of a into primes is clear by induction on deg a.

For the uniqueness assertion, we use induction on s, the result being clear if $s = 1$. Given (16.21) we apply (16.19) to conclude that p_1 divides some q_j, and we may assume that $j = 1$. Then $q_1 = p_1\epsilon_1$ for some unit ϵ_1. Then (16.21) becomes

$$p_1 \cdots p_s = \epsilon_1 p_1 q_2 \cdots q_t.$$

By the cancellation law we have

$$p_2 \cdots p_s = \epsilon_1 q_2 \cdots q_t = q_2' q_3 \cdots q_t$$

where $q_2' = \epsilon_1 q_2$. The result now follows, by the induction hypothesis.

We have followed the approach to the unique factorization theorem via the theory of the greatest common divisor because the greatest common divisor will be used in Chapter 5. It is interesting that the uniqueness of factorization can be proved by using nothing but the well-ordering principle for sets of natural numbers and the simplest facts concerning degrees of polynomials. Neither the division process nor the theory of the greatest common divisor is needed.

The following proof was discovered in 1960 by Charles Giffen while he was an undergraduate at the University of Wisconsin.

Suppose the uniqueness of factorization is false in $F[x]$. Then by the well-ordering principle there will be a polynomial of least degree

$$(16.22) \qquad f = p_1 \cdots p_r = q_1 \cdots q_s,$$

where the $\{p_i\}$ and $\{q_j\}$ are primes, which has two essentially different factorizations. We may assume that $r > 1$ and $s > 1$ and that no p_i coincides with a q_j, for otherwise we could cancel p_i and q_j and obtain a polynomial of lower degree than that of f with two essentially different factorizations. We may assume also that each p_i and q_j has leading coefficient (that is, the coefficient of the highest power of x) equal to 1. By interchanging the p's and q's, if necessary, we may arrange matters so that deg $p_r \leq$ deg q_s. Then for a suitable power x^i of x the coefficient of $x^{\deg q_s}$ in the polynomial $q_s - x^i p_r$ will cancel and we will have $0 \leq$ deg $(q_s - x^i p_r) <$ deg q_s. Now form the polynomial

$$f_1 = f - q_1 \cdots q_{s-1}(x^i p_r).$$

By (16.22) we have

$$(16.23) \qquad f_1 = q_1 \cdots q_{s-1}(q_s - x^i p_r)$$

and so, by what has been said, $f_1 \neq 0$ and deg $f_1 <$ deg f. But from the form of f_1 we see that $p_r \mid f_1$ and, since prime factorization is unique for polynomials of degree $<$ deg f, we conclude from (16.23) that $p_r \mid (q_s - x^i p_r)$, since p_r is distinct from all the primes $q_1, \cdots, q_{s-1}$. Then

$$q_s - x^i p_r = h p_r$$

and

$$q_s = p_r(h + x^i)$$

which is a contradiction. This completes the proof of unique factorization.*

We conclude this section with the observation familiar to us from high school algebra that, although $F[x]$ is not a field, $F[x]$ can be embedded in a field, and in exactly the way that the integers can be embedded in the field of rational numbers. Some of the details will be omitted.

Consider all pairs (f, g), for f and $g \in F[x]$, where $g \neq 0$. Define two such pairs (f, g) and (h, k) as *equivalent* if $fk = gh$; in this case we write $(f, g) \sim (h, k)$. Then the relation $\sim$ has the properties:

(1) $(f, g) \sim (f, g)$.
(2) $(f, g) \sim (h, k)$ implies $(h, k) \sim (f, g)$.
(3) $(f, g) \sim (h, k)$, $(h, k) \sim (p, q)$ imply $(f, g) \sim (p, q)$.

[For the proof of property 3 the cancellation law (16.6) is required.] Now define a fraction f/g, with $g \neq 0$, to be the set of all pairs (h, k), $k \neq 0$, such that $(h, k) \sim (f, g)$. Then we can state:

(4) Every pair (f, g) belongs to one and only one fraction f/g.
(5) Two fractions f/g and r/s coincide if and only if $fs = gr$.

Now we define:

(6) $f/g + r/s = (fs + gr)/gs$.
(7) $(f/g)(r/s) = fr/gs$.

It can be proved first of all that the operations of addition and multiplication of fractions are defined independently of the representatives of the fractions. In other words, one has to show that if $f/g = f_1/g_1$ and $r/s = r_1/s_1$ then

$$\frac{fs + gr}{gs} = \frac{f_1 s_1 + g_1 r_1}{g_1 s_1}$$

and that a similar statement holds for multiplication.

Now we shall state a result. The proof offers no difficulties, and will be omitted.

---

* Note that the same argument establishes the uniqueness of factorization in the ring of integers Z. In more detail, if uniqueness of factorization does not hold in Z, there exists a smallest positive integer $m = p_1 \cdots p_r = q_1 \cdots q_s$ which has two essentially different factorizations. Then we may assume that no p_i coincides with a q_j and that r and s are greater than 1. We may also assume that $p_r < q_s$ and form $m_1 = m - q_1 \cdots q_{s-1} p_r$. Then $m_1 < m$, and $p_r \mid m_1$. Since $m_1 = q_1 \cdots q_{s-1}(q_s - p_r)$, it follows that $p_r \mid (q_s - p_r)$, which is a contradiction. This argument first came to the to the attention of the author in Courant and Robbins (see Bibliography).

(16.24)   **Theorem.**   *The set of fractions f/g, $g \neq 0$, with respect to the operations of addition and multiplication previously defined, forms a field $F(x)$. The mapping $f \to fg/g = \varphi(f)$, where $f \in F[x]$, is a one-to-one mapping of $F[x]$ into $F(x)$ such that $\varphi(f + h) = \varphi(f) + \varphi(h)$ and $\varphi(fh) = \varphi(f)\varphi(h)$ for $f, h \in F[x]$.*

The field $F(x)$ we have constructed is called the *field of rational functions* in one variable with coefficients in F; it is also called the *quotient field* of the polynomial ring $F[x]$. If we identify the polynomial $f \in F[x]$ with the rational function $\varphi(f) = fg/g$, $g \neq 0$, then we may say that the field $F(x)$ contains the polynomial ring $F[x]$.

EXERCISES

1. Use the method of proof of theorem (16.8) to find the quotient Q and the remainder R such that
$$f = Qg + R$$
   where
   $$f = 2x^4 - x^3 + x - 1,$$
   $$g = 3x^3 - x^2 + 3.$$

2. Prove that a polynomial $f \in F[x]$ has at most $\deg f$ distinct zeros in F, where F is any field.

3. Let $f = ax^2 + bx + c$, for a, b, c real numbers and $a \neq 0$. Prove that f is a prime in $R[x]$ if and only if $b^2 - 4ac < 0$. Prove that if $b^2 - 4ac = D \geq 0$ then
$$f = a\left(x - \frac{-b + \sqrt{D}}{2a}\right)\left(x - \frac{-b - \sqrt{D}}{2a}\right).$$

4. Let F be any field and let $f \in F[x]$ be a polynomial of degree ≤ 3. Prove that f is a prime in $F[x]$ if and only if f has no zeros in F. Is the same result valid if $\deg f > 3$?

5. Prove that, if a rational number m/n, for m and n relatively prime integers, is a root of the polynomial equation
$$a_0x^r + a_1x^{r-1} + \cdots + a_r = 0$$
   where the $a_i \in Z$, then $n \mid a_0$ and $m \mid a_r$.* Use this result to list the possible rational roots of the equations

---

* This argument uses the fact that the law of unique factorization holds for the integers Z, as we pointed out in the footnote to Giffen's proof of unique factorization in $F[x]$.

$$2x^3 - 6x^2 + 9 = 0,$$
$$x^3 - 8x^2 + 12 = 0.$$

6. Prove that if m is a positive integer which is not a square in Z then $\sqrt{m}$ is irrational (use Exercise 5).

7. Factor the following polynomials into their prime factors in $Q[x]$ and $R[x]$.

   a. $2x^3 - x^2 + x + 1$.
   b. $3x^3 + 2x^2 - 4x + 1$.
   c. $x^6 + 1$.

8. Let A be the ring Z or $F[x]$ and let $a \in A$ and $b \in A$ be expressed in the forms

$$a = p_1^{a_1} \cdots p_r^{a_r},$$
$$b = p_1^{b_1} \cdots p_r^{b_r}, \qquad a_i, b_i \geq 0,$$

where the p_i are distinct primes. Prove that if (a, b) denotes the greatest common divisor of a and b then $(a, b) = p_1^{u_1} \cdots p_r^{u_r}$ for $u_i = \min \{a_i, b_i\}$, $1 \leq i \leq r$. Define the *least common multiple* $[a, b]$ of a, b. Prove that $[a, b]$ exists and is expressible as

$$[a, b] = p_1^{m_1} \cdots p_r^{m_r}, \qquad m_i = \max \{a_i, b_i\}.$$

Prove that $(a, b)[a, b] = ab$.

9. Let $a, b \in F[x]$ for $a, b \neq 0$. Apply the division process to obtain

$$a = bq_0 + r_0$$
$$b = r_0q_1 + r_1, \qquad \deg r_1 < \deg r_0$$
$$r_0 = r_1q_2 + r_2, \qquad \deg r_2 < \deg r_1$$
$$\cdots$$
$$r_i = r_{i+1}q_{i+2} + r_{i+2}, \qquad \deg r_{i+2} < \deg r_{i+1}$$

Show that for some i_0, $r_{i_0} \neq 0$ and $r_{i_0+1} = 0$. Prove that $r_{i_0} = (a, b)$.

10. Find the greatest common divisor of the following pairs of polynomials in the ring $R[x]$.

    a. $4x^3 + 2x^2 - 2x - 1, 2x^3 - x^2 + x + 1$.
    b. $x^3 - x + 1, 2x^4 + x^2 + x - 5$.

11. Let F be the field of two elements defined in Exercise 1, part c, of Section 15. Factor the following polynomials into primes in $F[x]$: $x^2 + x + 1$, $x^3 + 1$, $x^4 + x^2 + 1$, $x^4 + 1$.

12. Find the greatest common divisor of $x^5 + x^4 + x^3 + x^2 + x + 1$ and $x^3 + x^2 + x + 1$ in $F[x]$, where F is the field of two elements as in Exercise 11.

17. COMPLEX NUMBERS

The field of real numbers of R has the drawback that not every quadratic equation with real coefficients has a solution in R. This fact was circumvented by mathematicians of the eighteenth and nineteenth centuries by assuming that the equation $x^2 + 1 = 0$ had a solution i, and they investigated the properties of the new system of "imaginary" numbers obtained by considering the real numbers together with the new number i. Although today we do not regard the complex numbers as any more imaginary than real numbers, it was clear that mathematicians such as Euler used the "imaginary" number i with some hesitation, since it was not constructed in a clear way from the real numbers.

Whatever the properties of the new number system, the eighteenth- and nineteenth-century mathematicians insisted upon making the new numbers obey the same rules of algebra as the real numbers. In particular, they reasoned, the new number system had to contain all such expressions as

$$\alpha + \beta i + \gamma i^2 + \cdots$$

where α, β, γ, $\cdots$ were real numbers. Since $i^2 = -1$, $i^3 = -i$, etc., any such expression could be simplified to an expression like

$$\alpha + \beta i, \qquad \alpha, \beta \in R.$$

The rules of combination of these numbers were easily found to be

$$(\alpha + \beta i) + (\gamma + \delta i) = (\alpha + \gamma) + (\beta + \delta)i,$$
$$(\alpha + \beta i)(\gamma + \delta i) = \alpha\gamma + \beta\delta i^2 + \alpha\delta i + \beta i\gamma,$$
$$= (\alpha\gamma - \beta\delta) + (\alpha\delta + \beta\gamma)i.$$

This was the situation when the Irish mathematician W. H. Hamilton became interested in complex numbers in the 1840's. He realized first that the complex numbers would not seem quite so imaginary if there were a rigorous way of constructing them from the real numbers, and we shall give his construction.

(17.1) Definition. The system of *complex numbers* C is the two-dimensional vector space R_2 over the real numbers R together with two operations, called addition and multiplication, addition being the vector addition defined in R_2 and multiplication being defined by the rule

$$\langle \alpha, \beta \rangle \langle \gamma, \delta \rangle = \langle \alpha\gamma - \beta\delta, \alpha\delta + \beta\gamma \rangle.$$

(17.2)★   **Theorem.**   *The complex numbers form a field.*

The mapping $\alpha \rightarrow \langle \alpha, 0 \rangle = \alpha'$ of $R \rightarrow C$ is a one-to-one mapping such that

$$(\alpha + \beta)' = \alpha' + \beta', \qquad (\alpha\beta)' = \alpha'\beta'.$$

In this sense we may say that R is contained in C, and we shall write $\alpha = \langle \alpha, 0 \rangle$.

There is no longer anything mysterious about the equation $x^2 + 1 = 0$. Remembering that $1 = \langle 1, 0 \rangle$, we see that $\pm\langle 0, 1 \rangle$ are the solutions of the equation, so that if we define i by

$$i = \langle 0, 1 \rangle$$

then $i^2 = -1$. For all $\beta = \langle \beta, 0 \rangle \in R$ we have $\beta i = \langle 0, \beta \rangle$, and hence every complex number $z = \langle \alpha, \beta \rangle$ can be expressed as

$$z = \langle \alpha, \beta \rangle = \langle \alpha, 0 \rangle + \langle 0, \beta \rangle = \alpha \cdot 1 + \beta i.$$

We shall call α the *real part* of z and β the *imaginary part*. Moreover, $\alpha + \beta i = \gamma + \delta i$ if and only if $\alpha = \gamma$ and $\beta = \delta$.

Another point that Hamilton emphasized was that not only i but every complex number $z = \alpha + \beta i$ is a root of a quadratic equation with real coefficients. To find the equation, we compare

$$z^2 = (\alpha^2 - \beta^2) + (2\alpha\beta)i$$

with $z = \alpha + \beta i$. We find that

$$z^2 - 2\alpha z = -\alpha^2 - \beta^2$$

so that the equation satisfied by $z = \alpha + \beta i$ is

(17.3) $z^2 - 2\alpha z + (\alpha^2 + \beta^2) = 0.$

We know that there is another root of this equation, and we find that it is given by

$$\bar{z} = \alpha - \beta i.$$

Since the constant term of a quadratic polynomial $z^2 + Az + B$ is easily seen by the factor theorem to be the product of the zeros, we see at once that

$$z\bar{z} = \alpha^2 + \beta^2.$$

If we let $|z| = \sqrt{\alpha^2 + \beta^2}$, then $|z|$ is the length of the vector $\langle \alpha, \beta \rangle$, and we have shown that

(17.4) $z\bar{z} = |z|^2.$

From this formula we obtain a simple formula for z^{-1}, if $z \neq 0$, namely,

(17.5)
$$z^{-1} = \frac{\bar{z}}{|z|^2}.$$

The complex number $\bar{z}$ is called the *conjugate* of z; it is the other root of the quadratic equation with real coefficients satisfied by z. The operation of taking conjugates has the properties

$$\overline{z_1 + z_2} = \bar{z}_1 + \bar{z}_2, \qquad \overline{z_1 z_2} = \bar{z}_1 \bar{z}_2.$$

Thus $z \to \bar{z}$ is an isomorphism of C onto C, and we say it is an *automorphism* of C. Using this automorphism, we can derive the formula $|z_1 z_2| = |z_1|\,|z_2|$, since

$$|z_1 z_2|^2 = z_1 z_2 \overline{z_1 z_2} = z_1 z_2 \bar{z}_1 \bar{z}_2 = (z_1 \bar{z}_1)(z_2 \bar{z}_2) = |z_1|^2\,|z_2|^2.$$

If $z_1 = \alpha + \beta i$ and $z_2 = \gamma + \delta i$, then this formula gives the remarkable identity for real numbers,

$$(\alpha\gamma - \beta\delta)^2 + (\alpha\delta + \beta\gamma)^2 = (\alpha^2 + \beta^2)(\gamma^2 + \delta^2),$$

which asserts that a product of two sums of two squares can be expressed as a sum of two squares.*

We come next to the important *polar representation* of complex numbers. Let $z = \langle \alpha, \beta \rangle$; then letting $\rho = \sqrt{\alpha^2 + \beta^2} = |z|$, we can write

$$\alpha = \rho \cos \theta, \qquad \beta = \rho \sin \theta,$$

where θ is the angle determined by the rays joining the origin to the points $(1, 0)$ and (α, β). Thus,†

$$z = \alpha + \beta i = \rho\,(\cos \theta + i \sin \theta) = |z|\,(\cos \theta + i \sin \theta)$$

where we note that

$$|z| = |\rho|, \qquad |\cos \theta + i \sin \theta| = 1.$$

If $w = |w|\,(\cos \varphi + i \sin \varphi)$, then we obtain

$$zw = |z|\,|w|(\cos \theta + i \sin \theta)(\cos \varphi + i \sin \varphi)$$
$$= |zw|[(\cos \theta \cos \varphi - \sin \theta \sin \varphi) + i(\sin \theta \cos \varphi + \cos \theta \sin \varphi)].$$

With the addition theorems for the sine and cosine functions, this formula becomes

---

* For a discussion of this formula and analogous formulas for sums of four and eight squares, see the article by Curtis which appears in the first book listed in the Bibliography. It contains references to the original papers on these questions.

† We write $i \sin \theta$ instead of the more natural $(\sin \theta)i$ in order to keep the number of parentheses down to a minimum.

(17.6) $zw = |z||w|[\cos(\theta + \varphi) + i\sin(\theta + \varphi)]$

which says in geometrical terms that to multiply two complex numbers we must multiply their absolute values and add the angles they make with the "real" axis.

An important application of (17.6) is the following theorem.

(17.7)   De Moivre's Theorem. *For all positive integers n,*

$$(\cos\theta + i\sin\theta)^n = \cos n\theta + i\sin n\theta.$$

De Moivre's theorem has several important applications. If for a fixed n we expand $(\cos\theta + i\sin\theta)^n$ by using the binomial formula and compare real and imaginary parts on both sides of the equation in (17.7), we then obtain formulas expressing $\cos n\theta$ and $\sin n\theta$ as polynomials in $\sin\theta$ and $\cos\theta$.

Another important application is the construction of the *roots of unity*.

(17.8)★   Theorem. *For each positive integer n, the equation $x^n = 1$ has exactly n distinct complex roots, $z_1, z_2, \cdots, z_n$, which are given by*

$$z_1 = \cos\frac{2\pi}{n} + i\sin\frac{2\pi}{n}, \cdots, z_k = z_1^k = \cos\frac{2\pi k}{n} + i\sin\frac{2\pi k}{n},$$

$$k = 1, \cdots, n.$$

We come finally to what is perhaps the most important property of the field of complex numbers from the point of view of algebra.

(17.9)   Definition. A field F is said to be *algebraically closed* if every polynomial $f \in F[x]$ of positive degree has at least one zero in F.

The next theorem is sometimes called "the Fundamental Theorem of Algebra," and although modern algebra no longer extolls it in quite such glowing terms, it is nevertheless a basic result concerning the complex field.

(17.10)   Theorem. *The field of complex numbers is algebraically closed.*

Many proofs of this theorem have been found, all of which rest on the completeness axiom for the real numbers or on some topological property of the real numbers which is equivalent to the completeness axiom. The reader will find a proof very much in the spirit of this course in Schreier and Sperner's book, and other proofs may be found in Birkhoff and MacLane's (see Bibliography for both), or in any book on functions of a complex variable.

(17.11) Theorem. *Let F be an algebraically closed field. Then every prime polynomial in $F[x]$ has (up to a unit factor) the form $x - a$, $a \in F$. Every polynomial $f \in F[x]$ can be factored in the form*

$$\prod_{i=1}^{n} (x - a_i), \qquad a_i \in F.$$

Proof. Let F be algebraically closed and let $p \in F[x]$ be a prime polynomial. By definition (17.9) there is an element $a \in F$ such that $p(a) = 0$. By the factor theorem (16.14), $x - a$ is a factor of p. Since p is prime, p is a constant multiple of $x - a$, and the first statement is proved. The second statement is immediate from the first.

The disadvantage of this theorem is that, although it asserts the existence of the zeros of a polynomial, it gives no information about how the zeros depend on the coefficients of the polynomial f. This problem is the subject of the Galois theory (Van der Waerden, Chap. V; see Bibliography).

We conclude this section with an application of theorem (17.11) to polynomials with real coefficients.

(17.12) Theorem. *Let $f = \alpha_0 + \alpha_1 x + \cdots + \alpha_n x^n \in R[x]$. If $u \in C$ is a zero of f, then $\bar{u}$ is also a zero of f; if $u \neq \bar{u}$, then*

$$(x - u)(x - \bar{u}) = x^2 - (u + \bar{u})x + u\bar{u}$$

is a factor of f.

Proof. If u is a zero of f, then

$$\alpha_0 + \alpha_1 u + \cdots + \alpha_n u^n = 0.$$

Taking the conjugate of the left side and using the fact that $u \to \bar{u}$ is an automorphism of C such that $\bar{\alpha} = \alpha$ for $\alpha \in R$, we obtain

$$\alpha_0 + \alpha_1 \bar{u} + \cdots + \alpha_n \bar{u}^n = 0,$$

which is the first assertion of the theorem. The second is immediate by the factor theorem.

An important consequence of the last theorem is its corollary:

(17.13) Corollary. *Every prime polynomial in $R[x]$ has the form (up to a unit factor)*

$$x - \alpha, \qquad \text{or} \quad x^2 + \alpha x + \beta, \qquad \alpha^2 - 4\beta < 0.$$

Proof. Let $f \in R[x]$ be a prime polynomial; then f has a zero $u \in C$. If $u = \alpha \in R$, then $f = \xi(x - \alpha)$ for some $\xi \in R$. If $u \notin R$, then $\bar{u} \neq u$ and, by (17.12),

$$(x - u)(x - \bar{u}) = x^2 - (u + \bar{u})x + u\bar{u}$$

is a factor of f. Since $u + \bar{u}$ and $u\bar{u}$ belong to R, it follows that f is (up to a unit factor) $x^2 + \alpha x + \beta$. The condition $\alpha^2 - 4\beta < 0$ follows from the fact that f is prime in $R[x]$.

EXERCISES

1. Derive formulas for $\cos 3\theta$ and $\sin 3\theta$ in terms of $\cos \theta$ and $\sin \theta$.

2. Find all solutions of the equation $x^5 = 2$.

3. Let $a_0 + a_1 x + \cdots + a_{r-1}x^{r-1} + x^r = (x - u_1)(x - u_2) \cdots (x - u_r)$ be a polynomial in $C[x]$ with leading coefficient $a_r = 1$ and with zeros $u_1, \cdots, u_r$ in C. Prove that $a_0 = \pm u_1 u_2, \cdots u_r$ and $a_{r-1} = -(u_1 + u_2 + \cdots + u_r)$.

4. Prove that the field of complex numbers C is isomorphic* with the set of all 2-by-2 matrices with real coefficients of the form

$$\begin{pmatrix} \alpha & -\beta \\ \beta & \alpha \end{pmatrix}, \qquad \alpha, \beta \in R,$$

where the operations are addition† and multiplication of matrices.

5. Let $f(x) = \alpha_0 + \alpha_1 x + \cdots + \alpha_r x^r$ be a polynomial with coefficients $\alpha_i \in Q$, the field of rational numbers, and let $u \in C$ be a zero of f. Let $Q[u]$ be the set of complex numbers of the form

$$z = \beta_0 + \beta_1 u + \cdots + \beta_{r-1}u^{r-1}, \qquad \beta_i \in Q.$$

---

* Two fields F and F' are said to be isomorphic if there exists a one-to-one mapping $\alpha \to \alpha'$ of F onto F' such that $(\alpha + \beta)' = \alpha' + \beta'$ and $(\alpha\beta)' = \alpha'\beta'$ for all α, $\beta \in F$.

† Addition of two matrices (a_{ij}), (b_{ij}) is defined by $(a_{ij}) + (b_{ij}) = (c_{ij})$ where $c_{ij} = a_{ij} + b_{ij}$ for all i, j.

Prove that if z, $w \in Q[u]$ then $z \pm w$ and $zw \in Q[u]$. Prove that $Q[u]$ is a field if and only if f is a prime polynomial in $Q[x]$ (see Exercise 1, part **b**, of Section 15 for a special case). [*Hint:* In case $f(x)$ is a prime, the main difficulty is proving that if $z = \beta_0 + \beta_1 u + \cdots + \beta_{r-1} u^{r-1} \neq 0$ then there exists $w \in Q[n]$ such that $zw = 1$. Since $z \neq 0$, the polynomial

$$g(x) = \beta_0 + \beta_1 x + \cdots + \beta_{r-1} x^{r-1} \neq 0$$

in $Q[x]$. Since deg $f(x) = r$, it follows that $f(x)$ and $g(x)$ are relatively prime. Therefore there exist polynomials $a(x)$ and $b(x)$ such that

$$a(x)g(x) + b(x)f(x) = 1.$$

Upon substituting u for x, we obtain

$$a(u)g(u) = 1$$

and, since $g(u) = z$, we have produced an inverse for z.]

CHAPTER 5

VECTOR SPACES
and LINEAR
TRANSFORMATIONS

This chapter begins with the concept of an abstract vector space over an arbitrary field. Examples will be given to show that this idea includes many important mathematical systems besides the vector space of n-tuples that motivated much of this discussion.

The main topic of the chapter is an introduction to the theory of a single linear transformation on a vector space. We prove the simplest of the theorems on the classification of the invariant subspaces relative to a linear transformation and present several applications of this theorem. Among them is the computation of the exponential function of a matrix and its application to the solution of systems of first-order linear differential equations with constant coefficients.

18. ABSTRACT VECTOR SPACES

(18.1) Definition. Let F be an arbitrary field. A *vector space V over F* is a nonempty set V of objects $\{v\}$, called *vectors*, together

110

with two operations, one of which assigns to each pair of vectors v and w a vector $v + w$ called the *sum* of v and w, and the other of which assigns to each element $\alpha \in F$ and each vector $v \in V$ a vector αv called the *product* of v by the element $\alpha \in F$. The operations are assumed to satisfy the following axioms, for α, $\beta \in F$ and for u, $v \in V$.

(1) $u + (v + w) = (u + v) + w$, and $u + v = v + u$.
(2) There is a vector 0 such that $u + 0 = u$ for all $u \in V$.*
(3) For each vector u there is a vector $-u$ such that $u + (-u) = 0$.
(4) $\alpha(u + v) = \alpha u + \alpha v$.
(5) $(\alpha + \beta)u = \alpha u + \beta u$.
(6) $(\alpha\beta)u = \alpha(\beta u)$.
(7) $1u = u$.

These axioms should not surprise anyone who has worked through the earlier material in the course. We should check, however, that the elementary calculations which could be justified earlier by our particular interpretation of vectors can now be proved from the axioms. We list a few of these facts, which can be proved by the same arguments used to prove the corresponding facts for a field in Chapter 1, Section 2. In this discussion u, v, w stand for vectors and α, β stand for elements of F.

If $u + v = u + w$, then $v = w$.

The equation $u + x = v$ has a unique solution which we denote by $v - u$.

$-(-u) = u, \quad u \in V.$
$0u = 0.$
$-(\alpha u) = (-\alpha)u = \alpha(-u).$
$(-\alpha)(-u) = \alpha u, \quad \alpha \in F, u \in V.$

EXAMPLES OF VECTOR SPACES

(18.2) The vector space F_n of n-tuples, as defined in Section 15.

(18.3) Let $C[0, 1]$ be the set of continuous real-valued functions f defined on, for example, the closed interval $[0, 1]$. Then $C[0, 1]$ becomes a vector space V over the field of real numbers R if we define

$$(f + g)(x) = f(x) + g(x), \quad x \in [0, 1], \quad f, g \in V,$$
$$(\alpha f)(x) = \alpha f(x), \quad x \in [0, 1], \quad \alpha \in R.$$

---

* As before, we use the same symbol for the zero vector and for the zero element of F.

From calculus we know that one of the basic facts concerning continuous functions is that $f + g$ and αf belong to $C[0, 1]$ for all f, $g \in C[0, 1]$ and $\alpha \in R$. We omit the verification of the vector space axioms.

(18.4) Let r be a positive integer, and define $C^r[0, 1]$ to be the set of all continuous functions f on $[0, 1]$ which have continuous derivatives of order i on $[0, 1]$ for $i = 1, 2, \cdots, r$. The operations are defined as in (18.3).

(18.5) Let $V = F[x]$, the set of all polynomials with coefficients in F. If f, $g \in V$ and $\alpha \in F$, then $f + g$ is defined as the sum of the polynomials and αf as the polynomial obtained from f by multiplying all the coefficients of f by α.

(18.6) Let E be a field that contains F as a *subfield;* that is, F is a subset of E such that the operations on F are the operations of E restricted to pairs of elements in F. Then E becomes a vector space over F if for a and b in E we define $a + b$ as the sum of a and b, as elements of the field E, and define αa, where $a \in E$ and $\alpha \in F$, as the result of multiplying a by α in E. To check the axioms for a field in this case, it is necessary to show that the identity element $1 \in F$ is also the identity element in E.

Now we show that much of the material developed in Chapter 2 can be carried over to abstract vector spaces. The proofs of all statements are the same as in Chapter 2 and will not be repeated.

Let V be an (abstract) vector space over F. If $\{v_1, \cdots, v_r\}$ belong to V, we say that a vector v is a *linear combination of* $v_1, \cdots, v_r$ if there exist elements $\xi_1, \cdots, \xi_r$ in F such that

$$v = \xi_1 v_1 + \cdots + \xi_r v_r.$$

A *subspace* S of V is a subset of V such that, if r and $s \in S$, then $r \pm s \in S$ and, if $r \in S$, then $\alpha r \in S$ for all $\alpha \in F$. Evidently, if $v_1, \cdots, v_r$ belong to a subspace S, every linear combination of $v_1, \cdots, v_r$ belongs to S.

If $v_1, \cdots, v_r$ are vectors in V, then the set of all linear combinations of $v_1, \cdots, v_r$ is a subspace, which we shall call $S(v_1, \cdots, v_r)$, and is the smallest subspace containing $\{v_1, \cdots, v_r\}$. S is called the *subspace generated by* $\{v_1, \cdots, v_r\}$. A subspace S of V is called *finitely generated* if there exist vectors $s_1, \cdots, s_k$ in S such that $S = S(s_1, \cdots, s_k)$.

A set of vectors $\{v_1, \cdots, v_r\}$ is *linearly dependent* if there exist elements $\xi_1, \cdots, \xi_r \in F$, not all zero, such that

(18.7) $$\xi_1 v_1 + \cdots + \xi_r v_r = 0.$$

If no relation (18.7) holds unless $\xi_1 = \cdots = \xi_r = 0$, then the vectors $v_1, \cdots, v_r$ are *linearly independent*.

A set of vectors $b_1, \cdots, b_k$ is said to be a *basis* for a subspace S of V if $\{b_1, \cdots, b_k\}$ is a linearly independent set and if $S = S(b_1, \cdots, b_k)$.

We can now state some of the chief theorems of Chapter 2.

(18.8)   **Theorem.**   *Let $S = S(u_1, \cdots, u_s)$ be a finitely generated subspace of V and let $\{v_1, \cdots, v_r\}$ be a linearly independent subset of S; then $r \leq s$, and for a suitable arrangement of $\{u_1, \cdots, u_s\}$ we have*

$$S = S(v_1, \cdots, v_r, \quad u_{r+1}, \cdots, u_s).$$

(18.9)   **Corollary.**   *Any set of $s + 1$ (or more) vectors in a subspace $S(u_1, \cdots, u_s)$ with s generators, is a linearly dependent set.*

(18.10)   **Corollary.**   *Every finitely generated subspace $S(u_1, \cdots, u_s)$ has a basis of $r \leq s$ vectors which can be chosen from among the generators $\{u_1, \cdots, u_s\}$. Any two bases of $S(u_1, \cdots, u_s)$ contain the same number of vectors.**

(18.11)   **Definition.**   A vector space is called *finite-dimensional* if it is finitely generated. If V is finite-dimensional, the number of elements in a basis is called the *dimension* of V. A vector space which is not finite-dimensional is said to be *infinite-dimensional*.

(18.12)   **Theorem.**   *Let S be a finite-dimensional subspace of V and let $v_1, \cdots, v_k$ be linearly independent vectors in S; then there exist vectors $v_{k+1}, \cdots, v_r$ in S such that $\{v_1, \cdots, v_k, v_{k+1}, \cdots, v_r\}$ is a basis of S.*

(18.13)   **Definition.**   Let V and V' be vector spaces over F. The vector spaces V and V' are said to be *isomorphic* if there exists a one-to-one mapping T of V onto V' such that

$$T(v_1 + v_2) = T(v_1) + T(v_2), \qquad v_1, v_2 \in V,$$
$$T(\alpha v_1) = \alpha T(v_1), \qquad \alpha \in F.$$

---

* If S is the zero subspace, then S has a basis consisting of the empty set (we know from Chapter 2 that the empty set is linearly independent).

(18.14) Theorem. *Let V be a vector space of dimension n; then V is isomorphic with the vector space F_n of n-tuples with coefficients in F.*

Proof. Let $\{v_1, \cdots, v_n\}$ be a basis of V over F; then every vector $v \in V$ can be expressed uniquely in the form

$$v = \xi_1 v_1 + \cdots + \xi_n v_n, \qquad \xi_i \in F,$$

and the mapping $T: v \to \langle \xi_1, \cdots, \xi_n \rangle$ is easily seen to be the required isomorphism.

EXERCISES

1. Determine which of the following subsets of $C[0, 1]$ are subspaces of $C[0, 1]$; see the example of vector spaces, (18.3).

   a. The set of polynomial functions in $C[0, 1]$.
   b. The set of all $f \in C[0, 1]$ such that $f(\frac{1}{2})$ is a rational number.
   c. The set of all $f \in C[0, 1]$ such that $f(\frac{1}{2}) = 0$.
   d. The set of all $f \in C[0, 1]$ such that $\int_0^1 f(t)\, dt = 1$.
   e. The set of all $f \in C[0, 1]$ such that $\int_0^1 f(t)\, dt = 0$.
   f. The set of all $f \in C[0, 1]$ such that $df/dt = 0$.
   g. The set of all $f \in C[0, 1]$ such that

   $$\alpha \frac{d^2 f}{dt^2} + \beta \frac{df}{dt} + \gamma f = 0, \qquad \alpha, \beta, \gamma \in R.$$

   h. The set of all $f \in C[0, 1]$ such that

   $$\alpha \frac{d^2 f}{dt^2} + \beta \frac{df}{dt} + \gamma f = g$$

   for a fixed function $g \in C[0, 1]$.

2. Show that $C[0, 1]$ and $F[x]$ are both infinite-dimensional vector spaces over R and F, respectively. [*Hint:* Show that the functions (or polynomials) $x, x^2, x^3, \cdots$ are not contained in any finite-dimensional subspace.]

3. Prove that the set of all $f \in C[0, 1]$ such that $df/dt = 0$ is a one-dimensional subspace of $C[0, 1]$. (*Hint:* Use part **f** of Exercise 1 and a theorem from calculus.) Can you generalize this result? For example, what is the dimension of the subspace consisting of all f such that $d^2f/dt^2 = 0$? What do these subspaces look like

from a geometrical point of view; that is, how are the graphs of functions in the subspaces related?

4. What is the dimension of the field of complex numbers C viewed as a vector space over the field of real numbers R? What is a basis of C over R? See the example of vector spaces, (18.6).

19. LINEAR TRANSFORMATIONS

In this section, F denotes an arbitrary field.

(19.1) **Definition.**   Let V and W be vector spaces over F. A *linear transformation of V into W* is a function $T: V \to W$ which assigns to each vector $v \in V$ a unique vector $w = T(v) \in W$ such that*

$$T(v_1 + v_2) = T(v_1) + T(v_2), \qquad v_i \in V,$$
$$T(\alpha v) = \alpha T(v), \qquad \alpha \in F, \quad v \in V.$$

EXAMPLES OF LINEAR TRANSFORMATIONS

(19.2)   In Section 13 we showed that a system of m linear equations in n unknowns with coefficients in F may be used to define a linear transformation

$$T: F_n \to F_m.$$

The transformation T is defined as follows. We have, for $x = \langle x_1, \cdots, x_n \rangle \in F_n$,

$$T(x) = y.$$

The vector $y = \langle y_1, \cdots, y_m \rangle$ is given by

$$y_i = \sum_{j=1}^{n} \alpha_{ij} x_j, \qquad 1 \le i \le m,$$

where (α_{ij}) is the coefficient matrix of the system. In particular, if $m = 1$ we have a single linear equation

$$L(x) = \alpha_1 x_1 + \cdots + \alpha_n x_n$$

which defines a linear transformation of $F_n \to F_1$. A linear transformation of $F_n \to F_1$ is called a *linear function* on F_n. Some of our previous work can be viewed advantageously from the standpoint of

---

* In order to avoid forests of parentheses, we shall sometimes write Tv for $T(v)$.

linear functions. For example, an $(n - 1)$-dimensional subspace of F_n is simply the set of zeros of a single nonzero linear function. A hyperplane in F_n is the set of solutions x of an equation

$$L(x) = \beta$$

where L is a fixed nonzero linear function and β is a fixed element of F.

(19.3)   Let V be the vector space $C[0, 1]$ over the real field R; then the function

$$f \to I(f) = \int_0^1 f(t) \, dt, \qquad f \in C[0, 1]$$

is shown in elementary calculus to be a linear transformation of $C[0, 1] \to R_1$ or, in the language introduced in (19.2), a *linear function* on $C[0, 1]$. The set of functions $f \in C[0, 1]$ such that

$$I(f) = \int_0^1 f(t) \, dt = \beta$$

is therefore a generalization of our previous concept of a hyperplane.

(19.4)   Again let V be the vector space $C[0, 1]$ over R. For a differentiable function f, let Df denote the derivative of f. Then Df is a function on $[0, 1]$ which may or may not belong to $C[0, 1]$. The mapping $D:f \to Df$ clearly is not a linear transformation of $C[0, 1] \to C[0, 1]$, because Df is not defined for every element of V, and even for those functions for which Df is defined it is not clear whether $Df \in C[0, 1]$. To view D as a linear transformation, we must restrict ourselves to a set of functions on which D is defined. As in the example (18.4) of abstract vector spaces, let $C^1[0, 1]$ be the set of all functions $f \in C[0, 1]$ such that $Df \in C[0, 1]$. It is easily checked that $C^1[0, 1]$ is a subspace of $C[0, 1]$ and that D is a linear transformation of $C^1[0, 1]$ into $C[0, 1]$. We remark also that D does not carry $C^1[0, 1]$ into $C^1[0, 1]$. For example, let f be the function

$$f(x) = \begin{cases} -(x - \tfrac{1}{2}), & 0 \le x \le \tfrac{1}{2} \\ x - \tfrac{1}{2}, & \tfrac{1}{2} \le x \le 1 \end{cases}$$

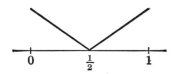

and define g by

$$g(x) = \int_0^x f(t)\, dt, \qquad 0 \le x \le 1.$$

Then $g \in C^1[0, 1]$ and $Dg = f \in C[0, 1]$, but $f \notin C^1[0, 1]$.

(19.5)   Let F be an arbitrary field and consider the vector space $F[x]$ over F as consisting of all polynomials

$$f = \alpha_0 + \alpha_1 x + \cdots + \alpha_r x^r, \qquad \alpha_i \in F.$$

For any such polynomial f, define its (formal) derivative Df by

$$Df = \alpha_1 + 2\alpha_2 x^2 + \cdots + r\alpha_r x^{r-1}.$$

We call Df the formal derivative since it is defined in a purely algebraic manner and can be studied even when the concept of limit is not defined in F. Of course, Df agrees with the usual concept of derivative if F is the field of real numbers and f is viewed as a polynomial function.

The importance of linear transformations comes partly from the fact that they can be combined by certain algebraic operations, and the resulting algebraic system has many properties not to be found in the other algebraic systems we have studied so far.*

(19.6)   Definition.   Let F be an arbitrary field and let V and W be vector spaces over F. Let S and T be linear transformations of $V \to W$. Define a mapping $S + T$ of $V \to W$ by the rule

$$(S + T)v = S(v) + T(v), \qquad v \in V.$$

Then $S + T$ is a linear transformation of $V \to W$ called the *sum* of the linear transformations S and T.

(19.7)   Definition.   Let M, N, P be vector spaces over F and let S be a linear transformation of $M \to N$ and T a linear transformation of $N \to P$; then the mapping $TS : M \to P$ defined by

$$(TS)(m) = T[S(m)]$$

is a linear transformation of $M \to P$ called the *product* of the linear transformations T and S.

---

* At this point the reader should review some of the definitions concerning functions on sets in Section 3.

(19.8) Theorem. *Let V, W be vector spaces over F and let $L(V, W)$ denote the set of all linear transformations of V into W; then $L(V, W)$ is a vector space over F, with respect to the operations*

$$S + T, \qquad S, T \in L(V, W), \quad \text{see definition (19.6)},$$

and

$$\alpha S, \qquad \alpha \in F, \quad S \in L(V, W),$$

where $(\alpha S)(v) = \alpha[S(v)]$.

Proof. We check first that $S + T$ and αS actually belong to $L(V, W)$; the argument is simply a thorough workout with the axioms for a vector space. Let v_1, $v_2 \in V$; then

$$
\begin{aligned}
(S + T)(v_1 + v_2) &= S(v_1 + v_2) + T(v_1 + v_2) \\
&= [S(v_1) + S(v_2)] + [T(v_1) + T(v_2)] \\
&= [S(v_1) + T(v_1)] + [S(v_2) + T(v_2)] \\
&= (S + T)(v_1) + (S + T)(v_2).
\end{aligned}
$$

For $\xi \in F$ we have

$$
\begin{aligned}
(S + T)(\xi v) &= S(\xi v) + T(\xi v) = \xi[S(v)] + \xi[T(v)] \\
&= \xi[S(v) + T(v)] = \xi[(S + T)(v)].
\end{aligned}
$$

Turning to the mapping αS, we have

$$(\alpha S)(v_1 + v_2) = \alpha[S(v_1) + S(v_2)] = \alpha S(v_1) + \alpha S(v_2)$$

and, for $\xi \in F$,

$$
\begin{aligned}
(\alpha S)(\xi v) &= \alpha[S(\xi v)] = \alpha[\xi S(v)] \\
&= (\alpha \xi)S(v) = (\xi \alpha)S(v) \\
&= \xi[(\alpha S)(v)],
\end{aligned}
$$

since F satisfies the commutative law for multiplication.

The linear transformation 0, which sends each $v \in V$ into the zero vector, satisfies the condition that*

$$T + 0 = T, \qquad T \in L(V, W)$$

and the transformation $-T$, defined by

$$(-T)v = -T(v)$$

satisfies the condition that

$$T + (-T) = 0.$$

The verification of the other axioms is left to the reader.

---

* The symbol 0 is given still another meaning, but the context will always indicate which meaning is intended.

A particular case of the preceding construction is of special importance and will be given a separate definition.

(19.9) Definition.   Let V be a vector space over F; then the vector space $L(V, F_1)$ is called the *dual space* of V and is denoted by V^*. The elements of V^* are called *linear functions*, or *linear functionals* on V.

(19.10) Theorem.   *Let V be a vector space over F, and let $S, T \in L(V, V)$ and $\alpha \in F$; then*

$$S + T, \qquad ST, \qquad \alpha S$$

are all elements of $L(V, V)$. With respect to the operations $S + T$ and αS, $L(V, V)$ is a vector space. Moreover, $L(V, V)$ has the further properties:

$$S(TU) = (ST)U \qquad \text{(associative law)};$$

there is a linear transformation 1 such that

$$1v = v, \qquad v \in V$$

and

$$1T = T1 = T, \qquad T \in L(V, V).$$

Finally, we have the distributive laws

$$S(T + U) = ST + SU, \qquad (S + T)U = SU + TU.$$

Proof.   Because the properties of $L(V, V)$ relative to the operations $S + T$ and αS were already described in the preceding theorem, it is sufficient to consider the properties of ST. First we check that ST is a linear transformation. For $v_1, v_2 \in V$ and $\alpha \in F$ we have

$$(ST)(v_1 + v_2) = S[T(v_1 + v_2)] = S[T(v_1) + T(v_2)]$$
$$= S[T(v_1)] + S[T(v_2)] = (ST)v_1 + (ST)v_2$$

and

$$(ST)(\alpha v_1) = S[T(\alpha v_1)] = S[\alpha T(v_1)]$$
$$= \alpha\{S[T(v_1)]\} = \alpha[ST(v_1)].$$

This completes the proof that $ST \in L(V, V)$. The same argument shows that TS in definition (19.7) is a linear transformation.

Now let S, T, U be elements of $L(V, V)$. The associative and distributive laws are verified by checking that the transformations $S(TU)$ and $(ST)U$, for example, have the same effect on an arbitrary vector in V. Let $v \in V$; then

$$[S(TU)](v) = S[(TU)(v)] = S\{T[U(v)]\}$$

while

$$[(ST)U](v) = ST[U(v)] = S\{T[U(v)]\}.$$

Similarly,

$$[S(T + U)](v) = S[(T + U)(v)] = S[T(v) + U(v)]$$
$$= S[T(v)] + S[U(v)] = (ST + SU)(v)$$

and

$$[(S + T)U](v) = (S + T)U(v) = S[U(v)] + T[U(v)]$$
$$= (SU)(v) + (TU)(v) = (SU + TU)(v)$$

This completes the proof of the theorem.

The previous result leads to the following general concept.

(19.11) Definition. A *ring* $\Re$ is a mathematical system consisting of a nonempty set $\Re = \{a, b, \cdots\}$ together with two operations, addition and multiplication, each of which assigns to a pair of elements a and b in $\Re$ other elements of $\Re$, denoted by $a + b$ in the case of addition and ab in the case of multiplication, such that the following formulas hold for all a, b, c in $\Re$.

(1) $a + b = b + a$.
(2) $(a + b) + c = a + (b + c)$.
(3) There is an element 0 such that $a + 0 = a$ for all $a \in \Re$.
(4) For each $a \in \Re$ there is an element $-a$ such that $a + (-a) = 0$.
(5) $(ab)c = a(bc)$.
(6) $a(b + c) = ab + ac$, $(a + b)c = ac + bc$.
(7) If the commutative law for multiplication, $ab = ba$, for a, $b \in \Re$, holds, then $\Re$ is called a *commutative ring*.

Any field is a commutative ring; the integers Z and polynomials $F[x]$ are commutative rings which are not fields. In the exercises at the end of this section, the reader is asked to show that the commutative law for multiplication does not hold in general for the linear transformations in $L(V, V)$. Theorem (19.10) now can be stated more concisely:

(19.10′) Theorem. $L(V, V)$ *is a ring.*

It is worth checking to what extent the proofs of the ring axioms for $L(V, V)$ depend on the assumption that the elements are *linear* transformations. To make this question more precise, let $M(V, V)$ be the set of *all* functions $T: V \rightarrow V$ and define $S + T$ and ST as for linear transformations. It can easily be verified that all the axioms for a ring hold for $M(V, V)$, with the exception of the one distributive law

$$S(T + U) = ST + SU,$$

which actually fails for suitably chosen S, T, and U in $M(V, V)$.

The mapping $T: \langle \alpha, \beta \rangle \rightarrow \langle \beta, 0 \rangle$, for $\alpha, \beta \in R$, is a linear transformation of R_2 such that $T^2 = 0$. It is impossible for T to have a reciprocal $\hat{T}$ such that $T\hat{T} = 1$, since $T\hat{T} = 1$ implies

$$T(T\hat{T}) = T \cdot 1 = T,$$

while, because of the associative law,

$$T(T\hat{T}) = T^2\hat{T} = 0 \cdot \hat{T} = 0,$$

which produces the contradiction $T = 0$. Because of this phenomenon, it is necessary to make the following definition.

(19.12) Definition. A linear transformation $T \in L(V, V)$ is said to be *invertible* (or *nonsingular*) if there exists a linear transformation $T^{-1} \in L(V, V)$ (called the *inverse* of T) such that

$$TT^{-1} = T^{-1}T = 1.$$

An exercise at the end of this section shows that $TU = 1$ does not imply always that $UT = 1$; so, if T' is to be shown the inverse of T, both the equations $TT' = 1$ and $T'T = 1$ must be checked.

Some other properties of invertible transformations can be best understood from the viewpoint of the following definition.

(19.13) Definition. A *group* G is a mathematical system consisting of a nonempty set G, together with one operation which assigns to each pair of elements S, T in G a third element ST in G, such that the following conditions are satisfied.

(A) $(ST)U = S(TU)$,   for $S, T, U \in G$.
(B) There is an element $1 \in G$ such that $S1 = 1S = S$ for all $S \in G$.
(C) For each $S \in G$ there is an element $S^{-1} \in G$ such that $SS^{-1} = S^{-1}S = 1$.

(19.14) Theorem. *Let G be the set of invertible linear transformations in $L(V, V)$; then G is a group.*

Proof. In view of the definition of invertible linear transformation and what has already been proved about $L(V, V)$, it is only necessary to check that if $S, T \in G$ then $ST \in G$. We have

$$(ST)T^{-1}S^{-1} = S \cdot 1S^{-1} = 1,$$
$$T^{-1}S^{-1}(ST) = T^{-1} \cdot 1T = 1.$$

Hence $ST \in G$ and $T^{-1}S^{-1}$ is an inverse of ST.

The next theorem, on the uniqueness of T^{-1}, etc., holds for groups in general.

(19.15)   Theorem. *Let G be an arbitrary group; then the equations*

$$AX = B, \qquad XA = B$$

have unique solutions $A^{-1}B$ and BA^{-1} respectively. In particular, $AX = 1$ implies that $X = A^{-1}$. Similarly, $XA = 1$ implies $X = A^{-1}$.

Proof.   We have

$$A(A^{-1}B) = (AA^{-1})B = 1B = B$$

and

$$(BA^{-1})A = B(A^{-1}A) = B \cdot 1 = B,$$

proving that solutions of the equations do exist. For the uniqueness, suppose that

$$AX' = B.$$

Then $A^{-1}(AX') = A^{-1}B$ and, since

$$A^{-1}(AX') = (A^{-1}A)X' = 1 \cdot X' = X',$$

we have $X' = A^{-1}B$. Similarly, $X'A = B$ implies $X' = BA^{-1}$. This completes the proof of the theorem.

Other important examples of groups will be considered in the next chapter.

EXERCISES

1. Which of the following mappings of $R_2 \to R_2$ are linear transformations?

    a. $\langle x_1, x_2 \rangle \to \langle y_1, y_2 \rangle$,   where $y_1 = 3x_1 - x_2 + 1$ and $y_2 = -x_1 + 2x_2$.

    b. $\langle x_1, x_2 \rangle \to \langle y_1, y_2 \rangle$,   where $y_1 = 3x_1 + x_2^2$ and $y_2 = -x_1$.

---

*Part of this theorem was proved for invertible matrices in Section 14.

2. Let T be a linear transformation of V into W. Prove that $T(0) = 0$ and $T(-v) = -T(v)$ for all $v \in V$ and that $T[S(v_1, v_2)] = S(T(v_1), T(v_2))$ where $T[S(v_1, v_2)]$ denotes the set of all images under T of the vectors in the subspace $S(v_1, v_2)$ generated by v_1 and v_2.

3. Let F be an arbitrary field. Prove that the polynomials of degree $\leq r - 1$ form an r-dimensional subspace S_r of $F[x]$. Prove that if D is the derivative defined in (19.5) then $Df \in S_r$ for all $f \in S_r$ and that $D^r f = [D(D \cdots (Df) \cdots)] = 0$ for $f \in S_r$.
$$\underbrace{\qquad}_{r\,D\text{'s}}$$

4. Let $f, g \in F[x]$. Prove that $D(fg) = (Df)g + f(Dg)$. (*Hint*: Since D is a linear transformation, it is sufficient to verify the formula when f and g are powers of x.)

5. Let $f = \alpha_0 + \alpha_1 x + \alpha_2 x^2 + \cdots + \alpha_k x^k \in R[x]$ where R is the real field. Define $I(f)$ by the rule

$$I(f) = \alpha_0 x + \frac{\alpha_1 x^2}{2} + \cdots + \frac{\alpha_k x^{k+1}}{k+1}.$$

Prove that I is a linear transformation of $R[x]$ such that $DI = 1$, but that D is not an invertible linear transformation of $R[x]$.

6. Let V be a finite-dimensional vector space with basis $\{v_1, \cdots, v_n\}$. For each i, let f_i be the linear function such that $f_i(\sum \xi_j v_j) = \xi_i$. Prove that $\{f_1, \cdots, f_n\}$ is a basis for the dual space V^* defined in (19.9).

20.   LINEAR TRANSFORMATIONS AND MATRICES

Throughout the rest of this chapter, V and W denote finite-dimensional vector spaces over F. The first result asserts that a linear transformation is completely determined if we know its effect on a set of basis elements and that, conversely, we may define a linear transformation by assigning arbitrary images for a set of basis elements.

(20.1) **Theorem.** *Let $\{v_1, \cdots, v_n\}$ be a basis of V over F. If S and T are elements of $L(V, W)$ such that $S(v_i) = T(v_i)$, $1 \leq i \leq n$, then $S = T$. Moreover, let $w_1, \cdots, w_n$ be arbitrary vectors in W. Then there exists one and only one linear transformation $T \in L(V, W)$ such that $T(v_i) = w_i$.*

Proof. Let $v = \sum_{1}^{n} \xi_i v_i$. Then $S(v_i) = T(v_i)$, $1 \leq i \leq n$, implies that

$$S(v) = S\left(\sum \xi_i v_i\right) = \sum \xi_i S(v_i) = \sum \xi_i T(v_i) = T(v).$$

Since this holds for all $v \in V$, we have $S = T$, and the first part of the theorem is proved.

To prove the second part, let $w_1, \cdots, w_n$ be given and define a mapping $T: V \rightarrow W$ by setting

$$T\left(\sum \xi_i v_i\right) = \sum \xi_i w_i, \qquad \xi_i \in F.$$

Since $\{v_1, \cdots, v_n\}$ is a basis of V, $\sum \xi_i v_i = \sum \eta_i v_i$ implies $\xi_i = \eta_i$, $1 \leq i \leq n$, and hence $T(\sum \xi_i v_i) = T(\sum \eta_i v_i)$, and we have shown that T is a single-valued function. It is immediate from the definition that T is a linear transformation of $V \rightarrow W$ such that $T(v_i) = w_i$, $1 \leq i \leq n$, and the uniqueness of T is clear by the first part of the theorem. This completes the proof.

Now consider a fixed basis $\{v_1, \cdots, v_n\}$ of V over F and for simplicity let $T \in L(V, V)$. Then for each i, $T(v_i)$ is a linear combination of $v_1, \cdots, v_n$, and the coefficients can be used to define the rows or columns of an n-by-n matrix which together with the basis $\{v_1, \cdots, v_n\}$ determines completely the linear transformation T, because of the preceding theorem. The question whether we should let $T(v_i)$ give the rows or columns of the matrix corresponding to T is answered by requiring that the matrix of a product of two transformations be the product of their corresponding matrices.

For example, let V be a two-dimensional vector space over F with basis $\{v_1, v_2\}$. Let S and T in $L(V, V)$ be defined by

$$S(v_1) = -v_1 + 2v_2, \qquad T(v_1) = 2v_1 + 3v_2,$$
$$S(v_2) = v_1 + v_2, \qquad T(v_2) = -v_2.$$

Then ST is the linear transformation given by

$$ST(v_1) = S(2v_1 + 3v_2) = 2(-v_1 + 2v_2) + 3(v_1 + v_2)$$
$$= v_1 + 7v_2,$$
$$ST(v_2) = S(-v_2) = -(v_1 + v_2) = -v_1 - v_2.$$

The matrices corresponding to S, T, ST, if we let $S(v_i)$ correspond to the *rows* of the matrix of S, etc., are respectively

$$\begin{pmatrix} -1 & 2 \\ 1 & 1 \end{pmatrix}, \quad \begin{pmatrix} 2 & 3 \\ 0 & -1 \end{pmatrix}, \quad \begin{pmatrix} 1 & 7 \\ -1 & -1 \end{pmatrix}$$

and we have

$$\begin{pmatrix} -1 & 2 \\ 1 & 1 \end{pmatrix} \cdot \begin{pmatrix} 2 & 3 \\ 0 & -1 \end{pmatrix} \neq \begin{pmatrix} 1 & 7 \\ -1 & -1 \end{pmatrix}.$$

Let us see if we have better luck by letting $S(v_i)$ correspond to the columns of the matrix of S, etc. In this case the matrices corresponding to S, T, ST are respectively

$$\begin{pmatrix} -1 & 1 \\ 2 & 1 \end{pmatrix}, \quad \begin{pmatrix} 2 & 0 \\ 3 & -1 \end{pmatrix}, \quad \begin{pmatrix} 1 & -1 \\ 7 & -1 \end{pmatrix}$$

and this time it is true that

$$\begin{pmatrix} -1 & 1 \\ 2 & 1 \end{pmatrix} \cdot \begin{pmatrix} 2 & 0 \\ 3 & -1 \end{pmatrix} = \begin{pmatrix} 1 & -1 \\ 7 & -1 \end{pmatrix}.$$

All this suggests the following definition.

(20.2) **Definition.** Let $\{v_1, \cdots, v_n\}$ be a basis of V and let $T \in L(V, V)$. The *matrix of T with respect to the basis* $\{v_1, \cdots, v_n\}$ of V is the n-by-n matrix whose ith column, for $1 \leq i \leq n$, is the set of coefficients obtained when $T(v_i)$ is expressed as a linear combination of $v_1, \cdots, v_n$. Thus the matrix (α_{rs}) of T is described by the equations

$$T(v_i) = \sum_{j=1}^{n} \alpha_{ji} v_j = \alpha_{1i} v_1 + \cdots + \alpha_{ni} v_n.$$

To give another example, let T be the linear transformation of a three-dimensional vector space with basis $\{v_1, v_2, v_3\}$ such that

$$\begin{aligned} T(v_1) &= 2v_1 - 3v_3 \\ T(v_2) &= v_2 + 5v_3 \\ T(v_3) &= v_1 - v_2. \end{aligned}$$

Then the matrix of T with respect to the basis $\{v_1, v_2, v_3\}$ is

$$\begin{pmatrix} 2 & 0 & 1 \\ 0 & 1 & -1 \\ -3 & 5 & 0 \end{pmatrix}.$$

One objective of the theory of a single linear transformation T is to find a basis such that the matrix of T with respect to this basis is as simple as possible; the "simplest possible" matrix is then called a *canonical form* of T. The vague notion of "simplest possible" matrix is open to several different interpretations, with the result that there are several different canonical forms that can be investigated.

To give one example, let $\{v_1, v_2\}$ be a basis for V and let T be a linear transformation such that

$$T(v_1) = v_2,$$
$$T(v_2) = v_1.$$

Then the matrix of T with respect to $\{v_1, v_2\}$ is

$$\begin{pmatrix} 0 & 1 \\ 1 & 0 \end{pmatrix}.$$

If we now consider the new basis,

$$w_1 = v_1 + v_2,$$
$$w_2 = v_1 - v_2,$$

then we see at once that

$$Tw_1 = w_1,$$
$$Tw_2 = -w_2,$$

and the matrix of T with respect to the basis $\{w_1, w_2\}$ is

$$\begin{pmatrix} 1 & 0 \\ 0 & -1 \end{pmatrix},$$

which is an improvement upon the original matrix of T in that $T(w_1)$, for example, is a multiple of w_1 and does not involve the other basis vector w_2.

We return now to some general remarks on the connection between linear transformations and matrices.

We recall that if A, B are n-by-n matrices with coefficients (α_{ij}) and (β_{ij}), respectively, their sum and product are defined by

$$(\alpha_{ij}) + (\beta_{ij}) = (\alpha_{ij} + \beta_{ij}),$$
$$(\alpha_{ij})(\beta_{ij}) = (\gamma_{ij}), \qquad \gamma_{ij} = \sum_{k=1}^{n} \alpha_{ik}\beta_{kj}.$$

In treating a matrix as an n^2-tuple, it is also natural to define

$$\alpha(\alpha_{ij}) = (\alpha\alpha_{ij}), \qquad \alpha \in F.$$

We come now to the result that links the algebraic structure of $L(V, V)$ introduced in the preceding section with the algebraic structure of the set $M_n(F)$ of all n-by-n matrices with coefficients in F.

(20.3) **Theorem.** *Let $\{v_1, \cdots, v_n\}$ be a fixed basis of V over F. The mapping $T \rightarrow (\alpha_{ij})$ which assigns to each linear transformation T its* *matrix* (α_{ij}) *with respect to the basis* $\{v_1, \cdots, v_n\}$ *is a one-to-one mapping of* $L(V, V)$ *onto* $M_n(F)$ *such that, if* $T \rightarrow (\alpha_{ij})$ *and* $S \rightarrow (\beta_{ij})$, *then*

$$T + S \rightarrow (\alpha_{ij}) + (\beta_{ij}),$$
$$TS \rightarrow (\alpha_{ij})(\beta_{ij}),$$
$$\alpha T \rightarrow \alpha(\alpha_{ij}).$$

Proof. The fact that the mapping is one-to-one and onto is clear by theorem (20.1). The fact that $T + S$ and αT map onto the desired matrices is clear from the definition and, of course, the result on TS should be true because this property motivated our definition of the matrix corresponding to T. However, we should check the details. We have

$$Tv_i = \sum_{j=1}^{n} \alpha_{ji} v_j, \qquad Sv_i = \sum_{j=1}^{n} \beta_{ji} v_j.$$

Then

$$(TS)v_i = T(Sv_i) = T\left(\sum_{j=1}^{n} \beta_{ji} v_j\right)$$

$$= \sum_{j=1}^{n} \beta_{ji} T(v_j) = \sum_{j=1}^{n} \beta_{ji} \sum_{k=1}^{n} \alpha_{kj} v_k$$

$$= \sum_{k=1}^{n} \left(\sum_{j=1}^{n} \alpha_{kj} \beta_{ji}\right) v_k.$$

Thus the (k, i) entry of the matrix of TS is $\sum_{j=1}^{n} \alpha_{kj}\beta_{ji}$, which is also the (k, i) entry of the product $(\alpha_{ij})(\beta_{ij})$. This completes the proof.

(20.4) Corollary. *Let* A, B, C *be n-by-n matrices with coefficients in* F; *then*

$$A(BC) = (AB)C$$
$$A(B + C) = AB + AC, \qquad (A + B)C = AC + BC.$$

The proof is immediate by theorems (20.3) and (19.10) and does not require any computation at all.

Some remarks on (20.3) are appropriate at this point. First, theorem (20.3) is simply the assertion that $L(V, V)$ is isomorphic with $M_n(F)$ as a ring and as a vector space over F. Theorem (20.3) asserts that all computations in $L(V, V)$ can equally well be carried out in $M_n(F)$. Experience shows that frequently the shortest and most elegant solution of a problem comes by working in $L(V, V)$, but the reader will find that there are times when calculations with matrices cannot be avoided. The preceding theorem also has the complication that the correspondence between $L(V, V)$ and $M_n(F)$ depends on the choice of a basis in V. Our next task is to work out this connection explicitly.

Let $\{v_1, \cdots, v_n\}$ be a basis of V over F and let $\{w_1, \cdots, w_n\}$ be a set of vectors in V. Then we have

$$(20.5) \qquad w_i = \sum_{j=1}^{n} \mu_{ji} v_j, \qquad 1 \leq i \leq n.$$

We assert that $\{w_1, \cdots, w_n\}$ is another basis of V if and only if the matrix (μ_{ij}) is invertible [the definition of invertible matrix is the same as for invertible transformation, (19.12), and was given in Section 14]. To see this, suppose first that $\{w_1, \cdots, w_n\}$ is a basis. Then we can express each

$$v_i = \sum_{j=1}^{n} \eta_{ji} w_j$$

where (η_{ij}) is an n-by-n matrix. Substituting in (20.5), we obtain

$$w_i = \sum_{j=1}^{n} \mu_{ji} v_j = \sum_{j=1}^{n} \mu_{ji} \left(\sum_{k=1}^{n} \eta_{kj} w_k \right) = \sum_{k=1}^{n} \left(\sum_{j=1}^{n} \eta_{kj} \mu_{ji} \right) w_k.$$

Since $\{w_1, \cdots, w_n\}$ are linearly independent, we obtain

$$\sum_{j=1}^{n} \eta_{kj} \mu_{ji} = \begin{cases} 1 & i = k \\ 0 & i \neq k \end{cases}$$

and we have proved that $(\eta_{ij})(\mu_{ij}) = I$. Similarly, $(\mu_{ij})(\eta_{ij}) = I$ and we have shown that (μ_{ij}) is an invertible matrix. We leave as an exercise the proof that if (μ_{ij}) is invertible then $\{w_1, \cdots, w_n\}$ is a basis.

(20.6) Theorem. *Let $\{v_1, \cdots, v_n\}$ be a basis of V and let $\{w_1, \cdots, w_n\}$ be another basis such that*

$$w_i = \sum_{j=1}^{n} \mu_{ji} v_j$$

where (μ_{rs}) is an invertible matrix. Let $T \in L(V, V)$, and let (α_{ij}) and (α'_{ij}) be the matrices of T with respect to the bases $\{v_1, \cdots, v_n\}$ and $\{w_1, \cdots, w_n\}$ respectively. Then we have

$$(\mu_{ij})(\alpha'_{ij}) = (\alpha_{ij})(\mu_{ij})$$

or
$$(\alpha'_{ij}) = (\mu_{ij})^{-1}(\alpha_{ij})(\mu_{ij}).$$

Proof. We have
$$T(w_i) = \sum_{j=1}^{n} \alpha'_{ji} w_j = \sum_{j=1}^{n} \alpha'_{ji} \sum_{k=1}^{n} \mu_{kj} v_k$$
$$= \sum_{k=1}^{n} \left(\sum_{j=1}^{n} \mu_{kj} \alpha'_{ji} \right) v_k,$$

while on the other hand we have
$$T(w_i) = T\left(\sum_{j=1}^{n} \mu_{ji} v_j \right) = \sum_{j=1}^{n} \mu_{ji} \left(\sum_{k=1}^{n} \alpha_{kj} v_k \right)$$
$$= \sum_{k=1}^{n} \left(\sum_{j=1}^{n} \alpha_{kj} \mu_{ji} \right) v_k.$$

Therefore
$$\sum_{j=1}^{n} \mu_{kj} \alpha'_{ji} = \sum_{j=1}^{n} \alpha_{kj} \mu_{ji}, \qquad 1 \le i, \quad k \le n,$$

and the theorem is proved.

(20.7) Definition. Two matrices A and B in $M_n(F)$ are *similar* if there exists an invertible matrix X in $M_n(F)$ such that
$$B = X^{-1}AX.$$

Theorem (20.6) asserts that, if A and B are matrices of $T \in L(V, V)$ with respect to different bases, then A and B are similar. The reader may verify that the converse of this statement is also true. Thus if A and B are similar matrices, then A and B can always be viewed as matrices of a single linear transformation with respect to different bases.

EXERCISES

Note. The results of Chapters 2 and 3 are needed to solve some of these problems. In all the problems, V denotes a finite-dimensional vector space over F.

1. What is the matrix of the differentiation operator D with respect to the basis of the set of polynomials in $F[x]$ of degree $\le n - 1$ consisting of $\{1, x, x^2, \cdots, x^{n-1}\}$?

2. Let V be a vector space over F with basis $\{v_1, \cdots, v_n\}$. Let T be the linear transformation such that

$$T(v_1) = v_2, \qquad T(v_2) = v_3, \qquad \cdots, T(v_n) = v_1.$$

What is the matrix of T with respect to this basis? Show that $T^n = 1$.

3. Let C be the field of complex numbers viewed as a vector space over the real numbers R. For a fixed complex number $c = \alpha + \beta i$, where $\alpha, \beta \in R$, show that the mapping

$$T_c: x \to cx, \qquad x \in C,$$

is a linear transformation of C over R. What is the matrix of T_c with respect to the basis $\{1, i\}$ of C over R (see Exercise 4 of Section 18 and Exercise 4 of Section 17)?

4. Let $T \in L(V, V)$ and let V^* be the dual space of V; see definition (19.9). For each $f \in V^*$, prove that the mapping T^*f of V into F defined by

$$(T^*f)(v) = f(Tv), \qquad v \in V,$$

is an element of V^* and that $T^*: f \to T^*f$ is a linear transformation of V^*. We call T^* the *transpose* of T. Let $\{v_1, \cdots, v_n\}$ be a basis of V and let $\{f_1, \cdots, f_n\}$ be the basis of V^* such that $f_i(\sum \xi_k v_k) = \xi_i, 1 \leq i \leq n$, as defined in Exercise 6 of Section 19. Show that, if A is the matrix of T with respect to $\{v_1, \cdots, v_n\}$, the matrix of T^* with respect to $\{f_1, \cdots, f_n\}$ is the transpose ${}^tA$ of A.

5. Let V be a vector space with basis $\{v_1, \cdots, v_n\}$ and let $T \in L(V, V)$ be a linear transformation such that

$$Tv_i = \sum_{j=1}^{n} \alpha_{ji} v_j, \qquad 1 \leq i \leq n, \quad \alpha_{ij} \in F.$$

If $v = \sum \xi_i v_i$ is a vector with components $\xi_1, \cdots, \xi_n$, then Tv can be expressed as

$$Tv = \sum_{i=1}^{n} \eta_i v_i$$

with uniquely determined components η_i. Show that

$$\eta_i = \sum_{j=1}^{n} \alpha_{ij} \xi_j, \qquad 1 = 2, \cdots, n.$$

(This problem establishes the connection between the definitions of linear transformations given in Sections 13 and 19.)

6. Let $\{v_1, \cdots, v_n\}$ be distinct, but not necessarily linearly independent, vectors. Discuss whether or not it is always possible to define a linear transformation $T \in L(V, V)$ such that $\{T(v_1), \cdots, T(v_n)\}$ is some prescribed set of vectors.

7. Let $T \in L(V, V)$. Prove that there exists a nonzero linear transformation $S \in L(V, V)$ such that $TS = 0$ if and only if there exists a nonzero vector $v \in V$ such that $T(v) = 0$.

8. Let $S, T \in L(V, V)$ be such that $ST = 1$. Prove that $TS = 1$. (Exercise 5, Section 19, shows that this result is not true unless V is finite-dimensional.) [*Hint:* Prove that $TSw = w$ for all vectors w of the form Tv. Then show that, if $\{v_1, \cdots, v_n\}$ is a basis for V, then $Tv_1, \cdots, Tv_n$ is also a basis of V and hence $TS = 1$.]

9. Let $T \in L(V, V)$. Prove that $T(V)$ is a subspace of V, which we shall call the *range space* $r(T)$ of T, and that the vectors $v \in V$, such that $T(v) = 0$ form a subspace which we call the *null space* $n(T)$ of T. Prove that

$$\dim(r(T)) + \dim(n(T)) = \dim V.$$

[*Hint:* Let $\{v_1, \cdots, v_k\}$ be a basis for $n(T)$ and find vectors $v_{k+1}, \cdots, v_n$ such that $\{v_1, \cdots, v_n\}$ is a basis for V. Prove that $\{T(v_{k+1}), \cdots, T(v_n)\}$ is a basis for $r(T)$.]

10. Give an example of a linear transformation which shows that it can happen that $r(T) \cap n(T) \neq 0$.

11. Prove that $T \in L(V, V)$ is one-to-one if and only if T is onto.

12. Let $T \in L(V, V)$. Define the *determinant of* T, $D(T)$, as the determinant $D(A)$ where A is the matrix of T with respect to some basis of V. Prove that if B is the matrix of T with respect to some other basis then $D(A) = D(B)$, so that the determinant of T is defined independently of the choice of basis. Prove that $D(TU) = D(T)D(U)$, for $T, U \in L(V, V)$. Prove that T is an invertible linear transformation if and only if $D(T) \neq 0$.

13. The dimension of the range space $r(T)$ is called the *rank* of T. Prove that the rank of T is equal to the rank of the matrix (as defined in Chapter 2) of T with respect to an arbitrary basis of V.

14. Let F be the field of two elements, and let V be an n-dimensional vector space over F. Show that there are exactly $(2^n - 1)(2^n - 2) \cdots (2^n - 2^{n-1})$ invertible linear transformations on V.

21. THE MINIMAL POLYNOMIAL

In this section, F denotes an arbitrary field, and V a finite-dimensional vector space over F. In Section 19 we saw that $L(V, V)$ is a vector space over F. Theorem (20.3) asserts that if we select a basis $\{v_1, \cdots, v_n\}$ of V then the mapping which assigns to $T \in L(V, V)$ its matrix with respect to the basis $\{v_1, \cdots, v_n\}$ is an isomorphism of the vector space $L(V, V)$ onto the vector space $M_n(F)$ of all n-by-n matrices, viewed as a vector space of n^2-tuples. From Chapter 2, $M_n(F)$ is an n^2-dimensional vector space. If $\{A_1, \cdots, A_{n^2}\}$ is a basis for $M_n(F)$ over F, then the linear transformations $T_1, \cdots, T_{n^2}$, whose matrices with respect to $\{v_1, \cdots, v_n\}$ are $A_1, \cdots, A_{n^2}$, respectively, form a basis of $L(V, V)$ over F. In particular, the matrices which have a 1 in one position and zeros elsewhere form a basis of $M_n(F)$; therefore the linear transformations $T_{ij} \in L(V, V)$ defined by

$$T_{ij}(v_j) = v_i, \qquad T_{ij}(v_k) = 0, \qquad k \neq j,$$

form a basis of $L(V, V)$ over F. It is instructive to prove directly that the set $\{T_{ij}\}$ forms a basis for $L(V, V)$.

For the rest of this section let T be a fixed linear transformation of V. Since $L(V, V)$ has dimension n^2 over F the $n^2 + 1$ powers of T,

$$1, \quad T, \quad T^2, \quad \cdots, T^{n^2}$$

are linearly dependent. That means that there exist elements of F, $\xi_0, \xi_1, \cdots, \xi_{n^2}$, not all zero, such that

$$\xi_0 1 + \xi_1 T + \xi_2 T^2 + \cdots + \xi_{n^2} T^{n^2} = 0.$$

In other words, there exists a nonzero polynomial

$$f(x) = \xi_0 + \xi_1 x + \cdots + \xi_{n^2} x^{n^2} \in F[x]$$

such that $f(T) = 0$.

As we shall see, the study of these polynomial equations is the key to most of the deeper properties of the transformation T.

Let us make the idea of substituting a linear transformation in a polynomial absolutely precise.

(21.1) Definition. Let $f(x) = \lambda_0 + \lambda_1 x + \cdots + \lambda_r x^r \in F[x]$ and let $T \in L(V, V)$; then $f(T)$ denotes the linear transformation

$$f(T) = \lambda_0 \cdot 1 + \lambda_1 T + \cdots + \lambda_r T^r$$

where 1 is the identity transformation on V. Similarly, we may define $f(A)$ where A is an n-by-n matrix over F, with 1 replaced by the identity matrix I.

(21.2) Lemma. *Let $T \in L(V, V)$ and let $f, g \in F[x]$; then:*

(A) $f(T)T = Tf(T)$.
(B) $(f \pm g)(T) = f(T) \pm g(T)$.
(C) $(fg)(T) = f(T)g(T)$.

Of course, the same lemma holds for matrices. The proof is similar to the proof of (16.12), and will be omitted.

(21.3) Theorem. *Let $T \in L(V, V)$; then $1, T, T^2, \cdots, T^{n^2}$ are linearly dependent in $L(V, V)$. Therefore there exists a uniquely determined integer $r \leq n^2$ such that*

$$1, T, T^2, \cdots, T^{r-1} \qquad \text{are linearly independent,}$$
$$1, T, T^2, \cdots, T^{r-1}, T^r \qquad \text{are linearly dependent.}$$

Then we have

$$T^r = \xi_0 1 + \xi_1 T + \cdots + \xi_{r-1}T^{r-1}, \qquad \xi_i \in F.$$

Let $m(x) = x^r - \xi_{r-1}x^{r-1} - \cdots - \xi_0 \cdot 1 \in F[x]$. Then $m(x)$ has the following properties:

(A) $m(x) \neq 0$ in $F[x]$ and $m(T) = 0$.
(B) *If $f(x)$ is any polynomial in $F[x]$ such that $f(T) = 0$, then $m(x) \mid f(x)$ in $F[x]$.*

Proof. The existence of the polynomial $m(x)$ and the statement (A) concerning it follow from the introductory remarks in this section. Now let $f(x)$ be any polynomial in $F[x]$ such that $f(T) = 0$. Because $1, T, \cdots, T^{r-1}$ are linearly independent, the only polynomial $R(x)$ of degree $< r$ such that $R(T) = 0$ is the zero polynomial. Now apply the division process to $f(x)$ and $m(x)$ and obtain

$$f(x) = m(x)Q(x) + R(x)$$

where either $R(x) = 0$ or deg $R(x) < r = $ deg $m(x)$. By lemma (21.2) we have
$$R(T) = (f - mQ)(T) = f(T) - m(T)Q(T) = 0$$

and by the preceding remark we have $R(x) = 0$ in $F[x]$. This proves that $m(x) \mid f(x)$, and the theorem is proved.

(21.4) Definition. Let $T \in L(V, V)$. The polynomial $m(x) \in F[x]$ defined in theorem (21.3) is called a *minimal polynomial* of T; $m(x)$ is characterized as the nonzero polynomial of least degree such that $m(T) = 0$, and it is uniquely determined up to a constant factor.

The remarks about the uniqueness of $m(x)$ are clear by part (B) of theorem (21.3). To see this, let $m(x)$ and $m'(x)$ be two nonzero polynomials of degree r such that $m(T) = m'(T) = 0$. Then by the proof of part B of theorem (21.3) we have $m(x) \mid m'(x)$ and $m'(x) \mid m(x)$. It follows from the discussion in Section 16 that $m(x)$ and $m'(x)$ differ by a unit factor in $F[x]$ and, since the units in $F[x]$ are simply the constant polynomials, the uniqueness of $m(x)$ is proved.

We remark that theorem (21.3) also holds for any matrix $A \in M_n(F)$. If $T \in L(V, V)$ has the matrix A with respect to the basis $\{v_1, \cdots, v_n\}$ of V, it follows from theorem (20.3) that T and A have the same minimal polynomial. Since we have in Chapter 2 an effective procedure for testing sets of n^2-tuples for linear dependence, the minimal polynomial of A (and hence the minimal polynomial of T) is—in principle, anyway—capable of being directly calculated by the methods we have developed earlier in the book.

A thorough understanding of the definition and properties of the minimal polynomial will be absolutely essential in the rest of this chapter.

EXERCISES

1. Let $T \in L(V, V)$ and $f, g \in F[x]$. Prove that $f(T)g(T) = g(T)f(T)$.

2. Let V and W be vector spaces over F of dimensions m and n respectively. Find a basis for $L(V, W)$.

3. Let:
$$A = \begin{pmatrix} \alpha & \beta \\ \gamma & \delta \end{pmatrix}, \qquad \alpha, \beta, \gamma, \delta \in F.$$

Prove that A satisfies the equation $f(A) = 0$ where
$$f(x) = x^2 - (\alpha + \delta)x + (\alpha\delta - \beta\gamma).$$

Prove that A is invertible if and only if $\Delta = \alpha\delta - \beta\gamma \neq 0$ and that, if $\Delta \neq 0$, then
$$A^{-1} = -\frac{1}{\Delta}[A - (\alpha + \delta)I]$$

where I is the 2-by-2 identity matrix.

4. Prove that if $T \in L(V, V)$ then T is invertible if and only if the constant term of the minimal polynomial of T is different from zero. Describe how to compute T^{-1} from the minimal polynomial. In particular, show that T^{-1} can always be expressed as a polynomial $f(T)$ in T.

5. Find the minimal polynomials of

$$\begin{pmatrix} 2 & 0 \\ 3 & -1 \end{pmatrix}, \quad \begin{pmatrix} 0 & 1 & 0 \\ 0 & 0 & 1 \\ 1 & 0 & 0 \end{pmatrix}, \quad \begin{pmatrix} 2 & -1 & 1 \\ 3 & 0 & 2 \\ -1 & 5 & 0 \end{pmatrix}.$$

6. Let $\{v_1, \cdots, v_n\}$ be a basis for V and let $T \in L(V, V)$ be such that $T(v_i) = \xi_i v_i$, for $\xi_i \in F$. Suppose that $\xi_1, \cdots, \xi_r$ are distinct and that each ξ_i, for $1 \leq i \leq n$, is equal to a ξ_j with $1 \leq j \leq r$. Prove that the minimal polynomial of T is

$$\prod_{j=1}^{r} (x - \xi_j) = (x - \xi_1) \cdots (x - \xi_r).$$

22. INVARIANT SUBSPACES

Let $T \in L(V, V)$ be such, for some basis $\{v_1, \cdots, v_n\}$ of V, that T has a diagonal matrix

$$\begin{pmatrix} \xi_1 & & 0 \\ & \cdot & \\ & & \cdot \\ 0 & & \xi_n \end{pmatrix}$$

with respect to this basis. What information does that give us about the action of T on V? It means that V has a basis $\{v_1, \cdots, v_n\}$ such that

$$Tv_i = \xi_i v_i, \qquad 1 \leq i \leq n.$$

In other words, each one-dimensional space $S(v_i)$ determined by a basis vector v_i is sent into itself by T. In the concrete example, considered in Section 20, of the linear transformation T of R_2 such that, for some basis $\{v_1, v_2\}$ of R_2,

$$T(v_1) = v_2,$$
$$T(v_2) = v_1,$$

we saw that if we take as a basis of R_2 the set $\{w_1, w_2\}$, where

$w_1 = v_1 + v_2$ and $w_2 = v_1 - v_2$, then the matrix A of T relative to this basis is given by

$$A = \begin{pmatrix} 1 & 0 \\ 0 & -1 \end{pmatrix}.$$

We can see that T is geometrically a reflection with respect to the line through the origin in the direction of the vector w_1; it sends each vector in $S(w_1)$ onto itself and sends w_2 onto its mirror image $-w_2$ with respect to the line $S(w_1)$. Figure 5.1 shows how the image $T(w)$ of an arbitrary vector w can be described geometrically.

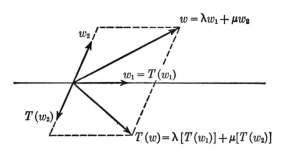

Figure 5.1

The concept illustrated here is the simplest case of the following basic idea.

(22.1) Definition. Let $T \in L(V, V)$. A subspace W of V is called an *invariant subspace relative* to T (or simply a *T-invariant subspace* or *T-subspace*) if $T(w) \in W$ for all $w \in W$. A generator $v \neq 0$ of a one-dimensional T-invariant subspace is called a *characteristic vector* of T. If $Tv = \xi v$ for $\xi \in F$, then ξ is called a *characteristic root* of T and v is said to *belong to* the *characteristic root* ξ.

The next result shows one way to construct T-invariant subspaces.

(22.2) Lemma. *Let* $T \in L(V, V)$ *and let* $f(x) \in F[x]$; *then the set of all vectors* $v \in V$ *such that* $f(T)(v) = 0$ *[that is, the null space of* $f(T)$] *is a T-invariant subspace—notation,* $n(f(T))$.

Proof. Since $f(T) \in L(V, V)$, the null space $n(f(T))$ is a subspace of V. We have to prove that if $w \in n(f(T))$ then $T(w) \in n(f(T))$. We have

$$f(T)(T(w)) = [f(T)T](w) = [Tf(T)](w) = T[f(T)(w)] = 0,$$

since $f(T)T = Tf(T)$ in $L(V, V)$, and the lemma is proved.

We observe in our example of the reflection that the basis vector w_1 generates the null space of the transformation $T - 1$ and w_2 generates the null space of the transformation $T + 1$. The polynomials $x + 1$ and $x - 1$ are exactly the prime factors of the minimal polynomial $x^2 - 1$ of T. The chief result of this section is a far-reaching generalization of this example.

(22.3) **Definition.** Let $V_1, \cdots, V_s$ be subspaces of V. The space V is said to be the *direct sum* of $\{V_1, \cdots, V_s\}$ (notation, $V = V_1 \oplus \cdots \oplus V_s$) if, first, every vector $v \in V$ can be expressed as a sum,

(22.4) $v = v_1 + \cdots + v_s,$ $v_i \in V_i,\ 1 \le i \le s,$

and if, second, the expressions (22.4) are unique, in the sense that if

$$v_1 + \cdots + v_s = v'_1 + \cdots + v'_s,   v_i, v'_i \in V_i,\ 1 \le i \le s$$

then

$$v_i = v'_i,   1 \le i \le s.$$

(22.5) **Lemma.** *Let* $V_1, \cdots, V_s$ *be subspaces of* V; *then* V *is the direct sum* $V_1 \oplus \cdots \oplus V_s$ *if and only if:*

(1) $V = V_1 + \cdots + V_s$, *that is, every vector* $v \in V$ *can be expressed in at least one way as a sum*

$$v = v_1 + \cdots + v_s,   v_i \in V_i,\ 1 \le i \le s.$$

(2) *If* $v_i \in V_i$, *for* $1 \le i \le s$, *are vectors such that*

$$v_1 + \cdots + v_s = 0$$

then $v_1 = v_2 = \cdots = v_s = 0$.

Proof. If V is the direct sum $V_1 \oplus \cdots \oplus V_s$, then part 1 is satisfied. If

$$v_1 + \cdots + v_s = 0,   v_i \in V_i,$$

then we have

$$v_1 + \cdots + v_s = 0 + \cdots + 0,   v_i, 0 \in V_i,\ 1 \le i \le s,$$

and by the second part of definition (22.3) we have $v_1 = \cdots = v_s = 0$, as required.

Now suppose that conditions 1 and 2 of the lemma are satisfied. To prove that $V = V_1 \oplus \cdots \oplus V_s$ it is sufficient to prove the uniqueness assertion of definition (22.3). If

$$v_1 + \cdots + v_s = v_1' + \cdots + v_s', \qquad v_i, v_i' \in V_i, \quad 1 \le i \le s,$$

then we can rewrite this equation as

$$(v_1 - v_1') + \cdots + (v_s - v_s') = 0, \qquad v_i - v_i' \in V_i, \quad 1 \le i \le s.$$

By condition 2 we have $v_i - v_i' = 0$ for $1 \le i \le s$ and hence $v_i = v_i'$ for all i. This completes the proof of the lemma.

Finally, we are ready to state our main theorem. It can be stated in the following intuitive way. Let $T \in L(V, V)$ and let $m(x)$ be the minimal polynomial of T. By the theorems of Section 16, $m(x)$ can be factored into primes in $F[x]$, say

$$m(x) = p_1(x)^{e_1} \cdots p_s(x)^{e_s}$$

where the $\{p_i\}$ are distinct primes and the e_i are positive integers. By lemma (22.2) the null spaces

$$n(p_i(T)^{e_i}), \qquad 1 \le i \le s,$$

are T-subspaces of V. The theorem asserts simply that V is their direct sum. As we shall see, although it is by no means the best theorem that can be proved in this direction, this theorem already goes a long way toward solving the problem of finding a basis of V such that the matrix of T with respect to this basis is as simple as possible. A formal statement of the theorem follows.

(22.6) Theorem. *Let $T \in L(V, V)$ and let*

$$m(x) = p_1(x)^{e_1} \cdots p_s(x)^{e_s}$$

be the minimal polynomial of T, factored into powers of distinct primes $p_i(x) \in F[x]$; then for each i, where $1 \le i \le s$, the null space of $p_i(T)^{e_i}$, or $n(p_i(T)^{e_i})$, is a T-subspace of V and we have

$$V = n(p_1(T)^{e_1}) \oplus \cdots \oplus n(p_s(T)^{e_s}).$$

Proof. Let

$$q_i(x) = \frac{m(x)}{p_i(x)^{e_i}}, \qquad 1 \le i \le s.$$

Then the $\{q_i(x)\}$ are polynomials in $F[x]$ with no common prime factors. Hence by corollary (16.18) there exist polynomials $a_i(x)$, $1 \le i \le s$, such that

$$1 = q_1(x)a_1(x) + \cdots + q_s(x)a_s(x).$$

Substituting T, we have by lemma (21.2) the result that

$$1 = q_1(T)a_1(T) + \cdots + q_s(T)a_s(T).$$

Now let $v \in V$; then we have

$$v = q_1(T)a_1(T)v + \cdots + q_s(T)a_s(T)v$$

and for each i,

$$p_i(T)^{e_i}q_i(T)a_i(T)v = m(T)a_i(T)v = 0.$$

Therefore

$$q_i(T)a_i(T)v \in n(p_i(T)^{e_i}), \qquad 1 \leq i \leq s,$$

and

$$V = n(p_1(T)^{e_1}) + \cdots + n(p_s(T)^{e_s}).$$

To prove the theorem it is now sufficient to prove that part 2 of lemma (22.5) is valid. Suppose that

$$v_1 + \cdots + v_s = 0, \qquad v_i \in n(p_i(T)^{e_i}), \quad 1 \leq i \leq s.$$

Find $a(x)$, $b(x) \in F[x]$ such that, by corollary (16.18),

$$1 = a(x)p_1(x)^{e_1} + b(x)p_2(x)^{e_2} \cdots p_s(x)^{e_s}.$$

Then we have

$$1 = a(T)p_1(T)^{e_1} + b(T)p_2(T)^{e_2} \cdots p_s(T)^{e_s},$$

and applying this linear transformation to v_1, we have

$$v_1 = 1 \cdot v_1 = a(T)p_1(T)^{e_1}v_1$$
$$+ b(T)p_2(T)^{e_2} \cdots p_s(T)^{e_s}(-v_2 - \cdots - v_s) = 0.$$

A similar argument proves that

$$v_2 = \cdots = v_s = 0$$

and the theorem is proved.

As a first application of this theorem, we consider the question of when a basis for V can be chosen that consists of characteristic vectors of T.

(22.7) Definition. A linear transformation $T \in L(V, V)$ is called *diagonable* if there exists a basis for V consisting of characteristic vectors of T. A matrix of T with respect to a basis of characteristic vectors is called a *diagonal matrix*; it has the form

$$\begin{pmatrix} \alpha_1 & & 0 \\ & \cdot & \\ & & \cdot \\ & & & \cdot \\ 0 & & \alpha_n \end{pmatrix}, \qquad \alpha_i \in F,$$

with zeros except in the (i, i) positions, $1 \leq i \leq n$.

(22.8) Theorem. *A linear transformation $T \in L(V, V)$ is diagonable if and only if the minimal polynomial of T has the form*

$$m(x) = (x - \xi_1) \cdots (x - \xi_s)$$

with distinct zeros $\xi_1, \cdots, \xi_s$ *in* F.

Proof. First suppose that T is diagonable and let $\{v_1, \cdots, v_n\}$ be a basis of T consisting of characteristic vectors belonging to characteristic roots $\xi_1, \cdots, \xi_n$ in F. Suppose the v_i are so numbered that $\xi_1, \cdots, \xi_s$ are distinct and every characteristic root ξ_j coincides with some ξ_i such that $1 \leq i \leq s$. Let

$$m(x) = (x - \xi_1) \cdots (x - \xi_s).$$

Since $T(v_i) = \xi_i v_i$, $1 \leq i \leq s$, we have

$$(T - \xi_i \cdot 1)v_i = 0$$

and hence

$$m(T)v_i = 0, \qquad 1 \leq i \leq n.$$

Therefore $m(T) = 0$ and by lemma (21.3) the minimal polynomial is a factor of $m(x)$. But it is clear that if any prime factor of $m(x)$ is deleted we obtain a polynomial $m^*(x)$ such that $m^*(T) \neq 0$. For example, if $m^*(x) = (x - \xi_1) \cdots (x - \xi_{s-1})$, then

$$\begin{aligned} m^*(T)v_s &= (T - \xi_1) \cdots (T - \xi_{s-1})v_s \\ &= (\xi_s - \xi_1) \cdots (\xi_s - \xi_{s-1})v_s \neq 0. \end{aligned}$$

It follows[*] that $m(x)$ is the minimal polynomial of T.

Now suppose that the minimal polynomial has the form

$$m(x) = (x - \xi_1) \cdots (x - \xi_s)$$

with distinct $\{\xi_i\}$ in F. By theorem (22.6) we have

$$V = n(T - \xi_1 \cdot 1) \oplus \cdots \oplus n(T - \xi_s \cdot 1).$$

Let $\{v_{11}, \cdots, v_{1d_1}\}$ be a basis for $n(T - \xi_1 \cdot 1)$, $\{v_{21}, \cdots, v_{2d_2}\}$ a basis for $n(T - \xi_2 \cdot 1)$, etc. Then because V is the direct sum of the subspaces $n(T - \xi_i \cdot 1)$ it follows that

$$\{v_{11}, \cdots, v_{1d_1}, v_{21}, \cdots, v_{2d_2}, \cdots\}$$

is a basis for V. Finally, $w \in n(T - \xi_i \cdot 1)$ implies that $(T - \xi_i \cdot 1)w = 0$ or $T(w) = \xi_i \cdot w$, so that if $w \neq 0$ then w is a characteristic vector of T. Thus all the basis vectors v_{ij} are characteristic vectors of T, and the theorem is proved.

It is worthwhile to translate theorems on linear transformations into theorems on matrices. We have

---

[*] This part of the theorem was already given as Exercise 6 in Section 21.

(22.9) Corollary. *A necessary and sufficient condition for a matrix* $A \in M_n(F)$ *to be similar to a diagonal matrix is that the minimal polynomial of A have the form*

$$m(x) = (x - \xi_1) \cdots (x - \xi_s)$$

with distinct $\xi_i \in F$.

EXERCISES

1. Test the following matrices to determine whether or not they are similar to diagonal matrices in $M_2(R)$.

$$\begin{pmatrix} 2 & 1 \\ 0 & -1 \end{pmatrix}, \quad \begin{pmatrix} 1 & -2 \\ 1 & -1 \end{pmatrix}, \quad \begin{pmatrix} 3 & -2 \\ 2 & -1 \end{pmatrix}.$$

2. Show that the matrices

$$\begin{pmatrix} 1 & -2 \\ 1 & -1 \end{pmatrix}, \quad \begin{pmatrix} 0 & 1 \\ -1 & 0 \end{pmatrix}$$

are similar to diagonal matrices in $M_2(C)$, where C is the complex field, but not in $M_2(R)$.

3. Prove that if $T \in L(V, V)$ and if $v_1, \cdots, v_r$ are characteristic vectors of T belonging to distinct characteristic roots then $\{v_1, \cdots, v_r\}$ are linearly independent. (*Hint:* Let $Tv_i = \xi_i v_i$; then $T^2 v_i = \xi_i^2 v_i$, etc. Use an appropriate van der Monde determinant.)

4. Let $T \in L(V, V)$. Prove that if T has at most $n = \dim V$ distinct characteristic roots and that if T has exactly n distinct characteristic roots then there exists a basis of V such that the matrix of T relative to this basis is a diagonal matrix. Suppose that, conversely, T has a diagonal matrix with respect to some basis of V. Does it follow that T has $n = \dim V$ distinct characteristic roots?

5. Let $T \in L(V, V)$ have the minimal polynomial $m(x) \in F[x]$. Let $f(x)$ be an arbitrary polynomial in $F[x]$. Prove that

$$n(f(T)) = n(d(T)),$$

where $d(x)$ is the greatest common divisor of $f(x)$ and $m(x)$.

23.   THE TRIANGULAR FORM THEOREM

There are two ways in which a linear transformation T can fail to be diagonable. One is that its minimal polynomial $m(x)$ cannot be factored into linear factors in $F[x]$ (for example, if $m(x) = x^2 + 1$ in $R[x]$ where R is the real field); the other is that $m(x) = (x - \xi_1)^{e_1} \cdots (x - \xi_s)^{e_s}$ with some $e_i > 1$. In the latter case it is desirable to have a theorem that applies to *all* linear transformations and that comes as close to the diagonal form theorem (22.8) as possible.

The main theorem is the following one.

(23.1)   Theorem (Triangular Form Theorem).   *Let $T \in L(V, V)$, where V is a finite-dimensional vector space over an arbitrary field F, and let the minimal polynomial of T be given by*

$$m(x) = (x - \alpha_1)^{e_1} \cdots (x - \alpha_s)^{e_s}$$

where the $\{e_i\}$ are positive integers and the $\{\alpha_i\}$ are distinct elements of F. Then there exists a basis of V such that the matrix A of T with respect to this basis has the form

$$A = \begin{pmatrix} A_1 & & & & 0 \\ & A_2 & & & \\ & & \cdot & & \\ & & & \cdot & \\ 0 & & & & A_s \end{pmatrix}$$

where each A_i is a d_i-by-d_i block for some integer $d_i \geq e_i$, where $1 \leq i \leq s$, and each A_i can be expressed in the form

$$A_i = \begin{pmatrix} \alpha_i & & & * \\ & \cdot & & \\ & & \cdot & \\ 0 & & & \alpha_i \end{pmatrix}$$

where the matrix A_i has zeros below the diagonal and, possibly, nonzero entries (*) above. All entries of A not contained in one of the blocks $\{A_i\}$ are zero. To express it all in another way, given a square matrix B there exists an invertible S such that $SBS^{-1} = A$ where A has the above-given form.

REMARK. A very important observation is that the hypothesis of theorem (23.1)—that the minimal polynomial of T can be factored into linear factors—is always satisfied if the field F is algebraically closed (see Section 17). The most common example of an algebraically closed field (and the only one we have discussed) is the field of complex numbers.

Proof. Let V_i be the null space of $(T - \alpha_i \cdot 1)^{e_i}$, for $1 \leq i \leq r$, and let d_i be the dimension of V_i. If we choose bases for the subspaces $V_1, V_2, \cdots, V_s$ separately then, as we pointed out in the proof of theorem (22.8), the totality of basis elements obtained form a basis of V because V is, by theorem (22.6), the direct sum of the subspaces $\{V_i\}$. Then let us arrange a basis for V so that the first d_1 elements form a basis for V_1, the next d_2 elements form a basis for V_2, and so on. Since each subspace V_i is invariant relative to T, it is clear that the matrix of T relative to this basis has the form

$$\begin{pmatrix} A_1 & & 0 \\ & \cdot & \\ & & \cdot \\ 0 & & A_s \end{pmatrix}.$$

It remains only to prove that the blocks A_i can be chosen to have the required form and that the inequalities $d_i \geq e_i$ hold, for $1 \leq i \leq s$.

Each space V_i is the null space of $(T - \alpha_i \cdot 1)^{e_i}$. In other words, if we let $N_i = T - \alpha_i \cdot 1$, then $N_i \in L(V_i, V_i)$ and we have $N_i^{e_i} = 0$. Such a linear transformation is called a *nilpotent linear transformation*.

Thus T, viewed as a linear transformation on V_i, is the sum of a constant times the identity transformation $\alpha_i \cdot 1$ and a nilpotent transformation N_i.

We now state a general result concerning nilpotent transformations, which will settle our problem.

(23.2) Lemma. *Let N be a nilpotent transformation on a finite-dimensional vector space W; then W has a basis $\{w_1, \cdots, w_t\}$ such that*

$$Nw_1 = 0, \qquad N(w_2) \in S(w_1), \cdots, N(w_i) \in S(w_1, \cdots, w_{i-1})$$

for $2 \leq i \leq t$.

We next present a proof of lemma (23.2). Notice that the matrix of N with respect to the basis $\{w_1, \cdots, w_t\}$ has the form (illustrated for $t = 4$),

$$\begin{pmatrix} 0 & * & * & * \\ 0 & 0 & * & * \\ 0 & 0 & 0 & * \\ 0 & 0 & 0 & 0 \end{pmatrix}$$

so that the lemma is a special case of the triangular form theorem. The point is that this special case implies the whole theorem. We prove lemma (23.2) by induction. First find $w_1 \neq 0$ such that $Nw_1 = 0$. Any vector will do for w_1 if $N = 0$ and, if $N^k \neq 0$ and $N^{k+1} = 0$, then let $w_1 = N^k(w) \neq 0$. Then $N(w_1) = N^{k+1}(w) = 0$. Suppose (as an induction hypothesis) that we have found linearly independent vectors $\{w_1, \cdots, w_i\}$ satisfying the conditions of the lemma and let $S = S(w_1, \cdots, w_i)$. If $S = W$ there is nothing more to prove. If $S \neq W$ and $N(W) \subset S$, then any vector not in S can be taken for w_{i+1}. Now suppose $N(W) \not\subset S$. Then there is an integer u such that $N^u(W) \not\subset S$, $N^{u+1}(W) \subset S$. Find $w_{i+1} \in N^u(W)$ such that $w_{i+1} \notin S$. Then $\{w_1, \cdots, w_{i+1}\}$ is a linearly independent set and $N(w_{i+1}) \in S$. This completes the proof of the lemma.

Let us apply lemma (23.2) to the task of selecting an appropriate basis for the subspace V_i of V. Since $N_i = T - \alpha_1 \cdot 1$ is nilpotent on V_i, the lemma implies that V_i has a basis $\{v_{i,1}, \cdots, v_{i,d_i}\}$ such that

$$N_i(v_{i,1}) = 0, \quad N_i(v_{i,2}) \in S(v_{i,1}), \quad \cdots, \quad N_i(v_{i,k}) \subset S(v_{i,1}, \cdots, v_{i,k-1})$$
$$\text{for } 2 \leq k \leq d_i.$$

Since $N_i = T - \alpha_i \cdot 1$, these equations yield the formulas

$$(T - \alpha_i \cdot 1)v_{i,1} = 0, \quad \cdots, \quad (T - \alpha_i \cdot 1)v_{i,k} \in S(v_{i,1}, \cdots, v_{i,k-1}),$$
$$\text{for } 2 \leq k \leq d_i - 1.$$

These in turn yield

(23.3)
$$\begin{aligned} Tv_{i,1} &= \alpha_i v_{i,1} \\ Tv_{i,2} &= \alpha_{12} v_{i,1} + \alpha_i v_{i,2} \\ &\cdots \qquad \cdots \\ Tv_{i,k} &= \alpha_{1k} v_{i,1} + \cdots + \alpha_{k-1,k} v_{i,k-1} + \alpha_i v_{i,k} \end{aligned}$$

and we have shown that, relative to this basis, the matrix of T on the space V_i has the required form.

It remains to prove the inequalities $d_i \geq e_i$, $1 \leq i \leq r$. From lemma (23.2) it follows that $N_i^{d_i} = 0$, where d_i is the dimension of V_i. Since $T = \alpha_i \cdot 1 + N_i$ on V_i we have $(T - \alpha_i \cdot 1)^{d_i} = 0$ on V_i, and since V is the direct sum of the subspaces V_i we have

(23.4) $(T - \alpha_1 \cdot 1)^{d_1} \cdots (T - \alpha_r \cdot 1)^{d_r} = 0.$

Therefore, the minimal polynomial $m(x) = \Pi(x - \alpha_i)^{e_i}$ divides the polynomial $\Pi(x - \alpha_i)^{d_i}$ and from the theory of unique factorization in $F[x]$ we have $d_i \geq e_i$. This completes the proof of the theorem.

This result has many important corollaries. The first shows that the minimal polynomial has degree $\leq \dim V$, although from the argument in Section 21 we could have predicted only that its degree is $\leq (\dim V)^2$.

(23.5) **Corollary.** *Let T be a linear transformation on a finite-dimensional vector space V over an algebraically closed field F; then the minimal polynomial $m(x)$ of T has degree $\leq \dim V$.*

We recall that an element $\alpha \in F$ is called a *characteristic root* of T if there exists a nonzero vector $v \in V$ such that $Tv = \alpha v$ or, in other words, if $(T - \alpha \cdot 1)v = 0$. If A is a matrix of T with respect to any basis, then $A - \alpha \cdot 1$ is the matrix of $T - \alpha \cdot 1$ with respect to this basis. The fact that $(T - \alpha \cdot 1)v = 0$ implies that $A - \alpha \cdot 1$ is not an invertible matrix and, hence, that the determinant $D(A - \alpha \cdot 1) = 0$. Conversely, if ξ is any element of F such that $D(A - \xi \cdot 1) = 0$, then $T - \xi \cdot 1$ is not invertible. From the exercises in Section 20 it follows that $n(T - \xi \cdot 1) \neq 0$ and hence that $(T - \xi \cdot 1)v = 0$ for some $v \neq 0$. Then ξ is a characteristic root of T. These considerations lead to the following definition.

(23.6) **Definition.** Let $T \in L(V, V)$ and let A be a matrix of T with respect to some basis of V; then the matrix $A - x \cdot I$ has coefficients in the quotient field (see Section 16) of the polynomial ring $F[x]$ and its determinant $h(x) = D(A - x \cdot I)$ is an element of $F[x]$ called the *characteristic polynomial* of T. The characteristic polynomial of T is independent of the choice of the matrix of T. The set of distinct zeros of the characteristic polynomial of T is identical with the set of distinct characteristic roots of T.

Several statements in the definition require proof. First of all, let A and B be matrices of T with respect to different bases. Then $B = SAS^{-1}$ for an invertible matrix S and we have

$$D(B - x \cdot I) = D(SAS^{-1} - x \cdot I)$$
$$= D[S(A - x \cdot I)S^{-1}]$$
$$= D(S)D(A - x \cdot I)D(S)^{-1} \qquad \text{[by (13.9)]}$$
$$= D(A - x \cdot I).$$

The statement about the zeros of the characteristic polynomial is clear from the introductory remarks. The fact that $D(A - x \cdot I) \in F[x]$ follows from the formula for the complete expansion of $D(A - x \cdot I)$ given in Section 12.

We now have the following basic corollary of theorem (23.1).

(23.7) Corollary. *Let V be a vector space over an algebraically closed field F. Let $T \in L(V, V)$, let $m(x)$ be the minimal polynomial of T, and let $h(x)$ be the characteristic polynomial; then:*

(A) *$m(x) \mid h(x)$.*
(B) *Every zero of $h(x)$ is a zero of $m(x)$.*
(C) *$h(T) = 0$.*

(The last statement is called the Cayley-Hamilton Theorem.)

The proof is immediate if we use the matrix of T given by theorem (23.1), for then

$$h(x) = \pm \prod (x - \alpha_i)^{d_i},$$
$$m(x) = \prod (x - \alpha_i)^{e_i},$$

and all the statements follow from the fact that $d_i \geq e_i$, as we proved in theorem (23.1).

We remark that the preceding corollary, and in particular the Cayley-Hamilton Theorem, is valid for a linear transformation on a finite-dimensional vector space over an arbitrary field F, even though our proof, based on theorem (23.1), works only when F is algebraically closed. For a proof in the general case, see Chapter X, Section 6, of Birkhoff and MacLane's book, listed in the Bibliography.

24. AN EXAMPLE

In this section an example is worked out, to indicate the general computational procedure for finding the triangular form of a matrix. Let V be a three-dimensional vector space over the complex field C with basis $\{v_1, v_2, v_3\}$ and let $T \in L(V, V)$ be defined by the equations

$$Tv_1 = -v_1 \qquad\quad + 2v_3$$
$$Tv_2 = 3v_1 + 2v_2 + \ v_3$$
$$Tv_3 = \qquad\qquad - \ v_3.$$

The matrix of T with respect to the basis $\{v_1, v_2, v_3\}$ is given by

$$A = \begin{pmatrix} -1 & 3 & 0 \\ 0 & 2 & 0 \\ 2 & 1 & -1 \end{pmatrix}.$$

We shall show how to find a **new** basis for V with respect to which the matrix of T is in the form given in theorem (23.1).

STEP 1. Find the distinct characteristic roots of A. This can be done either by finding the prime factors of the characteristic polynomial $h(x)$ or by finding the minimal polynomial $m(x)$ and determining its zeros since, by corollary (23.7), $m(x)$ and $h(x)$ have the same set of distinct zeros.

The characteristic polynomial $h(x)$ is given by

$$h(x) = D(A - x \cdot I) = \begin{vmatrix} -1 - x & 3 & 0 \\ 0 & 2 - x & 0 \\ 2 & 1 & -1 - x \end{vmatrix} = (1 + x)^2(2 - x).$$

At this point we know from corollary (23.7) that the distinct characteristic roots of T are $\{-1, 2\}$ and that the minimal polynomial of T is either

$$(1 + x)(2 - x) \quad \text{or} \quad (1 + x)^2(2 - x).$$

STEP 2. Find the null spaces of $T + 1$, $(T + 1)^2$, $T - 2$. If V turns out to be the direct sum of the null spaces of $T + 1$ and $T - 2$, we will know that the minimal polynomial is $(x + 1)(x - 2)$ (Why?) and if not then we will know that the minimal polynomial is $(x + 1)^2(x - 2)$ and will have to find the null space of $(T + 1)^2$.
We have

$$(T + 1)v_1 = \qquad\qquad 2v_3$$
$$(T + 1)v_2 = 3v_1 + 3v_2 + \ v_3$$
$$(T + 1)v_3 = \qquad\quad 0 \qquad .$$

The rank of $T + 1$ can now be found by determining the maximal number of linearly independent vectors among $\langle 0, 0, 2 \rangle$, $\langle 3, 3, 1 \rangle$, $\langle 0, 0, 0 \rangle$. In this case the number is obviously two and, by Exercise 9 of Section 20, the null space of $T + 1$ has dimension $3 - 2 = 1$.

Similarly, we have

$$(T - 2)v_1 = -3v_1 \qquad\qquad + 2v_3$$
$$(T - 2)v_2 = \quad 3v_1 \qquad\qquad + v_3$$
$$(T - 2)v_3 = \qquad\qquad\qquad - 3v_3$$

and we find that rank $(T - 2) = 2$, so that the null space of $T - 2$ has dimension 1.

At this point we have shown that V is not the direct sum of $n(T + 1)$ and $n(T - 2)$. We may conclude that the minimal polynomial is

$$m(x) = (x + 1)^2(x - 2)$$

and that, by theorem (22.8), it is impossible to find a basis of V with respect to which T has a diagonal matrix.

It remains to find the null spaces of $(T + 1)^2$ and $T - 2$. We have, from the computation of $T + 1$,

$$(T + 1)^2 v_1 = (T + 1)(2v_3) = 0,$$
$$(T + 1)^2 v_2 = (T + 1)(3v_1 + 3v_2 + v_3) = 9v_1 + 9v_2 + 9v_3,$$
$$(T + 1)^2 v_3 = 0.$$

Therefore $\{v_1, v_3\}$ is a basis for the null space of $(T + 1)^2$.

To find the null space of $T - 2$ we may suppose that $v = \xi_1 v_1 + \xi_2 v_2 + \xi_3 v_3 \in n(T - 2)$ and try to find ξ_1, ξ_2, ξ_3. We have

$$(T - 2)v = \xi_1(-3v_1 + 2v_3) + \xi_2(3v_1 + v_3) + \xi_3(-3v_3) = 0$$

and we have the following homogeneous system of equations to be solved for the ξ's:

$$-3\xi_1 + 3\xi_2 \qquad\quad = 0$$
$$2\xi_1 + \xi_2 - 3\xi_3 = 0.$$

This system has the solution vector $\langle 1, 1, 1 \rangle$. As a matter of fact, it is clear by inspection that $v_1 + v_2 + v_3$ is in $n(T - 2)$ and, since the dimension of $n(T - 2)$ is one, we know that $v_1 + v_2 + v_3$ generates $n(T - 2)$.

STEP 3.   Find the matrix of T with respect to the new basis. According to theorem (23.1), we should find a basis $\{w_1, w_2\}$ for $n((T + 1)^2)$ such that $(T + 1)w_1 = 0$, $(T + 1)w_2 \in S(w_1)$, and let w_3 be a basis of $n(T - 2)$. We see that we should have

$$w_1 = v_3, \qquad w_2 = v_1, \qquad w_3 = v_1 + v_2 + v_3.$$

The matrix relating these two bases is

$$S = \begin{pmatrix} 0 & 1 & 1 \\ 0 & 0 & 1 \\ 1 & 0 & 1 \end{pmatrix}$$

and the matrix of T with respect to $\{w_1, w_2, w_3\}$ is given by

$$B = \begin{pmatrix} -1 & 2 & 0 \\ 0 & -1 & 0 \\ 0 & 0 & 2 \end{pmatrix}.$$

We should now recall that either $SB = AS$ or $BS = SA$ (to remember which of the two holds is much too hard!). Checking the multiplications we see that

$$SB = AS$$

or

$$B = S^{-1}AS.$$

EXERCISES

1. Let T be a linear transformation on a vector space over the complex numbers such that

$$\begin{aligned} T(v_1) &= -v_1 - v_2 \\ T(v_2) &= v_1 - 3v_2 \end{aligned}$$

where $\{v_1, v_2\}$ is a basis for the vector space.

a. What is the characteristic polynomial of T?
b. What is the minimal polynomial of T?
c. What are the characteristic roots of T?
d. Does there exist a basis for the vector space consisting of characteristic vectors of T? Explain.
e. Find a characteristic vector of T.
f. Find a triangular matrix B and an invertible matrix S such that $SB = AS$ where A is the matrix of T with respect to the basis $\{v_1, v_2\}$.

2. Let V be a two-dimensional vector space over the real numbers R and let $T \in L(V, V)$ be defined by

$$\begin{aligned} T(v_1) &= \alpha v_2 \\ T(v_2) &= \beta v_1 \end{aligned}$$

where α and β are positive real numbers. Does there exist a basis of V consisting of characteristic vectors of T? Explain.

Note. In Exercises 3 to 8, V denotes a finite-dimensional vector space over the complex numbers C.

3. Let $T \in L(V, V)$ be a linear transformation whose characteristic roots are all equal to zero. Prove that T is nilpotent: $T^n = 0$ for some n.

4. Let $T \in L(V, V)$ be a linear transformation such that $T^2 = T$. Discuss whether or not there exists a basis of V consisting of characteristic vectors of T.

5. Answer the question of Exercise 4 for the case of a nilpotent transformation.

6. Answer the question of Exercise 4 for the case of a transformation T such that $T^r = 1$ for some positive integer r.

7. Let T be a linear transformation of rank 1, that is, dim $r(T) = 1$. Then $T(V) = S(v_0)$ for some vector $v_0 \neq 0$. In particular, $T(v_0) = \lambda v_0$ for some $\lambda \in C$. Prove that

$$T^2 = \lambda T.$$

Does there exist a basis of V consisting of characteristic vectors of T? Explain.

8. Prove that every linear transformation $T \in L(V, V)$ can be expressed in the form

$$T = D + N$$

where D is a diagonable transformation, N is nilpotent, and $DN = ND$. [*Hint:* This result follows almost at once from theorem (23.1).]

25. APPLICATION TO DIFFERENTIAL EQUATIONS*

We consider in this section a system of first-order linear differential equations with constant coefficients in the unknown functions $y_1(t), \cdots, y_n(t)$ where t is a real variable and the $y_i(t)$ are real-valued functions. All this means is that we are given differential equations

---

* This section is optional.

(25.1)
$$\frac{dy_1}{dt} = \alpha_{11}y_1 + \cdots + \alpha_{1n}y_n$$
$$\cdots\cdots\cdots\cdots\cdots\cdots\cdots$$
$$\frac{dy_n}{dt} = \alpha_{n1}y_1 + \cdots + \alpha_{nn}y_n$$

where $A = (\alpha_{ij})$ is a fixed n-by-n matrix with real coefficients. We shall discuss the problem of finding a set of solutions $y_1(t), \cdots, y_n(t)$ which take on a prescribed set of initial conditions $y_1(0), \cdots, y_n(0)$. For example, we are going to show, if t is the time and if $y_1(t), \cdots, y_n(t)$ describe the motion of some mechanical system, how to solve the equations of motion with the requirement that the functions take on specified values at time $t = 0$.

The simplest case of such a system is the case of one equation

$$\frac{dy}{dt} = \alpha y$$

and in this case we know from elementary calculus that the function

$$y(t) = y(0)\, e^{\alpha t}$$

solves the differential equation and takes on the initial value $y(0)$ when $t = 0$.

We shall show how matrix theory can be used to solve a general system (25.1) in an equally simple way. We should also point out that our discussion includes as a special case the problem of solving an nth-order linear differential equation with constant coefficients.

(25.2) $\alpha_0 \dfrac{d^n y}{dt^n} + \alpha_1 \dfrac{d^{n-1}y}{dt^{n-1}} + \cdots + \alpha_{n-1}\dfrac{dy}{dt} + \alpha_n y = 0, \qquad \alpha_0 \neq 0,$

where the α_i are real constants. This equation can be replaced by a system of the form (25.1) if we view $y(t)$ as the unknown function $y_1(t)$ and rename the derivatives as follows:

$$\frac{d^i y}{dt^i} = y_{i+1}(t), \qquad 1 \leq i \leq n - 1.$$

Then the functions $y_i(t)$ satisfy the system

(25.3)
$$\frac{dy_1}{dt} = y_2$$
$$\frac{dy_2}{dt} = y_3$$
$$\vdots$$
$$\frac{dy_n}{dt} = -\frac{\alpha_n}{\alpha_0}y_1 - \frac{\alpha_{n-1}}{\alpha_0}y_2 - \cdots - \frac{\alpha_1}{\alpha_0}y_n$$

and, conversely, any set of solutions of the system (25.3) will also yield a solution $y_1(t) = y(t)$ of the original equation (25.2). The initial conditions in this case amount to specifying the values of $y(t)$ and its first $n - 1$ derivatives at $t = 0$.

Now let us proceed with the discussion. We may represent the functions $y_1(t), \cdots, y_n(t)$ in vector form (or as an n-by-1 matrix):

$$\vec{y}(t) = \begin{pmatrix} y_1(t) \\ \cdot \\ \cdot \\ \cdot \\ y_n(t) \end{pmatrix}.$$

We have here a function which, viewed abstractly, assigns to a real number t the vector $\vec{y}(t) \in R_n$. We may define limits of such functions as follows:

$$\lim_{t \to t_0} \vec{y}(t) = \begin{pmatrix} \lim_{t \to t_0} y_1(t) \\ \cdot \\ \cdot \\ \lim_{t \to t_0} y_n(t) \end{pmatrix}$$

provided all the limits $\lim_{t \to t_0} y_i(t)$ exist.

It will be useful to generalize all this slightly. We may consider functions

$$t \to A(t) = \begin{pmatrix} a_{11}(t) \cdots a_{1r}(t) \\ \cdots\cdots\cdots\cdots \\ \cdots\cdots\cdots\cdots \\ \cdots\cdots\cdots\cdots \\ a_{s1}(t) \cdots a_{sr}(t) \end{pmatrix}$$

which assign to a real number t an s-by-r matrix $A(t)$ whose coefficients are complex numbers $a_{ij}(t)$. For a 1-by-1 matrix function we may define

$$\lim_{t \to t_0} a(t) = u$$

for some complex number u, provided that for each $\epsilon > 0$ there exists a $\delta > 0$ such that $0 < |t - t_0| < \delta$ implies $|a(t) - u| < \epsilon$ where $|a(t) - u|$ denotes the distance between the points $a(t)$ and u in the complex plane. By using the fact (to be proved in Section 27) that

$$|u + v| \le |u| + |v|$$

for complex numbers u and v, it is easy to show that the usual limit theorems of elementary calculus carry over to complex-valued functions. We may then define, as in the case of a vector function $\vec{y}(t)$,

$$\lim_{t \to t_0} A(t),$$

$$\frac{dA}{dt} = \lim_{h \to 0} \frac{A(t+h) - A(t)}{h} = \begin{pmatrix} \dfrac{da_{11}}{dt} & \cdots & \dfrac{da_{1r}}{dt} \\ \cdots\cdots\cdots\cdots \\ \cdots\cdots\cdots\cdots \\ \cdots\cdots\cdots\cdots \\ \dfrac{da_{s1}}{dt} & \cdots & \dfrac{da_{sr}}{dt} \end{pmatrix}$$

and

$$\lim_{n \to \infty} A_n(t) = \begin{pmatrix} \lim_{n \to \infty} a_{11}^n(t) & \cdots & \lim_{n \to \infty} a_{1r}^n(t) \\ \cdots\cdots\cdots\cdots\cdots\cdots \\ \cdots\cdots\cdots\cdots\cdots\cdots \\ \lim_{n \to \infty} a_{s1}^n(t) & \cdots & \lim_{n \to \infty} a_{sr}^n(t) \end{pmatrix}$$

where $\{A_n(t)\}$ is a sequence of matrix-valued functions $A_n(t) = (a_{ij}^{(n)}(t))$.

We can now express our original system of differential equations (25.1) in the more compact form

(25.4)
$$\frac{d\vec{y}}{dt} = A\vec{y}$$

where

$$\vec{y}(t) = \begin{pmatrix} y_1(t) \\ \cdot \\ \cdot \\ \cdot \\ y_n(t) \end{pmatrix}$$

is a vector-valued function and $A\vec{y}$ denotes the product of the constant n-by-n matrix A by the n-by-1 matrix $\vec{y}(t)$.

The remarkable thing is that the equation (25.4) can be solved exactly as in the one-dimensional case. Let us begin with the following definition.

(25.5) Definition. Let B be an n-by-n matrix with complex coefficients (β_{ij}). Define the sequence of matrices

$$E^{(n)} = I + B + \frac{1}{2}B^2 + \cdots + \frac{1}{n!}B^n, \qquad n = 0, 1, 2, \cdots.$$

Define the *exponential matrix*

$$e^B = \lim_{n \to \infty} E^{(n)} = \lim_{n \to \infty} \left(I + B + \frac{1}{2} B^2 + \cdots + \frac{1}{n!} B^n \right).$$

Of course, it must first be verified that e^B exists, that, in other words, the limit of the sequence $\{E^{(n)}\}$ exists. Let ρ be some upper bound for the $\{|\beta_{ij}|\}$; then $|\beta_{ij}| \leq \rho$ for all (i, j). Let $B^n = (\beta_{ij}^{(n)})$. Then the (i, j) entry of $E^{(n)}$ is

$$\beta_{ij}^{(0)} + \beta_{ij}^{(1)} + \frac{1}{2} \beta_{ij}^{(2)} + \cdots + \frac{1}{n!} \beta_{ij}^{(n)}$$

and we have to show that this sequence tends to a limit. This means that the infinite series

$$\sum_{k=0}^{\infty} \frac{1}{k!} \beta_{ij}^{(k)}$$

converges, and this can be checked by making a simple comparison test as follows. By induction on k we show first that for $k = 1, 2, \cdots$,

$$|\beta_{ij}^{(k)}| \leq n^{k-1} \rho^k, \qquad 1 \leq i, \; j \leq n.$$

Then each term of the series

$$\sum_{k=0}^{\infty} \frac{1}{k!} \beta_{ij}^{(k)}$$

is dominated in absolute value by the corresponding term in the series of positive terms

$$\sum_{k=0}^{\infty} \frac{1}{k!} n^{k-1} \rho^k$$

and this series converges for all ρ by the ratio test. This completes the proof that e^B exists for all matrices B.

We now list some easily verified properties of the function $B \to e^B$.

(25.6)* $\dfrac{d}{dt} e^{tB} = B e^{tB}$ *for all n-by-n matrices B.*

(25.7)* $e^{A+B} = e^A e^B$ *provided that $AB = BA$.*

(25.8)* $S^{-1} e^A S = e^{S^{-1}AS}$ *for an arbitrary invertible matrix S.*

The solution of (25.4) can now be given as follows.

(25.9) **Theorem.** *The vector differential equation*

$$\frac{d\vec{y}}{dt} = A\vec{y},$$

where A is an arbitrary constant matrix with real coefficients, has the solution

$$\vec{y}(t) = e^{tA} \cdot \vec{y}_0,$$

which takes on the initial value $\vec{y}_0$ when $t = 0$.

Proof. It is clear that $\vec{y}(0) = \vec{y}_0$, and it remains to check that $\vec{y}(t)$ is actually a solution of the differential equation. We note first that, if $A(t)$ is a matrix function and B is a constant vector, then

$$\frac{d}{dt}[A(t)B] = \frac{dA}{dt} \cdot B.$$

Applying this to $\vec{y}(t) = e^{tA} \cdot \vec{y}_0$ and using (25.6), we have

$$\frac{d\vec{y}}{dt} = \left(\frac{d}{dt} e^{tA}\right) \cdot \vec{y}_0 = (A\,e^{tA})\vec{y}_0 = A\vec{y}(t).$$

This completes the proof of the theorem.

Theorem (25.9) solves the problem stated at the beginning of the section, but the solution is still not of much practical importance because of the difficulty of computing the matrix e^{tA}. We show now how theorem (23.1) can be used to give a general method for calculating e^{tA}, provided that the complex roots of the minimal polynomial of the matrix A are known. Let

$$m(x) = (x - \alpha_1)^{e_1} \cdots (x - \alpha_s)^{e_s}, \qquad e_i > 0,$$

be the minimal polynomial of A. Then there exists an invertible matrix S, possibly with complex coefficients, such that, by theorem (23.1),

$$S^{-1}AS = D + N$$

where

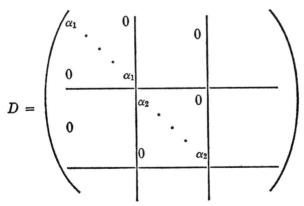

$$D = \begin{pmatrix} \alpha_1 & & 0 & & 0 \\ & \ddots & & & \\ 0 & & \alpha_1 & & \\ \hline & & & \alpha_2 & & 0 \\ 0 & & & & \ddots & \\ & & & 0 & & \alpha_2 \\ \hline & & & & & \end{pmatrix}$$

is a diagonal matrix, N is nilpotent, and $DN = ND$ (see Exercise 8 of Section 24). Moreover, S, D, and N can all be calculated by the methods of Sections 23 and 24. Then

$$A = S(D + N)S^{-1}$$

and, by (25.7) and (25.8), we have

(25.10) $e^{tA} = e^{tS(D+N)S^{-1}} = S(e^{tD+tN})S^{-1}$

$$= S\, e^{tD}\, e^{tN} S^{-1}.$$

The point of all this is that e^{tD} and e^{tN} are both easy to compute; e^{tD} is simply the diagonal matrix

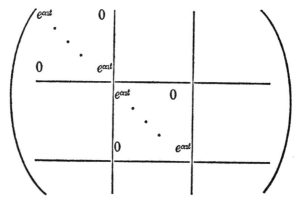

while $e^{tN} = I + tN + \dfrac{t^2 N^2}{2} + \cdots + \dfrac{t^{r-1} N^{r-1}}{(r-1)!}$ if $N^r = 0$. The solution vector $\vec{y}(t) = S\, e^{tD} e^{tN} S^{-1} \vec{y}_0$.

These remarks, of course, serve only as an introduction to the modern theory of vector differential equations. The point of it for us is to show how the triangular form theorem is used to make enormous simplifications in a seemingly impossible computational problem. For a more thorough (and advanced) treatment, see Coddington and Levinson (listed in the bibliography).

EXERCISES

1. Let

$$A = \begin{pmatrix} 0 & 1 \\ 0 & 0 \end{pmatrix}, \qquad B = \begin{pmatrix} -1 & 0 \\ 0 & 0 \end{pmatrix}.$$

Show that $AB \neq BA$. Calculate e^A, e^B, e^{A+B}, and show that $e^{A+B} \neq e^A e^B$. Thus (25.7) does not hold without some hypothesis like $AB = BA$.

2. Show that $D(e^A) = e^{\Sigma \alpha_i}$ where the $\{\alpha_i\}$ are the characteristic roots of A. [*Hint:* Use the triangular form theorem (23.1) together with (25.8).]

3. Show that e^A is always invertible and that $(e^A)^{-1} = e^{-A}$ for all $A \in M_n(C)$.

4. Apply the methods of this section to compute a solution for the differential equation

$$\frac{d^2y}{dt^2} + y = 0$$

such that $y(0) = 0$, $y'(0) = 1$. (Of course, this problem can also be done directly as a check.)

5. Solve the system

$$\begin{cases} \dfrac{dy_1}{dt} = -y_1 + y_2 \\[2mm] \dfrac{dy_2}{dt} = -y_1 - 3y_2 \end{cases} \qquad y_1(0) = 0,\ y_2(0) = 1.$$

(Note that the matrix

$$\begin{pmatrix} -1 & 1 \\ -1 & -3 \end{pmatrix}$$

is the same as the matrix involved in Exercise 1 of Section 24.)

6. Let A be the coefficient matrix of the vector differential equation equivalent to

$$\alpha_0 \frac{d^n y}{dt^n} + \alpha_1 \frac{d^{n-1}y}{dt^{n-1}} + \cdots + \alpha_n y = 0.$$

Prove that the characteristic polynomial of A is

$$\alpha_0 x^n + \alpha_1 x^{n-1} + \cdots + \alpha_n.$$

7. (Optional). Verify the following derivation of a particular solution of the "nonhomogeneous" vector differential equation

$$\frac{d\vec{y}}{dt} = A\vec{y} + \vec{f}(t)$$

where $\vec{f}(t)$ is a given continuous vector function of t. Attempt to find a solution of the form $\vec{y}(t) = e^{At}\vec{c}(t)$, where $\vec{c}(t)$ is a vector function to be determined. Differentiate to obtain

$$\frac{d\vec{y}}{dt} = A\,e^{At}\vec{c}(t) + e^{At}\frac{d\vec{c}(t)}{dt} = A\vec{y} + \vec{f}(t).$$

Since $Ae^{At}\vec{c}(t) = A\vec{y}$, we obtain [since $(e^{At})^{-1} = e^{-At}$]

$$\frac{d\vec{c}}{dt} = e^{-At}\vec{f}(t).$$

Thus $\vec{c}(t)$ is an indefinite integral of $e^{-At}\vec{f}(t)$ and can be expressed as

$$\vec{c}(t) = \int_{t_0}^{t} e^{-As}\vec{f}(s)\ ds.$$

Then $\vec{y}(t) = e^{At}\int_{t_0}^{t} e^{-As}\vec{f}(s)\ ds = \int_{t_0}^{t} e^{A(t-s)}\vec{f}(s)\ ds$. Finally, verify that $\vec{y}(t)$ is a solution of the differential equation.

Appendix:
The Jordan Normal Form*

Let T be a linear transformation on a finite-dimensional vector space V over an algebraically closed field F. From the Triangular Form Theorem, it follows that the matrix A of T is similar to $D + N$, where D is a diagonal matrix, N is nilpotent, and $DN = ND$. The entries along the diagonal of D are the characteristic roots of T, with each characteristic root α repeated as many times as the linear factor $x - \alpha$ appears in a factorization of the characteristic polynomial of T into primes. Apart from the order in which the characteristic roots appear on the diagonal of D, D is completely determined by the characteristic polynomial of T. The matrix N, on the other hand, is not uniquely determined and depends on the choice of the bases for the null spaces of $(T - \alpha \cdot 1)^m$ where $(x - \alpha)^m$ is a prime power factor of the minimal polynomial of T. For the applications to differential equations and the computation of e^A, and for other purposes as well, it is desirable to know the simplest possible choice for the nilpotent matrix N. We present a solution of this problem here.

We begin with a close study of a nilpotent linear transformation T on a finite-dimensional space V over an arbitrary field F. Let v be a nonzero vector in V, and consider the set of vectors $\{v, Tv, T^2v, \cdots\}$. These vectors generate a T-subspace of V called the *cyclic subspace generated by* v. An arbitrary T-subspace W of V is called a *cyclic subspace relative to* T (or simply a *cyclic T-subspace*) if there exists a vector $w \in W$ such that W is generated by the vectors w, Tw, T^2w, $\cdots$.

---

* The material in this appendix is optional, and several steps in the discussion are left as exercises for the reader.

(A.1)   Lemma.   *Let W be a cyclic subspace relative to T. Then there exists a vector $w \in W$ and a positive integer k such that $T^k w = 0$, and such that $\{T^{k-1}w, T^{k-2}w, \cdots, Tw, w\}$ is a basis of W. The matrix of the transformation of W determined by T with respect to this basis is*

$$\begin{pmatrix} 0 & 1 & 0 & \cdots & 0 \\ \cdot & 0 & 1 & & \cdot \\ \cdot & \cdot & 0 & & \cdot \\ \cdot & \cdot & \cdot & & 1 \\ 0 & 0 & 0 & \cdots & 0 \end{pmatrix}.$$

Proof.   Since W is cyclic, there exists a vector $w \in W$ such that W is generated by the vectors $w, Tw, \cdots$. Since W is finite-dimensional, there exists a positive integer k such that $\{w, Tw, \cdots, T^{k-1}w\}$ is a linearly independent set, and $T^k w \in S(w, Tw, \cdots, T^{k-1}w)$. It is clear that for all integers $m \geq k$, $T^m w \in S(w, Tw, \cdots, T^{k-1}w)$, and hence $\{w, Tw, \cdots, T^{k-1}w\}$ is a basis for W. Now let T_1 be the linear transformation defined by T on the space W; then $T_1(u) = T(u)$ for all $u \in W$. Since T is nilpotent on V, T_1 is nilpotent on W, and hence the minimal polynomial of T_1 on W has the form x^t, for some $t \leq \dim W$. Since $\dim W = k$, we have $t \leq k$, and hence $T_1^k = T^k = 0$ on W. In particular, $T^k w = 0$. The form of the matrix of T_1 relative to the basis given in the statement of the lemma is clear by the definition of the matrix of a linear transformation. This completes the proof of the lemma.

The main theorem in the appendix can now be stated.

(A.2)   Theorem.   *Let T be a nilpotent linear transformation on a finite-dimensional space V over an arbitrary field F. Then V can be expressed as a direct sum $V = V_1 \oplus \cdots \oplus V_s$, where each V_i is a cyclic T-subspace.*

Proof.   We define a T-subspace W of V to be *indecomposable* if $W \neq 0$ and if it is impossible to express W as a direct sum of two nonzero T-subspaces. We first prove, by induction on $\dim V$, that V is either indecomposable or a direct sum of indecomposable invariant subspaces. We shall then prove that every indecomposable invariant subspace is cyclic.

If $\dim V = 1$, then V is indecomposable. Suppose now that $\dim V > 1$ and that every T-subspace $W \neq V$ is either indecomposable or a direct sum of indecomposable subspaces relative to T. If V is indecomposable, there is nothing to prove. If V is not indecomposable, then there exist invariant subspaces V_1 and V_2, both different from zero, such that $V = V_1 \oplus V_2$. Then both V_1 and V_2 have dimensions less than dim V. Upon applying the induction hypothesis to V_1 and V_2, it follows that V is a direct sum of indecomposable invariant subspaces, as required.

In order to prove that if V is indecomposable then V is cyclic, we shall prove instead that if V is not cyclic then V is not indecomposable. Let x^k be the minimal polynomial of T on V. Then there exists a cyclic subspace W of V with a basis $\{w, Tw, \cdots, T^{k-1}w\}$. Otherwise, by lemma (A.1), $T^{k-1} = 0$ on V, contrary to the assumption that x^k is the minimal polynomial of T. Since by assumption V is not cyclic, $W \neq V$.

Now let V^* be the dual space of V [see definition (19.9)], and let $W^\perp$ be the set of all linear functions $f \in V^*$ such that $f(W) = 0$. Then $W^\perp$ is a subspace of V^*. Let $\{v_1, \cdots, v_n\}$ be a basis of V such that $\{v_1, \cdots, v_k\}$ is a basis of W, and let $\{f_1, \cdots, f_n\}$ be the corresponding basis of V^* defined in Exercise 6 of Section 19. Then the reader can verify that $\{f_{k+1}, \cdots, f_n\}$ is a basis of $W^\perp$, so that dim $W^\perp = n - k$.

Now let T^* be the transpose of T, defined in Exercise 4 of Section 20. The reader can show that for all integers $i \geq 1$, $(T^*)^i = (T^i)^*$. Therefore $(T^*)^k = 0$. On the other hand, we shall prove that for some linear function $f \in V^*$, $(T^*)^{k-1}f \notin W^\perp$. Otherwise $(T^*)^{k-1}f \in W^\perp$ for all $f \in V^*$. Then $0 = [(T^*)^{k-1}f](w) = f(T^{k-1}w)$ for all $f \in V^*$. It follows that $T^{k-1}w = 0$ (Why?). But this is contrary to the definition of the vector w. Thus $(T^*)^{k-1}f \notin W^\perp$ for some $f \in V^*$.

We prove next that if

$$\alpha_0 f + \alpha_1(T^*f) + \cdots + \alpha_{k-1}[(T^*)^{k-1}f] \in W^\perp,$$

then $\alpha_0 = \cdots = \alpha_{k-1} = 0$. Suppose we have such a relation, with $\alpha_0 = \cdots = \alpha_{i-1} = 0$, $\alpha_i \neq 0$. Then

$$\alpha_i(T^*)^i f + \cdots + \alpha_{k-1}(T^*)^{k-1}f \in W^\perp,$$

and multiplying by $(T^*)^{k-1-i}$ and using the fact that $(T^*)^k = 0$, we obtain

$$\alpha_i(T^*)^{k-1}f \in W^\perp$$

where $\alpha_i \neq 0$, contrary to our choice of f. It follows that if S is the subspace of V^* generated by $f, T^*f, \cdots, (T^*)^{k-1}f$, then $S \cap W^\perp = 0$, and dim $S = k$. Therefore $V^* = W^\perp + S$, by (7.17), and

(A.3) $$V^* = W^\perp \oplus S.$$

Moreover, since $(T^*)^k = 0$, S is a T^*-subspace of V^*.

Finally, let $S^\perp$ be the set of vectors v in V such that $g(v) = 0$ for all $g \in S$. Then $S^\perp$ is a T-subspace of V, since S is a T^*-subspace of V^*. We shall complete the argument by showing that

$$V = W \oplus S^\perp$$

and hence that V is not indecomposable.

First of all, let $v \in W \cap S^\perp$. Then, by (A.3), $\varphi(v) = 0$ for all $\varphi \in V^*$, and hence $v = 0$. Thus $W \cap S^\perp = 0$. Now let $\{\varphi_1, \cdots, \varphi_k\}$ be a basis for S. Then the reader can check that

$$\varphi_1(x) = 0, \quad \cdots, \quad \varphi_k(x) = 0$$

is a system of homogeneous equations whose coefficient matrix has rank k, and whose solution space is exactly $S^\perp$. It follows that $\dim S^\perp = n - k$. Since $\dim W = k$ and $W \cap S^\perp = 0$, we have $V = W \oplus S^\perp$. This completes the proof of the theorem.

(A.4) Corollary. *Let T be a nilpotent transformation on a finite-dimensional space V. Then V has a basis such that the matrix of T relative to this basis has the form*

$$\begin{pmatrix} A_1 & & & & 0 \\ & A_2 & & & \\ & & \cdot & & \\ & & & \cdot & \\ & & & & \cdot \\ 0 & & & & A_r \end{pmatrix}$$

with zeros except in the diagonal blocks, and each diagonal block has the form

$$A_i = \begin{pmatrix} 0 & 1 & 0 & \cdot & \cdot & \cdot & 0 \\ & 0 & 1 & & & & \cdot \\ & & 0 & & & & \cdot \\ & & & \cdot & & & \cdot \\ & & & & \cdot & & \\ & & & & & \cdot & 1 \\ 0 & & & & & & 0 \end{pmatrix}.$$

Using the main theorem of Section 22, we obtain the following result:

(A.5) Corollary. *Let T be a linear transformation on a finite-dimensional space V over a field F whose minimal polynomial has the form $\prod_{i=1}^{s} (x - \alpha_i)^{d_i}$, where the $\{\alpha_i\}$ are the characteristic roots of T. (This hypothesis is satisfied, for example, if F is an algebraically closed field.)*

Then there exists a basis of V such that the matrix of T with respect to this basis has the form

$$B = \begin{pmatrix} B_1 & & & 0 \\ & \cdot & & \\ & & \cdot & \\ 0 & & & B_l \end{pmatrix}$$

with zeros except in the diagonal blocks, and the blocks $\{B_j\}$ have the form

$$\begin{pmatrix} \alpha & 1 & 0 & & & & 0 \\ & \alpha & 1 & & & & \cdot \\ & & \alpha & & & & \cdot \\ & & & \cdot & & & \cdot \\ & & & & \cdot & & \cdot \\ & & & & & \cdot & 1 \\ & & & & & & \alpha \end{pmatrix}$$

where α is one of the characteristic roots of T.

Proof. By theorem (22.6), V can be expressed as the direct sum of the null spaces $V_i = n((T - \alpha_i \cdot 1)^{d_i})$. On the space V_i, $T - \alpha_i 1$ is a nilpotent transformation. Apply corollary (A.4) to $T - \alpha_i \cdot 1$ on the space V_i. There exists a basis of V_i such that the matrix A of $T - \alpha_i 1$ on V_i has the form

$$A = \begin{pmatrix} A_1 & & & 0 \\ & \cdot & & \\ & & \cdot & \\ 0 & & & A_r \end{pmatrix}$$

where the A_i are as in corollary (A.4). If B is the matrix of T on the space V_i relative to this basis, then $A = B - \alpha_i \cdot I$, and

$$B = \alpha_i I + A.$$

It follows that

$$B = \begin{pmatrix} B_1 & & & 0 \\ & \cdot & & \\ & & \cdot & \\ 0 & & & B_r \end{pmatrix}$$

where each B_j has the form

$$\begin{pmatrix} \alpha_i & 1 & 0 & \cdot & \cdot & \cdot & 0 \\ & \alpha_i & 1 & & & & \cdot \\ & & \alpha_i & & & & \cdot \\ & & & \cdot & & & \cdot \\ & & & & \cdot & & 1 \\ 0 & & & & & & \alpha_i \end{pmatrix}$$

Combining these bases for the various spaces $n((T - \alpha_i 1)^{d_i})$, we obtain a basis of V with respect to which the matrix of T has the required form. This completes the proof of the corollary.

It follows from earlier results in this chapter that every n-by-n matrix A whose minimal polynomial has the form $\Pi(x - \alpha_i)^{d_i}$ is similar to a matrix in the form given in corollary (A.4). This form is called the *Jordan normal form* of the matrix of T. Our result proves only the existence of the Jordan normal form. It leaves open the questions of how to give an algorithm for putting a matrix in its Jordan normal form, the uniqueness of the blocks in the Jordan normal form, and what can be said for linear transformations over fields which are not necessarily algebraically closed. For a discussion of these questions, the reader may consult one of the more advanced books on linear algebra such as Jacobson or Schreier and Sperner (see the Bibliography).

CHAPTER 6

VECTOR SPACES
with an
INNER PRODUCT

This chapter begins with an optional section on symmetry of plane figures, which shows how some natural geometrical questions lead to the problem of studying linear transformations that preserve length. The concept of length in a general vector space over the real numbers is introduced in the next section, where it is shown how length is related to an inner product. A classification is given for the linear transformations that preserve length. Applications are given to quadratic forms and to the classification of symmetry groups in three dimensions.

26. THE CONCEPT OF SYMMETRY*

The word "symmetry" has rich associations for most of us. A person familiar with sculpture and painting knows the importance of sym-

---

* This section is optional.

metry to the artist and how the distinctive features of certain types of architecture and ornaments result from the use of symmetry. A geologist knows that crystals are classified according to the symmetry properties they possess. A naturalist knows the many appearances of symmetry in the shapes of plants, shells, and fish. The chemist knows that the symmetry properties of molecules are related to their chemical properties. In this section we shall consider the mathematical concept of symmetry, which will provide some worthwhile insight into all of the preceding examples.

Let us begin with a simple example from analytic geometry, Figure 6.1. What does it mean to say the graph of the parabola

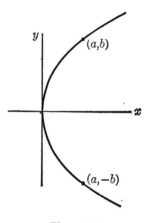

Figure 6.1

$y^2 = x$ is symmetric about the x-axis? One way of looking at it is to say that if we fold the plane along the x axis the two halves of the curve $y^2 = x$ fit together. But this is a little too vague. A more precise description comes from the observation that the operation of plane-folding defines a transformation T, of the points in the plane, which assigns to a point (a, b) the point $(a, -b)$ which meets it after the plane is folded. The symmetry of the parabola is now described by asserting that if (a, b) is a point on the parabola so is the transformed point $(a, -b)$. This sort of symmetry is called *bilateral symmetry*.

Now consider the example of a triod, Figure 6.2. What sort of symmetry does it possess? It clearly has bilateral symmetry about the three lines joining the center with the points a, b, and c. The triod has also a new sort of symmetry, *rotational symmetry*. If we rotate points in the plane through an angle of 120°, leaving the center fixed, then the triod is carried onto itself. Does the triod have the

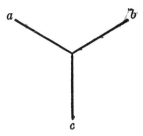

Figure 6.2

same symmetry properties as the winged triod of Figure 6.3? Clearly not; the winged triod has only rotational symmetry and does not possess the bilateral symmetry of the triod. Thus we see that the symmetry properties of figures may serve to distinguish them.

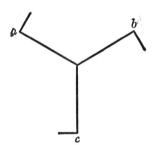

Figure 6.3

We have not yet arrived at a precise definition of symmetry. Another example suggests the underlying idea. The circle with center 0, Figure 6.4, possesses all the kinds of symmetry we have discussed so far. However, we can look at the symmetry of the circle from another viewpoint. The circle is carried onto itself by any transformation T which preserves distance and which leaves the center fixed, for the circle consists of precisely those points p whose distances

from 0 are a fixed constant r and, if T is a distance preserving transformation such that $T(0) = 0$, then the distance of $T(p)$ from 0 will
again be r and $T(p)$ is on the circle. This suggests the following
definition.

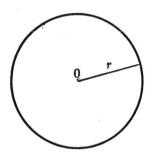

Figure 6.4

(26.1) Definition. By a *figure* X we mean a set of points in the
plane. A *symmetry* of a figure X is a transformation T of the plane
into itself such that:

(A) $T(X) = X$; that is, T sends every point in X onto another
point in X, and every point in X is the image of some point
in X under T.

(B) T preserves distance; that is, if $d(p, q)$ denotes the distance
between the points p and q, then

$$d(T(p), T(q)) = d(p, q)$$

for all points p and q.

(26.2) Theorem. *The set G of all symmetries of a figure X form a
group G, called the symmetry group of the figure* [*see definition* (19.13)].

Proof. We show first that if $S, T \in G$ then the product ST
defined by

$$ST(p) = S[T(p)]$$

belongs to G. We have $ST(X) = S[T(X)] = S(X) = X$ and
$d(ST(p), ST(q)) = d(S[T(p)], S[T(q)]) = d(T(p), T(q)) = d(p, q)$
and hence $ST \in G$. We have to check also that

$$S(TU) = (ST)U, \qquad \text{for } S, T, U \in G,$$

which is a consequence of the fact that both mappings send $p \to$ $S\{T[U(p)]\}$. The transformation 1 such that $1(p) = p$ for all p belongs, clearly, to G and satisfies

$$S \cdot 1 = 1 \cdot S = S, \qquad S \in G.$$

Finally, if $S \in G$, there exists a symmetry S^{-1} of X which unwinds whatever S has done (the reader can give a more rigorous proof) such that

$$SS^{-1} = S^{-1}S = 1.$$

This completes the proof of the theorem.

The vague question, What kinds of symmetry can a figure possess? is now replaced by the precise mathematical question, What are the possible symmetry groups? We shall investigate a simple case of this problem in this section. First we look at some examples of symmetry groups.

The symmetry group of the triod, Figure 6.5, consists of the three bilateral symmetries about the arms of the triod and three

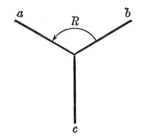

Figure 6.5

rotations through angles of 120°, 240°, and 360°. By means of the group operation we show that the symmetries of the triod all can be built up from two of the symmetries. For example, let R be the counterclockwise rotation through an angle of 120° and let S be the bilateral symmetry about the arm a. The reader may verify that the symmetry group G of the triod consists of the symmetries

$$\{1, R, R^2, S, SR, SR^2\}.$$

We may also verify that $S^2 = 1$, $R^3 = 1$, and $SR = R^{-1}S$ and that these rules suffice to multiply arbitrary elements of G.

The symmetry group of the winged triod is easily seen to consist of exactly the symmetries

$$\{1, R, R^2\}.$$

More generally, let X be the n-armed figure, Figure 6.6, S the bi-

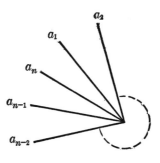

Figure 6.6

lateral symmetry about the arm a_1, and R the rotation carrying $a_2 \to a_1$. Then the group of X consists exactly of the symmetries

(26.3) $\{1, R, R^2, \cdots, R^{n-1}, S, SR, \cdots, SR^{n-1}\}$

and these symmetries are multiplied according to the rules

$$R^n = 1, \qquad S^2 = 1, \qquad SR = R^{-1}S.$$

The symmetry group of the corresponding winged figure consists of precisely the rotations

(26.4) $\{1, R, R^2, \cdots, R^{n-1}\}.$

The group (26.3) is called the *dihedral group* D_n; the group (26.4) is called the *cyclic group* C_n. We shall sketch a proof that these are the only *finite* symmetry groups of plane figures.

We require first some general remarks. It will be convenient to identify the plane with the vector space R_2 of all pairs of real numbers $\langle \alpha, \beta \rangle$. If p is a vector $\langle \alpha, \beta \rangle$, then the *length* $||p||$ is defined by

$$||p|| = \sqrt{\alpha^2 + \beta^2}$$

and the distance from p to q (see Figure 6.7) is then given by

$$d(p, q) = ||p - q||.$$

We require also the fact from plane analytic geometry that $p =$

$\langle \alpha, \beta \rangle$ is perpendicular to $q = \langle \gamma, \delta \rangle$ (notation: $p \perp q$) if and only if

$$\alpha\gamma + \beta\delta = 0.$$

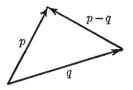

Figure 6.7

(26.5) *A distance preserving transformation T of R_2 which leaves the zero element fixed is a linear transformation.*

Proof. A point p in the plane is completely determined by its distances from 0, $e_1 = \langle 1, 0 \rangle$, and $e_2 = \langle 0, 1 \rangle$. Therefore $T(p)$ is completely determined by $T(e_1)$ and $T(e_2)$, since $T(0) = 0$. From Chapter 5 we can define a linear transformation $\tilde{T}$ such that

$$T(e_1) = \tilde{T}(e_1), \qquad T(e_2) = \tilde{T}(e_2).$$

Since both T and $\tilde{T}$ are determined by their action on e_1 and e_2, we have $T = \tilde{T}$.

We prove next the following characterization of a distance preserving transformation.

(26.6) *A linear transformation T preserves distances if and only if:*

(26.7) $\|T(e_1)\| = \|T(e_2)\| = 1 \quad and \quad T(e_1) \perp T(e_2).$

Proof. If T preserves distances, then it is clear that (26.7) holds. Conversely, suppose T is a linear transformation such that (26.7) holds. To prove that T preserves distances it is sufficient to prove that, for all vectors p,

$$\|T(p)\| = \|p\|,$$

for then

$$d(T(p), T(q)) = \|T(p) - T(q)\| = \|T(p - q)\| = \|p - q\| = d(p, q).$$

Now let $p = \xi e_1 + \eta e_2$ and let $T(e_1) = \langle \alpha, \beta \rangle$, $T(e_2) = \langle \gamma, \delta \rangle$. Then (26.7) implies that

$$\alpha^2 + \beta^2 = \gamma^2 + \delta^2 = 1, \qquad \alpha\gamma + \beta\delta = 0.$$

Then
$$\begin{aligned}
||T(p)||^2 &= ||\xi T(e_1) + \eta T(e_2)||^2 = ||\langle \xi\alpha + \eta\gamma, \xi\beta + \eta\delta\rangle||^2 \\
&= (\xi\alpha + \eta\gamma)^2 + (\xi\beta + \eta\delta)^2 \\
&= \xi^2\alpha^2 + 2\xi\alpha\eta\gamma + \eta^2\gamma^2 + \xi^2\beta^2 + 2\xi\beta\eta\delta + \eta^2\delta^2 \\
&= \xi^2(\alpha^2 + \beta^2) + \eta^2(\gamma^2 + \delta^2) + 2\xi\eta(\alpha\gamma + \beta\delta) \\
&= \xi^2 + \eta^2 = ||p||^2.
\end{aligned}$$
This completes the proof of (26.6).

Now let T be a distance preserving transformation and leaving the origin fixed, and let $T(e_1) = \langle \alpha, \beta \rangle$. Then $T(e_2)$ is a point on the

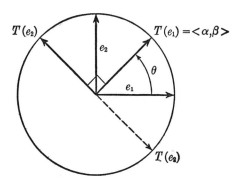

Figure 6.8

unit circle whose radius vector is perpendicular to $T(e_1)$, Figure 6.8. It follows that either
$$T(e_2) = \langle -\beta, \alpha \rangle$$
or
$$T(e_2) = \langle \beta, -\alpha \rangle.$$
In the former case the matrix of T with respect to $\{e_1, e_2\}$ is
$$A = \begin{pmatrix} \alpha & -\beta \\ \beta & \alpha \end{pmatrix}, \qquad D(A) = \alpha^2 + \beta^2 = 1,$$
while in the latter case the matrix is
$$A = \begin{pmatrix} \alpha & \beta \\ \beta & -\alpha \end{pmatrix}, \qquad D(A) = -\alpha^2 - \beta^2 = -1.$$
In the former case T is a rotation through an angle θ such that $\cos \theta = \alpha$, while in the latter case T is a bilateral symmetry about

the line making an angle $\frac{1}{2}\theta$ with e_1. Notice that in the second case the matrix of T^2 is

$$\begin{pmatrix} \alpha & \beta \\ \beta & -\alpha \end{pmatrix} \begin{pmatrix} \alpha & \beta \\ \beta & -\alpha \end{pmatrix} = \begin{pmatrix} \alpha^2 + \beta^2 & 0 \\ 0 & \alpha^2 + \beta^2 \end{pmatrix} = I$$

so that $T^2 = 1$. The second kind of transformation will be called a *reflection*, the first a *rotation*. The above computations show that:

(26.8)   *A distance preserving linear transformation T has determinant ± 1; it has determinant $+1$ if and only if T is a rotation and determinant -1 if and only if T is a reflection.*

The multiplication theorem for determinants implies the following.

(26.9)   *Let S and T be distance-preserving linear transformations; then:*

(A)   *If S, T are rotations, then ST is a rotation.*
(B)   *If S, T are reflections, ST is a rotation.*
(C)   *If one of S, T is a rotation and the other is a reflection, then ST is a reflection.*

Now we are ready to determine the possible finite symmetry groups G of plane figures. We assume that all the elements of G are linear transformations (and so leave the origin fixed). To determine a group means to show that it is *isomorphic* with a group that has previously been constructed, in the sense that a one-to-one correspondence exists between the two groups which preserves the multiplication laws of the two groups.

(26.10)   **Theorem.**   *Let G be a finite group of distance-preserving linear transformations. Then G is isomorphic with one of the following:*

(A)   *The cyclic group $C_n = \{1, R, R^2, \cdots, R^{n-1}\}$, $R^n = 1$, consisting of the powers of a single rotation.*
(B)   *The dihedral group $D_n = \{1, R, \cdots, R^{n-1}, S, SR, \cdots, SR^{n-1}\}$ where R is a rotation, S a reflection, and $R^n = 1$, $S^2 = 1$, $SR = R^{-1}S$.*

Proof.   We may suppose $G \neq \{1\}$. First suppose all the elements of G are rotations and let R be a rotation in G through the least positive angle. Consider the powers of R, $\{1, R, R^2, \cdots\}$. These exhaust G, as will be seen. Suppose $T \in G$ is a rotation different from all the powers of R. If φ is the angle of T and θ the angle of R, then, for some i, $i\theta < \varphi < (i + 1)\theta$, Figure 6.9. Then G contains

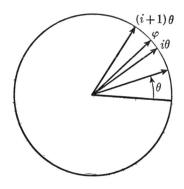

Figure 6.9

TR^{-i} which is a rotation in G through an angle $\varphi - i\theta$ smaller than θ, contrary to our assumption. Therefore G consists of the powers of R and is a cyclic group.

Now suppose G contains a reflection S. Let H be the set of all rotations contained in G. Then H itself is a group and, by the first part of the proof, there exists a rotation R in H such that

$$H = \{1, R, R^2, \cdots, R^{n-1}\}, \qquad R^n = 1.$$

Now let $X \in G$; either $X \in H$, or X is a reflection. In the latter case SX is a rotation. Hence $SX = R^i$ for some i, and since $S^2 = 1$ we have

$$X = S(SX) = SR^i$$

and we have proved that

$$G = \{1, R, \cdots, R^{n-1}, S, SR, \cdots, SR^{n-1}\}.$$

Finally, SR is a reflection; hence $(SR)^2 = 1$ or $SRSR = 1$, and we have $SR = R^{-1}S$. It follows that G is isomorphic with a dihedral group, and the theorem is proved.

For further discussion of this topic, the reader is urged to consult the books of Weyl and of Coxeter listed in the bibliography.

EXERCISE

Prove that the mapping

$$\begin{pmatrix} \cos\theta & -\sin\theta \\ \sin\theta & \cos\theta \end{pmatrix} \rightarrow \cos\theta + i\sin\theta$$

is an isomorphism between the group of rotations in the plane and the multiplicative group of complex numbers of absolute value 1.

27. INNER PRODUCTS

Let V be a vector space over the real numbers R.

(27.1) Definition. An *inner product* on V is a function which assigns to each pair of vectors u, v in V a real number (u, v) such that the following conditions are satisfied.

(A) (u, v) is a *bilinear function;* that is,

$$\begin{aligned} (u + v, w) &= (u, w) + (v, w), \\ (u, v + w) &= (u, v) + (u, w), \\ (\alpha u, v) &= (u, \alpha v) = \alpha(u, v), \end{aligned}$$

for all $u, v, w \in V$ and $\alpha \in R$.

(B)   The function (u, v) is *symmetric;* that is,

$$(u, v) = (v, u), \qquad u, v \in V.$$

(C)   The function is *positive definite;* that is,

$$(u, u) \geq 0$$

and

$$(u, u) = 0 \text{ if and only if } u = 0.$$

EXAMPLES.   (1) Let $\{e_1, \cdots, e_n\}$ be a basis for V over R and let

$$(u, v) = \sum_{i=1}^{n} \xi_i \eta_i$$

where $u = \sum \xi_i e_i$, $v = \sum \eta_i e_i$.

(2) Let V be a subspace of $C[0, 1]$, and define

$$(f, g) = \int_0^1 f(t)g(t)\, dt, \qquad f, g \in V.$$

In both cases the reader may verify that the functions defined are actually inner products.

In the case of R_2 the inner product defined in Example 1 is known to be connected with the angle between the vectors u and v; indeed, if u and v have length 1, then $(u, v) = \cos \theta$ where θ is the angle between u and v. Thus $|(u, v)| \leq 1$ if both u and v have length 1. Our next task is to verify that this same inequality holds in general.

(27.2) Definition. Let (u, v) be a fixed inner product on V. Define the *length* $||u||$ of a vector $u \in V$ by

$$||u|| = \sqrt{(u, u)}.$$

Note that by part C of definition (27.1) we have

$$||u|| \geq 0, \qquad ||u|| = 0 \text{ if and only if } u = 0.$$

Moreover, we have

$$||\alpha u|| = |\alpha| \cdot ||u||$$

where $|\alpha|$ is the absolute value of α in R.

We prove now an important inequality.

(27.3) Lemma. *If $||u|| = ||v|| = 1$, then $|(u, v)| \leq 1$.*

Proof. We have

$$(u - v, u - v) \geq 0.$$

This implies

$$(u, u) + (v, v) - 2(u, v) \geq 0$$

and since $(u, u) = (v, v) = 1$ we obtain

$$(u, v) \leq 1.$$

Similarly, from $(u + v, u + v) \geq 0$ we have

$$-(u, v) \leq 1.$$

Combining these inequalities we have $|(u, v)| \leq 1$.

(27.4) Theorem (Cauchy-Schwarz Inequality). *For arbitrary vectors, $u, v \in V$ we have*

(27.5) $$|(u, v)| \leq ||u|| \cdot ||v||.$$

Proof. The result is trivial if either $||u||$ or $||v||$ is zero. Therefore, assume that $||u|| \neq 0$, $||v|| \neq 0$. Then

$$\frac{u}{||u||}, \qquad \frac{v}{||v||}$$

are vectors of length 1, and by lemma (27.3) we have

$$\left| \left(\frac{u}{||u||}, \frac{v}{||v||} \right) \right| \leq 1.$$

It follows that $|(u, v)| \leq ||u|| \cdot ||v||$, and (27.5) is proved.

As a corollary we obtain the triangle inequality, which has already been used for R_2 in Section 25 on differential equations.

(27.6) Corollary (Triangle Inequality). *For all vectors* $u, v \in V$ *we have*

$$||u + v|| \leq ||u|| + ||v||.$$

Proof. By the Cauchy-Schwarz inequality and by the triangle inequality for R_1 we have

$$\begin{aligned}
||u + v||^2 &= |(u + v, u + v)| = |(u, u) + (v, v) + 2(u, v)| \\
&\leq |(u, u)| + |(v, v)| + 2|(u, v)| \\
&\leq ||u||^2 + ||v||^2 + 2||u|| \cdot ||v|| = (||u|| + ||v||)^2.
\end{aligned}$$

Therefore, by Exercise 4 of Section 2,

$$||u + v|| \leq ||u|| + ||v||,$$

as required.

(27.7) Definition. Let $u, v \in V$. Define the *angle* θ between u and v as the angle, for $0 \leq \theta \leq \pi$, such that

$$\cos \theta = \frac{(u, v)}{||u|| \; ||v||}.$$

[Note that $|\cos \theta| \leq 1$ by (27.5).] The vectors u and v are defined *orthogonal* if $(u, v) = 0$ or, in other words, if the cosine of the angle between them is zero. A basis $\{u_1, \cdots, u_n\}$ for a finite-dimensional space V is called an *orthonormal basis* if:

> (A) $||u_i|| = 1, \quad 1 \leq i \leq n.$
> (B) $(u_i, u_j) = 0, \quad i \neq j.$

Note that any *orthonormal set of vectors* (which satisfy the conditions A and B) are linearly independent (Why?).

(27.8) Theorem. *Every finite-dimensional vector space* V *with an inner product* (u, v) *has an orthonormal basis.*

Proof. Pick $u \neq 0$ in V. Then $u_1 = ||u||^{-1}u$ has length 1. Let

V_1 be the set of vectors w in V such that $(u_1, w) = 0$. Then V_1 is a subspace of V and we have $V = S(u_1) \oplus V_1$. To see this, consider the following. It is clear that $\xi u_1 + v_1 = 0$, for $\xi \in R$ and $v_1 \in V_1$, implies $\xi u_1 = v_1 = 0$ (Why?). Next let $v \in V$. Then $v = (u_1, v)u_1 + (v - (u_1, v)u_1)$ where $v - (u_1, v)u_1 \in V_1$, and we have shown that $V = S(u_1) \oplus V_1$. Then (u, v), for $u, v \in V_1$, is an inner product on V_1 and by induction we may assume that V_1 has an orthonormal basis $\{u_2, \cdots, u_n\}$. Then $\{u_1, \cdots, u_n\}$ is an orthonormal basis for V.

REMARKS.   The last theorem shows that in a sense the inner product defined in Example 1 following definition (27.1) is the only example of an inner product. For, let V be a vector space with an inner product (u, v), and let $\{u_1, \cdots, u_n\}$ be an orthonormal basis of V. Then if $u = \sum \xi_i u_i$, $v = \sum \eta_i v_i$, the reader may verify that

$$(u, v) = \sum \xi_i \eta_i.$$

Theorem (27.8) has the disadvantage that it affords no construction for the orthonormal basis. The next theorem gives an inductive procedure for constructing an orthonormal basis from a given set of basis vectors.

(27.9)   Theorem (Gram-Schmidt Orthogonalization Process).   *Let V be a finite-dimensional vector space with an inner product (u, v), and let $\{w_1, \cdots, w_n\}$ be a basis. Suppose $\{u_1, \cdots, u_r\}$ is an orthonormal basis for the subspace $S(w_1, \cdots, w_r)$. Define*

$$u_{r+1} = \frac{w}{||w||}$$

where

$$w = w_{r+1} - \sum_{i=1}^{r} (w_{r+1}, u_i)u_i.$$

Then $\{u_1, \cdots, u_{r+1}\}$ is an orthonormal basis for $S(w_1, \cdots, w_{r+1})$.

Proof.   We have three statements to prove: first, that u_{r+1} has length 1; second, that $(u_{r+1}, u_i) = 0$ for $1 \leq i \leq r$; and third, that $S(w_1, \cdots, w_{r+1}) = S(u_1, \cdots, u_{r+1})$ (it follows from the last statement that $\{u_1, \cdots, u_{r+1}\}$ is a linearly independent set). Since $S(u_1, \cdots, u_r) = S(w_1, \cdots, w_r)$, it is clear that $w = w_{r+1} - \sum_1^r (w_{r+1}, u_i)u_i$ is different from zero. Then $u_{r+1} = w/||w||$ has length 1. To prove that $(u_{r+1}, u_j) = 0$ for $1 \leq j \leq r$ it is sufficient to prove that $(w, u_j) = 0$. We have

$$(w, u_j) = \left(w_{r+1} - \sum_{i=1}^{r} (w_{r+1}, u_i) u_i, u_j \right)$$

$$= (w_{r+1}, u_j) - \sum_{i=1}^{r} (w_{r+1}, u_i)(u_i, u_j)$$

$$= (w_{r+1}, u_j) - (w_{r+1}, u_j) = 0.$$

Finally, it is clear that $u_{r+1} \in S(w_1, \cdots, w_{r+1})$ and that $w_{r+1} \in S(u_1, \cdots, u_{r+1})$. Since $S(w_1, \cdots, w_r) = S(u_1, \cdots, u_r)$ by assumption, we have $S(u_1, \cdots, u_{r+1}) = S(w_1, \cdots, w_{r+1})$, as required. This completes the proof.

(27.10)   Definition.   Let V be a vector space with an inner product (u, v). A linear transformation $T \in L(V, V)$ is called an *orthogonal transformation*, provided that T preserves length, that is, that $\|T(u)\| = \|u\|$ for all $u \in V$.

(27.11)   Theorem.   *The following statements concerning a linear transformation $T \in L(V, V)$, where V is finite-dimensional, are equivalent.*

(A)   *T is an orthogonal transformation.*
(B)   *$(T(u), T(v)) = (u, v)$ for all $u, v \in V$.*
(C)   *For some orthonormal basis $\{u_1, \cdots, u_n\}$ of V, the vectors $\{T(u_1), \cdots, T(u_n)\}$ also form an orthonormal set.*
(D)   *The matrix A of T with respect to an orthonormal basis satisfies the condition ${}^t A \cdot A = I$ where ${}^t A$ is the transpose matrix of A.*

Proof.   Statement A implies statement B. We are given that $\|T(u)\| = \|u\|$ for *all* vectors $u \in V$. This implies that $(T(u), T(u)) = (u, u)$ for all vectors u. Replacing u by $u + v$ we obtain

$$(T(u + v), T(u + v)) = (u + v, u + v).$$

Now expand, using the bilinear and symmetric properties of the inner product, to obtain

$$(T(u), T(u)) + 2(T(u), T(v)) + (T(v), T(v))$$
$$= (u, u) + 2(u, v) + (v, v).$$

Since $(T(u), T(u)) = (u, u)$ and $(T(v), T(v)) = (v, v)$, the last equation implies that $(T(u), T(v)) = (u, v)$ for all u and v.

Statement B implies statement C. Let $\{u_1, \cdots, u_n\}$ be an orthonormal basis of V; then:

$$(u_i, u_i) = 1, \qquad (u_i, u_j) = 0, \qquad i \neq j.$$

By statement B we have

$$(T(u_i), T(u_i)) = 1, \qquad (T(u_i), T(u_j)) = 0, \qquad i \neq j,$$

and $\{T(u_1), \cdots, T(u_n)\}$ is an orthonormal set.

Statement C implies statement A. Suppose that for some orthonormal basis $\{u_1, \cdots, u_n\}$ of V the image vectors $\{T(u_1), \cdots, T(u_n)\}$ form an orthonormal set. Let

$$v = \xi_1 u_1 + \cdots + \xi_n u_n$$

be an arbitrary vector in V. Then

$$||v||^2 = (v, v) = (\xi_1 u_1 + \cdots + \xi_n u_n, \xi_1 u_1 + \cdots + \xi_n u_n) = \sum_1^n \xi_i^2$$

since $\{u_1, \cdots, u_n\}$ is an orthonormal set. Similarly, we have

$$||T(v)||^2 = (T(v), T(v)) = \left(\sum_1^n \xi_i T(u_i), \sum_1^n \xi_i T(u_i) \right) = \sum_1^n \xi_i^2.$$

Thus statement A is proved and we have shown the equivalence of all three statements.

Finally, we prove that statements C and D are equivalent. Suppose that statement C holds and let $\{u_1, \cdots, u_n\}$ be an orthonormal basis for V. Let

$$T(u_i) = \sum_{j=1}^n \alpha_{ji} u_j.$$

Since $\{T(u_1), \cdots, T(u_n)\}$ is an orthonormal set, we have

$$(T(u_i), T(u_i)) = \left(\sum_{j=1}^n \alpha_{ji} u_j, \sum_{j=1}^n \alpha_{ji} u_j \right) = \sum_{j=1}^n \alpha_{ji}^2 = 1$$

and, if $i \neq j$,

$$(T(u_i), T(u_j)) = \left(\sum_{k=1}^n \alpha_{ki} u_k, \sum_{k=1}^n \alpha_{kj} u_k \right) = \sum_{k=1}^n \alpha_{ki} \alpha_{kj} = 0.$$

These equations imply that ${}^t A A = I$. Conversely, ${}^t A A = I$ implies that the equations above are satisfied and hence that $\{T(u_1), \cdots, T(u_n)\}$ is an orthonormal set. This completes the proof of the theorem.

(27.12) **Definition.** A matrix $A \in M_n(R)$ is called an *orthogonal matrix* if ${}^t A \cdot A = I$; then A is simply the matrix of an orthogonal transformation with respect to an orthonormal basis of V.

EXERCISES

In these exercises V denotes always a real vector space with an inner product.

1. Find an orthornormal basis for the subspace of $C[0, 1]$ generated by $\{1, x, x^2\}$, with respect to the inner product $(f, g) = \int_0^1 f(t)g(t)\, dt$.

2. Prove that if $\{u_1, \cdots, u_n\}$ is an orthonormal basis for V then every vector $v \in V$ can be expressed as

$$v = \sum_{i=1}^{n} (v, u_i)u_i.$$

3. Prove that if $\alpha \in R$ is a characteristic root of an orthogonal transformation then $\alpha = \pm 1$.

4. Prove that if v_1 and v_2 are characteristic vectors belonging to distinct real characteristic roots of an orthogonal transformation then $(v_1, v_2) = 0$.

5. Let $O(V)$ be the set of all orthogonal transformations on V. Prove the following statements.
   a. $O(V)$ is a group with respect to the operation of multiplication.
   b. $T \in O(V)$ implies $D(T) = \pm 1$ (see Exercise 3 of Section 13).

6. Prove that the *unit ball* in R_n consisting of all vectors u such that $\|u\| \leq 1$ is a convex set.

7. Prove that, if W_1 and W_2 are subspaces of V such that $\dim W_1 = \dim W_2$, then there exists an orthogonal transformation T such that $T(W_1) = W_2$.

8. Prove Hadamard's inequality for determinants: if $u_1, \cdots, u_n \in R_n$, then

$$|D(u_1, \cdots, u_n)| \leq \|u_1\| \cdots \|u_n\|.$$

[*Hint:* Show first that it is sufficient to prove that if $\|u_i\| = 1$ for $1 \leq i \leq n$ then $|D(u_1, \cdots, u_n)| \leq 1$. Assume the result for $n - 1$ vectors of length one in R_{n-1}. Prove that if T is an orthogonal transformation then, by part b of Exercise 5 and the multiplication theorem for determinants,

$$|D(Tu_1, \cdots, Tu_n)| = |D(u_1, \cdots, u_n)|.$$

We may assume that $\{u_1, \cdots, u_n\}$ are linearly independent. Then by Exercise 7 there exists an orthogonal transformation T such that $T(u_i) \in S(e_2, \cdots, e_n)$ for $i = 2, \cdots, n$, so that the matrix whose rows are $Tu_1, \cdots, Tu_n$ has the form

$$X = \begin{pmatrix} \lambda_{11} & \lambda_{12} & \cdots & \lambda_{1n} \\ 0 & \lambda_{22} & \cdots & \lambda_{2n} \\ \cdots & \cdots & \cdots & \cdots \\ \cdots & \cdots & \cdots & \cdots \\ \cdots & \cdots & \cdots & \cdots \\ 0 & \lambda_{n2} & \cdots & \lambda_{nn} \end{pmatrix}$$

where the sum of the squares of the entries in each row is 1 (Why?). Then

$$|D(X)| = |\lambda_{11}| \begin{vmatrix} \lambda_{22} & \cdots & \lambda_{2n} \\ \cdots & \cdots & \cdots \\ \cdots & \cdots & \cdots \\ \lambda_{n2} & \cdots & \lambda_{nn} \end{vmatrix} \le 1$$

by the induction hypothesis and the fact that $|\lambda_{11}| \le 1$.]

9. Let T be an invertible transformation which "preserves orthogonality" in the sense that $(u, v) = 0$ implies $(Tu, Tv) = 0$ for all u, v. Prove that there exists a constant $\lambda \in R$ and $U \in O(V)$ such that $T = \lambda U$.

28. THE STRUCTURE OF ORTHOGONAL TRANSFORMATIONS

In Section 26 we showed that every orthogonal transformation of the plane is either a rotation or a reflection. We wish to find in this section a geometrical description of orthogonal transformations on an n-dimensional real vector space V with an inner product (u, v). From the point of view of Chapter 5, given an orthogonal transformation T we look for an orthonormal basis of V with respect to which the matrix of T is as simple as possible.

The matrix

$$A = \begin{pmatrix} \cos\dfrac{2\pi}{3} & -\sin\dfrac{2\pi}{3} \\ \sin\dfrac{2\pi}{3} & \cos\dfrac{2\pi}{3} \end{pmatrix} = \begin{pmatrix} -\dfrac{1}{2} & -\dfrac{\sqrt{3}}{2} \\ \dfrac{\sqrt{3}}{2} & -\dfrac{1}{2} \end{pmatrix}$$

is an orthogonal matrix such that $A^3 = I$. Its minimal polynomial is

$$x^2 + x + 1$$

which is a prime in the polynomial ring $R[x]$. Therefore, by theorem (22.8), A cannot be diagonalized over the real field and cannot even be put in triangular form, since a triangular 2-by-2 orthogonal matrix can easily be shown to be diagonal. Thus the methods of Chapter 5 yield little new information, even in this simple case.

The difficulty is that the real field is not algebraically closed. It is here that, as Hermann Weyl remarked, Euclid enters the scene, brandishing his ruler and his compass. The ideas necessary to treat orthogonal transformations on a real vector space will throw additional light on the problems considered in Chapter 5, as well. We begin with some general definitions and theorems.

(28.1) Definition. Let $T \in L(V, V)$ be a linear transformation on an arbitrary finite-dimensional vector space V over an arbitrary field F. A nonzero invariant subspace $W \subset V$ (relative to T) is called *irreducible* if the only T-invariant subspaces contained in W are $\{0\}$ and W.

(28.2) Theorem. *(A) If V is a vector space over an algebraically closed field F, then every irreducible invariant subspace W relative to $T \in L(V, V)$ has dimension 1. (B) If V is a vector space over the real field R and if W is an irreducible invariant subspace relative to $T \in L(V, V)$, then W has dimension 1 or 2.*

Proof of A. Let W be an irreducible invariant subspace relative to T; then T defines a linear transformation T_W of W into itself, where

$$T_W(w) = T(w), \qquad w \in W.$$

From Section 23, W contains a characteristic vector w relative to T; then $S(w)$ is an invariant subspace contained in W, and hence $W = S(w)$ because W is irreducible. This proves part A.

Proof of B. Let W be an irreducible invariant subspace relative to T and let $m(x)$ be the minimal polynomial of T_W. From theorem (22.6), $m(x) = p(x)^e$ where $p(x)$ is a prime polynomial in $R[x]$; otherwise, W would be the direct sum of subspaces, contrary to the assumption that W is irreducible. If $m(x) = p(x)^e$ is the minimal polynomial of T_W, then $e = 1$; otherwise, the null space of $p(T)^{e-1}$ would be an invariant subspace different from $\{0\}$ and W. Thus we have, by corollary (17.13), either

$$m(x) = x - \alpha \quad \text{or} \quad m(x) = x^2 + \alpha x + \beta, \qquad \alpha^2 - 4\beta < 0.$$

Let w be a nonzero vector of W. Then, if $m(x) = x - \alpha$, w is a characteristic vector of T, and $W = S(w)$ as in part A. If $m(x) = x^2 + \alpha x + \beta$ for $\alpha^2 - 4\beta < 0$, then $S(w, T(w))$ is an invariant subspace, and hence $W = S(w, T(w))$. Therefore W has dimension either 1 or 2, and the theorem is proved.

Now we apply this theorem to orthogonal transformations as follows.

(28.3)   Theorem.   *Let T be an orthogonal transformation on a real vector space V with an inner product and let W be an irreducible invariant subspace relative to T; then either of the two following holds.*

(1)   dim $W = 1$ *and, if $w \neq 0$ in W, then $T(w) = \pm w$.*
(2)   dim $W = 2$ *and there is an orthonormal basis $\{w_1, w_2\}$ for W such that the matrix of T with respect to $\{w_1, w_2\}$ has the form*

$$\begin{pmatrix} \cos\theta & -\sin\theta \\ \sin\theta & \cos\theta \end{pmatrix}.$$

In other words, T_W is a rotation in the two-dimensional space W (see Section 26).

Proof.   By theorem (28.2), dim W is either 1 or 2. In case 1 of the theorem, $T(w) = \lambda w$ for some $\lambda \in R$, and

$$\|T(w)\| = \|w\|$$

implies $|\lambda| = 1$. Therefore, $\lambda = \pm 1$ and $T(w) = \pm w$.

If dim $W = 2$, then the minimal polynomial of T has the form

$$x^2 + \alpha x + \beta, \qquad \alpha^2 - 4\beta < 0.$$

Let $\{w_1, w_2\}$ be an orthonormal basis for W and let

$$T(w_1) = \lambda w_1 + \mu w_2.$$

Then $\lambda^2 + \mu^2 = 1$ and, since $(T(w_1), T(w_2)) = 0$, $T(w_2)$ is either $-\mu w_1 + \lambda w_2$ or $\mu w_2 - \lambda w_2$. In the first case, the matrix of T is

$$\begin{pmatrix} \lambda & -\mu \\ \mu & \lambda \end{pmatrix}$$

and we can find θ such that $\cos\theta = \lambda$, $\sin\theta = \mu$, since $\lambda^2 + \mu^2 = 1$. In the latter case, the matrix is

$$\begin{pmatrix} \lambda & \mu \\ \mu & -\lambda \end{pmatrix}$$

which satisfies the equation $x^2 - 1 = 0$, and since $x^2 - 1 = (x + 1)(x - 1)$ is not a prime this case cannot occur. This completes the proof of the theorem.

The last theorem becomes of especial interest when combined with the following result.

(28.4) Theorem. *Let T be an orthogonal transformation on a real vector space V with an inner product; then V is a direct sum of irreducible invariant subspaces $\{W_1, \cdots, W_s\}$, for $s \geq 1$, such that vectors belonging to distinct subspaces W_i and W_j are orthogonal.*

Proof. We prove the theorem by induction on dim V, the result being obvious if dim $V = 1$. Assume the theorem for subspaces of dimension $<$ dim V and let T be an orthogonal transformation on V. Let W_1 be a nonzero invariant subspace of least dimension; then W_1 is an irreducible invariant subspace. Let $W_1^\perp$ be the subspace consisting of all vectors orthogonal to the vectors in W_1. We prove that

$$W = W_1 \oplus W_1^\perp.$$

Clearly, $W_1 \cap W_1^\perp = \{0\}$, since $(w, w) \neq 0$ if $w \neq 0$. Now let $w \in W$ and let $\{w_1, \cdots, w_s\}$ be an orthonormal basis for W_1 where $s = 1$ or 2. Then

$$w = \sum_{i=1}^{s} (w, w_i)w_i + \left(w - \sum_{i=1}^{s} (w, w_i)w_i \right)$$

and since $\sum_1^s (w, w_i)w_i \in W_1$ and $w - \sum_1^s (w, w_i)w_i \in W_1^\perp$ we have $W = W_1 + W_1^\perp$. This fact together with the result that $W_1 \cap W_1^\perp = \{0\}$ implies that $W = W_1 \oplus W_1^\perp$.

Now we prove the key result that $W_1^\perp$ is also an invariant subspace. Let $w' \in W_1^\perp$. Since T is orthogonal, $T(W_1) = W_1$ and $(W_1, w') = (T(W_1), T(w')) = (W_1, T(w')) = 0$. Therefore $T(w')$ is also orthogonal to all the vectors in W_1.

Since $T(W_1^\perp) \subset W_1^\perp$, T is an orthogonal transformation of $W_1^\perp$ and, by the induction hypothesis, $W_1^\perp$ is a direct sum of pairwise orthogonal irreducible invariant subspaces. Since $V = W_1 \oplus W_1^\perp$, the same is true for V, and the theorem is proved.

Combining theorems (28.3) and (28.4) we obtain the following determination of the form of the matrix of an orthogonal transformation.

(28.5) Theorem. *Let T be an orthogonal transformation of a real vector space V with an inner product; then there exists an orthonormal basis for V such that the matrix of T with respect to this basis has the form*

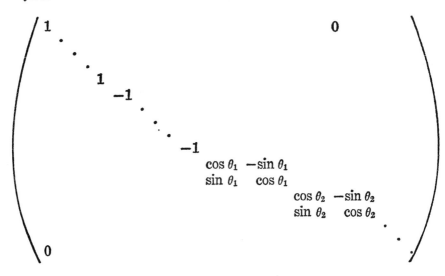

with zeros except in the 1-by-1 or 2-by-2 blocks along the diagonal.

Proof. The proof is immediate by theorems (28.3) and (28.4), since we can choose orthonormal bases for the individual subspaces W_i in theorem (28.4) which, when taken together, will form an orthonormal basis of V.

EXERCISES

1. Prove that, if T is an orthogonal transformation on R_2 such that $D(T) = -1$, there exists an orthonormal basis for R_2 such that the matrix of T with respect to this basis is

$$\begin{pmatrix} -1 & 0 \\ 0 & 1 \end{pmatrix}.$$

2. An orthogonal transformation T of R_3 is called a *rotation* if $D(T) = 1$. Prove that if T is a rotation in R_3 there exists an orthonormal basis of R_3 such that the matrix of T with respect to this basis is

$$\begin{pmatrix} 1 & 0 & 0 \\ 0 & \cos\theta & -\sin\theta \\ 0 & \sin\theta & \cos\theta \end{pmatrix}$$

for some real number θ.

3. Prove that an orthogonal transformation T in R_m has 1 as a characteristic root if $D(T) = 1$ and m is odd. What can you say if m is even?

Note. Exercises 4 to 12 give an important generalization of orthogonal transformations to complex vector spaces. In these exercises, $V = \{u, v, \cdots\}$ denotes a finite-dimensional vector space over the complex field $C = \{a, b, \cdots\}$ and $\bar{a}$ denotes the complex conjugate of $a \in C$.

4. If $a \in C$ is viewed as a vector in R_2, then its length is given by $\sqrt{a\bar{a}}$. Now let C_n be the vector space of n-tuples over C. Then in order to define an inner product on C_n which is related to length in the case of C_1, we define

$$(u, v) = \sum_{i=1}^{n} a_i \bar{b}_i$$

where $u = \langle a_1, \cdots, a_n \rangle$, $v = \langle b_1, \cdots, b_n \rangle$. Prove that (u, v) has the properties:

(1) $(u_1 + u_2, v) = (u_1, v) + (u_2, v)$, $(u, v_1 + v_2) = (u, v_1) + (u, v_2)$; $(u, v) = \overline{(v, u)}$, $(au, v) = a(u, v)$, $(u, av) = \bar{a}(u, v)$, for all $u, v \in V$, $a \in C$.

(2) For all $u \in V$, (u, u) is real and nonnegative. Moreover, $(u, u) = 0$ if and only if $u = 0$. We define the *length* $||u||$ of u by $||u|| = \sqrt{(u, u)}$, $u \in V$.

5. Let V be an arbitrary finite-dimensional vector space over C. A mapping (u, v) which assigns to each pair of vectors $\{u, v\}$ a complex number (u, v) is called a *hermitian scalar product* (after the French mathematician C. Hermite) if (u, v) has the properties 1 and 2 in Exercise 4. A set of vectors $\{u_1, \cdots, u_s\}$ in V is called an *orthonormal set* if $||u_i|| = 1$ for all i and $(u_i, u_j) = 0$ for $i \neq j$. Prove that every subspace W of V has an orthonormal basis. Let $\{u_1, \cdots, u_s\}$ be an orthonormal basis for W and let $v = \sum a_i u_i$ and $w = \sum b_i u_i$ be arbitrary vectors in W. Prove that $(v, w) = \sum a_i \bar{b}_i$.

6. A linear transformation $U \in L(V, V)$ is called a *unitary transformation* on V if $||U(v)|| = ||v||$ for all v. Prove that $U \in L(V, V)$ is unitary if and only if $(Uv, Uw) = (v, w)$ for all $v, w \in V$. [*Hint:* Suppose $||Uv|| = ||v||$ for all v. Applying this formula to $v + w$ and $v + iw$, show that

$$(Uv, Uw) + (Uw, Uv) = (v, w) + (w, v)$$

and that

$$i(Uw, Uv) - i(Uv, Uw) = i(w, v) - i(v, w).$$

Comparing these formulas, show that $(Uv, Uw) = (v, w)$.]

7. Prove that the unitary transformations on V form a group under multiplication.

8. Let $\{v_1, \cdots, v_n\}$ be an orthonormal basis for V. Prove that the following statements concerning $U \in L(V, V)$ are equivalent.

   (A) U is a unitary transformation.
   (B) $\{U(v_1), \cdots, U(v_n)\}$ is an orthonormal set of vectors.

   (C) If $U(v_i) = \sum_{j=1}^{n} a_{ji}v_j$, then the matrix $A = (a_{ij})$ has the property that

$$A \cdot {}^t\overline{A} = I$$

   where the (i, j) entry in ${}^t\overline{A}$ is $\overline{a}_{ji}$. A matrix $A \in M_n(C)$ such that $A \cdot {}^t\overline{A} = I$ is called a *unitary matrix*; it is the matrix of a unitary transformation with respect to an orthonormal basis.

9. Let a be a characteristic root of a unitary transformation U. Prove that $a\overline{a} = 1$.

10. Let U be a unitary transformation on V. Prove that there exists an orthonormal basis for V consisting of characteristic vectors of U. [*Hint:* First show that, if v and w belong to distinct characteristic roots of U, then $(v, w) = 0$. It is now sufficient to prove that U is diagonable (Why?). Let a be a characteristic root of U. Then $a\overline{a} = 1$ by Exercise 9. It is sufficient, by the results of Section 23, to prove that, if w is a vector such that $(U - a \cdot 1)^2 w = 0$, then $(U - a \cdot 1)w = 0$. Let $x = U(w) - aw$. If $x = 0$ we are done. If $x \neq 0$, then $U(x) = ax$. Then

$$[U(w), U(x)] = (w, x) = (x + aw, ax) = \overline{a}(x, x) + a\overline{a}(w, x)$$

which implies that $(x, x) = 0$ and contradicts the assumption that $x \neq 0$. Therefore $x = 0$, and U is diagonable.]

11. Prove that if A is a unitary matrix there exists a unitary matrix B such that BAB^{-1} is a diagonal matrix whose nonzero entries all have absolute value 1.

12. Show that

$$A = \begin{pmatrix} 0 & i \\ -i & 0 \end{pmatrix}$$

is a unitary matrix. Find a unitary matrix B such that BAB^{-1} is a diagonal matrix.

29. PRINCIPAL-AXIS THEOREM

In a beginning course in analytic geometry the following problem is considered. Let

$$f(x_1, x_2) = ax_1^2 + bx_1x_2 + cx_2^2 + dx_1 + ex_2 + f = 0$$

be an equation of the second degree in x_1 and x_2. The problem is to find a new coordinate system

$$X_1 = (\cos \theta)\, x_1 + (\sin \theta)x_2 + c_1$$
$$X_2 = (-\sin \theta)x_1 + (\cos \theta)x_2 + c_2$$

obtained by a rotation and a translation from the original one, such that in the new coordinate system the equation becomes either of the following.

(29.1) $$f(X_1, X_2) = AX_1^2 + BX_2^2 + C = 0.$$

(29.2) $$f(X_1, X_2) = AX_2^2 - DX_1 = 0.$$

The graph of $f(X_1, X_2) = 0$ can then be classified as a circle, ellipse, hyperbola, parabola, etc. It is clear that, if we can first find a rotation of axes

$$X_1 = (\cos \theta)x_1 + (\sin \theta)x_2$$
$$X_2 = (-\sin \theta)x_1 + (\cos \theta)x_2$$

such that the second-degree terms $ax_1^2 + bx_1x_2 + cx_2^2$ become

(29.3) $$AX_1^2 + BX_2^2,$$

then the new equation has the form

$$f(X_1, X_2) = AX_1^2 + BX_2^2 + CX_1 + DX_2 + D$$

and can be put in the form (29.1) or (29.2) by a translation of axes: $X'_1 = X_1 + c_1$, $X'_2 = X_2 + c_2$.

The problem we shall consider in this section is a generalization of the problem of finding a rotation of axes that will put the second-degree terms of $f(x_1, x_2)$ in the form (29.3).

(29.4) Definition. Let V be an n-dimensional vector space over the real numbers R. A *quadratic form* on V is a function Q which assigns to each vector $a \in V$ a real number $Q(a)$ such that the following conditions are satisfied.

(A) $Q(\alpha a) = \alpha^2 Q(a)$, $\quad \alpha \in R$, $a \in V$.
(B) If we define $B(a, b) = \frac{1}{2}[Q(a + b) - Q(a) - Q(b)]$, then B is a *bilinear function* on V, that is,*

$$B(\alpha a_1 + \beta a_2, b) = \alpha B(a_1, b) + \beta B(a_2, b),$$
$$B(a, \alpha b_1 + \beta b_2) = \alpha B(a, b_1) + \beta B(a, b_2),$$

for all $a, b \in V$ and $\alpha, \beta \in R$.

(29.5) Theorem. *Let Q be a quadratic form on V and let $\{e_1, \cdots, e_n\}$ be a basis of V over R. Define an n-by-n matrix $S = (\sigma_{ij})$ by setting*

$$\sigma_{ij} = B(e_i, e_j), \qquad 1 \le i, \ j \le n,$$

where B is the bilinear function defined in part B of definition (29.4). Then ${}^tS = S$, and for all $a = \sum \alpha_i e_i \in V$ we have

$$\textbf{(29.6)}\quad Q(a) = B(a, a) = \sum_{i,j=1}^{n} \alpha_i \alpha_j \sigma_{ij} = \sum_{i=1}^{n} \alpha_i^2 \sigma_{ii} + 2 \sum_{i<j} \alpha_i \alpha_j \sigma_{ij}.$$

Conversely, if $S = (\sigma_{ij})$ is an arbitrary n-by-n real matrix such that ${}^tS = S$, then (29.6) defines a quadratic form Q such that if we set $B(a, b) = \frac{1}{2}[Q(a + b) - Q(a) - Q(b)]$ then $B(e_i, e_j) = \sigma_{ij}$.

REMARK. Assuming the truth of the theorem, the function

$$f(x_1, x_2) = ax_1^2 + bx_1x_2 + cx_2^2$$

defines a quadratic form on R_2 such that if $\{x_1, x_2\}$ are the coordinates of a vector x with respect to the basis $\{e_1, e_2\}$ then the matrix of f defined in the theorem is given by

$$\begin{pmatrix} a & \frac{1}{2}b \\ \frac{1}{2}b & c \end{pmatrix}.$$

---

* Bilinear functions are sometimes called *bilinear forms*.

Proof of Theorem (29.5). The first part of the theorem is immediate from definition (29.4). For the converse, let $S = {}^tS$ be given and define a function

$$B(a, b) = \sum_{i,j=1}^{n} \alpha_i \beta_j \sigma_{ij}$$

for $a = \sum \alpha_i e_i$, $b = \sum \beta_i e_i$. Then B is a bilinear function on V such that $B(e_i, e_j) = \sigma_{ij}$ and $B(a, b) = B(b, a)$, for $a, b \in V$. It is also clear that if we define

$$Q(a) = B(a, a)$$

then Q is a quadratic form such that $B(a, b) = \frac{1}{2}[Q(a + b) - Q(a) - Q(b)]$, since $B(a, b) = B(b, a)$. This completes the proof.

(29.7) **Definition.** A real n-by-n matrix S is called *symmetric* if ${}^tS = S$. The *matrix* $S = (\sigma_{ij})$ of a *quadratic form* Q with respect to the basis $\{e_1, \cdots, e_n\}$ is defined by

$$\sigma_{ij} = B(e_i, e_j)$$

where

$$B(a, b) = \frac{1}{2}[Q(a + b) - Q(a) - Q(b)]$$

is the bilinear function associated with Q.

(29.8) **Theorem.** *Let Q be a quadratic form on V whose matrix with respect to the basis $\{e_1, \cdots, e_n\}$ is $S = (\sigma_{ij})$. Let $\{f_1, \cdots, f_n\}$ be another basis of V such that*

$$f_i = \sum_{j=1}^{n} \gamma_{ji} e_j, \qquad 1 \le i \le n.$$

Then the matrix of Q with respect to the basis $\{f_1, \cdots, f_n\}$ is given by

$$S' = {}^tCSC$$

where $C = (\gamma_{ij})$.

Proof. Let $S' = (\sigma'_{ij})$. Then

$$\sigma'_{ij} = B(f_i, f_j) = B\left(\sum_{k=1}^{n} \gamma_{ki} e_k, \sum_{l=1}^{n} \gamma_{lj} e_l\right)$$

$$= \sum_{k=1}^{n} \sum_{l=1}^{n} \gamma_{ki} \gamma_{lj} B(e_k, e_l)$$

$$= \sum_{k=1}^{n} \sum_{l=1}^{n} \gamma_{ki} \sigma_{kl} \gamma_{lj},$$

and the theorem is proved.

Now we can state the main theorem of this section.

(29.9)   Principal-Axis Theorem.* *Let V be a vector space over R with an inner product (a, b) and let $\{e_1, \cdots, e_n\}$ be an orthonormal basis of V. Let Q be a quadratic form on V whose matrix with respect to $\{e_1, \cdots, e_n\}$ is $S = (\sigma_{ij})$. Then there exists an orthonormal basis $\{f_1, \cdots, f_n\}$ such that the matrix of Q with respect to $f_1, \cdots, f_n$ is*

$$S' = \begin{pmatrix} \sigma_1 & & & & 0 \\ & \sigma_2 & & & \\ & & \cdot & & \\ & & & \cdot & \\ 0 & & & & \sigma_n \end{pmatrix}$$

where the σ_i are the characteristic roots of S. If

$$f_i = \sum_{j=1}^{n} \gamma_{ji} e_j, \qquad 1 \leq i \leq n,$$

then $C = (\gamma_{ij})$ is an orthogonal matrix. If $a \in V$ is expressed in terms of the new basis $\{f_1, \cdots, f_n\}$ by $a = \sum_{i=1}^{n} \alpha_i f_i$, then $Q(a) = \sum_{i=1}^{n} \alpha_i^2 \sigma_i$. The vectors $f_1, \cdots, f_n$ are called the principal axes of Q.

(29.10)   Definition. A linear transformation T on a real vector space with an inner product (a, b) is called a *symmetric transformation* if

$$(Ta, b) = (a, Tb), \qquad a, b \in V.$$

(29.11) *Let $\{e_1, \cdots, e_n\}$ be an orthonormal basis of V. A linear transformation $T \in L(V, V)$, whose matrix with respect to $\{e_1, \cdots, e_n\}$ is $S = (\sigma_{ij})$, is a symmetric transformation if and only if S is a symmetric matrix.*

The proof is similar to the proof of part D of theorem (27.11) and will be omitted.

(29.12)   Theorem. *Let T be a symmetric transformation on a real vector space V; then there exists an orthonormal basis of V consisting of characteristic vectors of V.*

---

* For a different proof and an application of this theorem to mechanics, see Synge and Griffith, p. 318 (listed in Bibliography).

We shall first prove that theorem (29.12) implies theorem (29.9) and then we shall prove theorem (29.12).

Proof that (29.12) *implies* (29.9).   In the notation of theorem (29.9) let Q be a quadratic form on V with the matrix S with respect to the orthonormal basis $\{e_1, \cdots, e_n\}$. By theorems (29.8) and (29.5) and the results of Section 27 it is sufficient to construct an *orthogonal* matrix C such that

$$
{}^tCSC = \begin{pmatrix} \sigma_1 & & 0 \\ & \cdot & \\ & & \cdot \\ 0 & & \sigma_n \end{pmatrix}
$$

where $\sigma_1, \cdots, \sigma_n$ are the characteristic roots of S. For an *orthogonal* matrix C, ${}^tC = C^{-1}$ and therefore it is sufficient to find an orthogonal matrix C such that

$$
C^{-1}SC = \begin{pmatrix} \sigma_1 & & 0 \\ & \cdot & \\ & & \cdot \\ 0 & & \sigma_n \end{pmatrix}.
$$

This is a problem on the linear transformation T whose matrix with respect to $\{e_1, \cdots, e_n\}$ is S. By (29.11), T is a symmetric transformation and from the results of Section 27 the task of finding C is exactly the problem stated in theorem (29.12).

Proof of theorem (29.12).   We first prove that V is a direct sum of pairwise orthogonal irreducible invariant subspaces relative to T. The argument is the same as the proof of theorem (28.4); we have only to check that, if W is invariant relative to T, then $W^\perp$ is invariant relative to T. Let $w' \in W^\perp$ and $w \in W$; then

$$(w, Tw') = (Tw, w') = 0$$

since $Tw \in W$ and $w' \in W^\perp$. We may now conclude that V is the direct sum of pairwise orthogonal irreducible invariant subspaces $\{W_1, \cdots, W_s\}$.

It is now sufficient to prove that for all i, where $1 \leq i \leq s$, dim $W_i = 1$. Since dim $W_i = 1$ or 2, it is sufficient to prove that a symmetric transformation T on a two-dimensional real vector space W always has a characteristic vector. Let $\{w_1, w_2\}$ be an orthonormal basis for W; then, relative to $\{w_1, w_2\}$, T has a symmetric matrix

$$
\begin{pmatrix} \lambda & \xi \\ \xi & \mu \end{pmatrix}, \qquad \lambda, \mu, \xi \in R.
$$

This matrix satisfies the equation
$$x^2 - (\lambda + \mu)x + (\lambda\mu - \xi^2) = 0.$$
Letting $A = -(\lambda + \mu)$ and $B = \lambda\mu - \xi^2$, we have
$$A^2 - 4B = (\lambda + \mu)^2 - 4(\lambda\mu - \xi^2)$$
$$= \lambda^2 - 2\lambda\mu + \mu^2 + 4\xi^2 = (\lambda - \mu)^2 + 4\xi^2 \geq 0$$
for all real numbers λ, ξ, μ. Therefore the polynomial $x^2 + Ax + B$ factors into linear factors in $R[x]$, and it follows from Section 22 that W contains a characteristic vector. This completes the proof of the theorem.

EXERCISES

1. Consider the symmetric matrix
$$X = \begin{pmatrix} -1 & -3 & 0 \\ -3 & -1 & 0 \\ 0 & 0 & 1 \end{pmatrix}.$$

   a. Find the characteristic roots of X.

   b. Define a symmetric transformation T in R_3 whose matrix with respect to the orthonormal basis of unit vectors $\{e_1, e_2, e_3\}$ is X. Find by the methods of Chapter 5 a basis of R_3 consisting of characteristic vectors of T [we know that can be done, by theorem (29.12)]. Modify this basis to obtain an orthonormal basis $\{f_1, f_2, f_3\}$ of R_3 consisting of characteristic vectors of T. Let
$$f_i = \sum_{j=1}^{3} \mu_{ji} e_j$$
   and
$$Tf_i = \alpha_i f_i, \qquad \alpha_i \in R, \quad i = 1, 2, 3.$$
   Then $M = (\mu_{ij})$ is an orthogonal matrix, such that MXM^{-1} is diagonal. Since M is orthogonal, $M^{-1} = {}^t M$, so this computational procedure also can be applied to find the principal axes of a vector space with respect to a quadratic form.

2. Find an orthonormal basis of R_2 which exhibits the principal axes of the quadratic form
$$8x_1^2 + 8x_1x_2 + 2x_2^2.$$

30. FINITE SYMMETRY GROUPS IN THREE DIMENSIONS*

We begin with some general remarks about orthogonal transformations on an n-dimensional real vector space V with an inner product (u, v). If $S \subset V$, we denote by $S^\perp$ the set of all vectors $v \in V$ such that $(s, v) = 0$ for all $s \in S$. Then $S^\perp$ is always a subspace and, as we have shown in Section 28, if S is a subspace then

$$V = S \oplus S^\perp.$$

In particular, if x is a nonzero vector, then $(x)^\perp$ is an $(n-1)$-dimensional subspace such that

$$V = S(x) \oplus (x)^\perp.$$

In the language of Section 10, $(x)^\perp$ is a hyperplane passing through the origin. Perhaps the simplest kind of orthogonal transformation on V is a transformation T such that, for some nonzero vector x,

$$Tx = -x$$
$$Tu = u, \qquad u \in (x)^\perp.$$

If H denotes the hyperplane $(x)^\perp$, then T is called a *reflection with respect to* H.† Geometrically, T sends each point of V onto its mirror image with respect to H, leaving the elements of H fixed. The matrix of a reflection T, with respect to a basis containing a basis for the hyperplane left fixed by T and a vector orthogonal to the hyperplane, is given by

$$\begin{pmatrix} 1 & & & & 0 \\ & 1 & & & \\ & & \ddots & & \\ & & & 1 & \\ 0 & & & & -1 \end{pmatrix}$$

so that we have

$$T^2 = 1, \qquad D(T) = -1$$

---

* This section is optional.

† The question of the uniqueness of a reflection with respect to a given hyperplane is settled in the exercises.

for all reflections T. Our first important result is the following theorem, due to E. Cartan and J. Dieudonné, which asserts that every orthogonal transformation is a product of reflections.

(30.1) Theorem. *Every orthogonal transformation on an n-dimensional vector space V with an inner product is a product of at most n reflections.*

*Proof.** We use induction on n, the result being clear if $n = 1$, since the only orthogonal transformations on a one-dimensional space are ± 1. Suppose dim $V > 1$ and that the theorem is true for orthogonal transformations on an $(n - 1)$-dimensional space. Let T be a given orthogonal transformation on V and let $x \neq 0$ be a vector in V.

Case 1:   Suppose $Tx = x$; then if $u \in H = (x)^{\perp}$ we have

$$(Tu, x) = (Tu, Tx) = (u, x) = 0,$$

so that $Tu \in H$, and T defines an orthogonal transformation on the $(n - 1)$-dimensional space H. By the induction hypothesis there exist reflections $T_1, \cdots, T_s$, for $s \leq n - 1$ of H, such that

$$(30.2) \qquad Tu = T_1 \cdots T_s u, \qquad u \in H.$$

Extend each T_i to a linear transformation T_i' on V by defining $T_i' x = x$ and $T_i' u = T_i u$, for $u \in H$, $i = 1, \cdots, s$. We show now that each T_i' is a reflection on V. There exists an $(n - 2)$-dimensional subspace $H_i \subset H = (x)^{\perp}$ whose elements are left fixed by T_i; then T_i' leaves fixed the vectors in the hyperplane $H_i' = H_i + S(x)$ of V. Moreover, if x_i generates $H_i^{\perp}$ in H, then $x_i \in (H_i')^{\perp}$ and $T_i' x_i = T_i x_i = -x_i$. These remarks show that T_i' is a reflection with respect to H_i'. Finally, from the definition of the transformations T_i' and (30.2) it follows that

$$T = T_1' \cdots T_s'.$$

Thus we have shown that an orthogonal transformation which leaves a vector fixed is a product of at most $n - 1$ reflections.

Case 2:   Suppose $Tx \neq x$; then $u = Tx - x \neq 0$. Let $H = (u)^{\perp}$ and let U be a reflection with respect to H. We have

$$(Tx + x, Tx - x) = (Tx, Tx) + (x, Tx) - (Tx, x) - (x, x)$$
$$= 0$$

---

*This proof and a more general version of this theorem are given by Artin (listed in Bibliography).

because T is orthogonal and the form is symmetric. Therefore, $Tx + x \in H = (u)^{\perp}$ where $u = Tx - x$ and we have

$$U(Tx + x) = Tx + x.$$

Since U is a reflection with respect to $H = (Tx - x)^{\perp}$ we have

$$U(Tx - x) = -(Tx - x).$$

Adding these equations, we obtain

$$2UT(x) = 2x$$

and hence

$$UT(x) = x.$$

By case 1 there exist $s \leq n - 1$ reflections $T_1, \cdots, T_s$ such that

$$UT = T_1 \cdots T_s.$$

Since $U^2 = 1$ we have

$$T = U(UT) = UT_1 \cdots T_s$$

which is a product of at most n reflections. This completes the proof.

As a corollary, we obtain some geometrical insight into the the following result, which was proved in another way in the exercises of Section 28.

(30.3) **Corollary.** *Let T be an orthogonal transformation of a three-dimensional real vector space such that $D(T) = +1$. Then there exists a nonzero vector $v \in V$ such that $Tv = v$.*

Proof. We may assume $T \neq 1$. By theorem (30.1), T is a product of one, two, or three reflections of determinant -1. It follows that T is a product of exactly two reflections, $T = T_1 T_2$, where T_i is a reflection with respect to a two-dimensional space H_i for $i = 1, 2$. By theorem (7.17),

$$\dim (H_1 + H_2) + \dim (H_1 \cap H_2) = \dim H_1 + \dim H_2 = 4$$

and since $\dim (H_1 + H_2) \leq 3$ we have $\dim (H_1 \cap H_2) \geq 1$. Let x be a nonzero vector in $H_1 \cap H_2$; then $Tx = x$, and the corollary is proved.

We define a *rotation* in a three-dimensional space as an orthogonal transformation of determinant $+1$. Then the corollary asserts that every rotation in three dimensions is a rotation about an axis, the axis being the line determined by the vector left fixed. This fact is of fundamental importance in mechanics and was proved with the use of an interesting geometrical argument by Euler.* We shall see that it is also the key to the classification of finite symmetry groups in R_3. Our presentation of this material is based on the introductory discussion in Section 26, and the proof of the main theorem is taken from Weyl's book (see Bibliography). Apart from its geometrical interest, Weyl's argument gives a penetrating introduction to the theory of finite groups.

Let us make the problem precise. By a *finite symmetry group* in three dimensions we mean a finite group of orthogonal transformations in R_3. For simplicity we shall determine the *finite groups of rotations* in R_3 and indicate in the exercises the connection with the general problem. Let us begin with a list of some examples of finite rotation groups in R_3. By the *order* of a finite group we mean the number of elements in the group. The cyclic group $\mathcal{C}_n$ of order n and the dihedral group $\mathcal{D}_n$ of order $2n$, discussed in Section 26, are the first examples.

For our purposes in this section it is better to think of $\mathcal{D}_n$ as the symmetry group of a regular n-sided polygon. Although the transformation S in $\mathcal{D}_n$ which flips the polygon over along a line of symmetry is a reflection when viewed as a transformation in the plane, S is a rotation when viewed as a transformation in R_3.

The next examples are the symmetry groups of the regular polyhedra in R_3. There are exactly five of these, which are listed in the following table along with the number of vertices V, edges E, and faces F.

	F	E	V
tetrahedron	4	6	4
cube	6	12	8
octahedron	8	12	6
dodecahedron	12	30	20
icosahedron	20	30	12

(For a derivation of this list, based on Euler's formula for polyhedra "without holes," $F - E + V = 2$, see Courant and Robbins and also Weyl and Coxeter, listed in the Bibliography.) The faces are equilateral triangles in the case of the tetrahedron, squares in the case of the cube, equilateral triangles in the case of the octahedron, pentagons in the dodecahedron, and equilateral triangles in the case of the icosahedron; see Figure 6.10.

Apparently, we should obtain five different groups of rotations

---

* See Synge and Griffith, pp. 279–280 (listed in Bibliography).

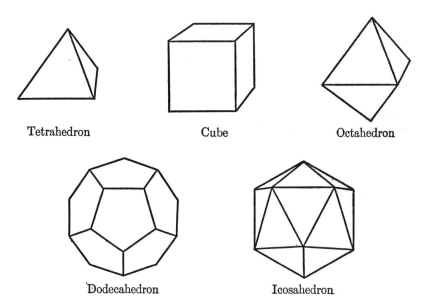

Tetrahedron   Cube   Octahedron

Dodecahedron   Icosahedron

Figure 6.10

from these figures, the group in each case being the set of all rotations
that carry the figure onto itself. On closer inspection we see that this
is not the case. For example, the cube and the octahedron are dual
in the sense that, if we take either figure and connect the centers of
the faces with line segments, these line segments are the edges of the

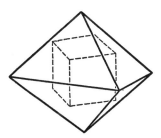

Figure 6.11

other; see Figure 6.11. Thus, any rotation carrying the cube onto
itself will also be a symmetry of the octahedron, and conversely.
Similarly, the dodecahedron and the icosahedron are dual figures.

So, from the regular polyhedra we obtain only three additional groups: the group $\mathfrak{I}$ of rotations of the tetrahedron, the group $\mathfrak{O}$ of rotations of the octahedron, and the group $\mathfrak{I}$ of rotations of the icosahedron.

Our main theorem can now be stated.

(30.4)   Theorem.   *Let* $\mathfrak{G}$ *be a finite group of rotations in* R_3; *then* $\mathfrak{G}$ *is isomorphic with one of the groups in the following list:*

$$\mathfrak{C}_n, \quad n = 1, 2, \cdots,$$
$$\mathfrak{D}_n, \quad n = 1, 2, \cdots,$$
$$\mathfrak{I}, \mathfrak{O}, \text{ or } \mathfrak{I}.$$

Proof.   Let S be the unit sphere in R_3 consisting of all points* $x \in R_3$ such that $||x|| = 1$. If $T \in \mathfrak{G}$, then $Tx \in S$ for every $x \in S$, and T is completely determined by its action on the elements of the sphere S because S contains a basis for R_3. Every $T \in \mathfrak{G}$ such that $T \neq 1$ leaves fixed two antipodal points on the sphere, by corollary (30.3), and no others. These points are called the *poles* of T. Since $\mathfrak{G}$ is finite, the set of all poles of all elements T of $\mathfrak{G}$ such that $T \neq 1$ is a finite set of points on the sphere S; we proceed to examine this set in great detail.

Let p be a pole on S. The set of all elements T of $\mathfrak{G}$ such that p is a pole of T, together with the identity element 1, is clearly a *subgroup* of $\mathfrak{G}$, that is, a subset of $\mathfrak{G}$ which itself forms a group under the operation defined on $\mathfrak{G}$. The order of this subgroup is called the *order of the pole* p and is denoted by v_p.

Next we define two poles p and p' *equivalent* and we write $p \sim p'$ if and only if $p = Tp'$ for some $T \in \mathfrak{G}$. The set of all poles equivalent to p is called the *equivalence class* of p. We prove that each pole belongs to one and only one equivalence class. Since $1 \in \mathfrak{G}$, $p = 1p$, and so p belongs to the equivalence class of p. Now we have to show that if a pole p belongs to the equivalence classes of p' and p'' these equivalence classes coincide. Let q belong to the equivalence class of p'; then $q \sim p'$, and $q = Tp'$ for some $T \in \mathfrak{G}$. Since $p \sim p'$ and $p \sim p''$, we have $p = T'p'$ and $p = T''p''$ for T' and $T'' \in \mathfrak{G}$, and hence $p' = (T')^{-1}T''p''$. Then $q = T(T')^{-1}T''p''$ so that $q \sim p''$. We have shown that the equivalence class of p' is contained in the equivalence class of p'', and a similar argument establishes the reverse inclusion. This completes the proof that a pole belongs to one and only one equivalence class.

---

* We shall speak of the elements in R_3 as points in this discussion.

(30.5) **Lemma.** *Equivalent poles have the same order.*

Proof of Lemma (30.5). Let $p \sim p'$, let $\mathfrak{K}$ be the subgroup of $\mathfrak{G}$ consisting of the identity 1 together with the elements which have p as a pole, and let $\mathfrak{K}'$ be the corresponding subgroup for p'. Let $p = Tp'$. Then an easy verification shows that the mapping $X \to TXT^{-1}$ is a one-to-one mapping of $\mathfrak{K}'$ onto $\mathfrak{K}$, and this establishes the lemma.

(30.6) **Lemma.** *Let p be a pole of order v_p and let n_p be the number of poles equivalent to p; then $v_p n_p = N$ where N is the order of $\mathfrak{G}$.*

Proof of Lemma (30.6). Let $\mathfrak{K}$ be the subgroup associated with p and, for $X \in G$, let $X\mathfrak{K}$ denote the set of all elements $Y \in \mathfrak{G}$ such that $Y = XT$ for some $T \in \mathfrak{K}$. We observe first that, for all $X \in \mathfrak{G}$, Xp is a pole and that poles Xp and $X'p$ are the same if and only if $X' \in X\mathfrak{K}$. Thus the number of poles equivalent to p is equal to the number of distinct sets of the form $X\mathfrak{K}$. The set $X\mathfrak{K}$ is called the *left coset of $\mathfrak{K}$ containing X*. We prove now that each element of $\mathfrak{G}$ belongs to one and only one left coset and that the number of elements in each left coset is v_p. If $X \in \mathfrak{G}$, then $X = X \cdot 1 \in X\mathfrak{K}$ since $1 \in \mathfrak{K}$. Now suppose $X \in X'\mathfrak{K} \cap X''\mathfrak{K}$; we show that $X'\mathfrak{K} = X''\mathfrak{K}$. We have, for $Y \in X'\mathfrak{K}$, $Y = X'T$ for some $T \in \mathfrak{K}$. Moreover, $X \in X'\mathfrak{K} \cap X''\mathfrak{K}$ implies that $X = X'T' = X''T''$ for T' and $T'' \in \mathfrak{K}$. Then $Y = X'T = X(T')^{-1}T = X''T''(T')^{-1}T \in X''\mathfrak{K}$. Thus, $X'\mathfrak{K} \subset X''\mathfrak{K}$ and, similarly, $X''\mathfrak{K} \subset X'\mathfrak{K}$. Therefore $X'\mathfrak{K} = X''\mathfrak{K}$ and we have proved that each element of $\mathfrak{G}$ belongs to a unique left coset. Now let $X\mathfrak{K}$ be a left coset. Then the mapping $T \to XT$ is a one-to-one mapping of $\mathfrak{K}$ onto $X\mathfrak{K}$ and each left coset contains v_p elements where v_p is the order of $\mathfrak{K}$.

We have shown that the number of poles equivalent to p is equal to the number of left cosets of $\mathfrak{K}$ in $\mathfrak{G}$. From what has been shown, this number is equal to N/v_p, and lemma (30.6) is proved.

Now we can finish the proof of theorem (30.4). Consider the set of all pairs (T, p) with $T \in \mathfrak{G}$, $T \neq 1$, and p a pole of T. Counting the pairs in two different ways* we obtain

$$2(N - 1) = \sum_p (v_p - 1)$$

---

*We use first the fact that each $T \neq 1$ is associated with two poles and next that with each pole are associated $(v - 1)$ elements $T \in \mathfrak{G}$ such that $T \neq 1$.

and collecting terms on the right-hand side according to the equivalence classes of poles, C, we have

$$2(N - 1) = \sum n_C(v_C - 1)$$

where n_C is the number of poles in an equivalence class C, v_C is the order of a typical pole in C [see lemma (30.5)], and the sum is taken over the different equivalence classes of poles. Applying (30.6) we obtain

$$2(N - 1) = \sum_C (N - n_C) = \sum_C \left(N - \frac{N}{v_C}\right).$$

Dividing by N we obtain

(30.7) $$2 - \frac{2}{N} = \sum_C \left(1 - \frac{1}{v_C}\right).$$

The left side is >1 and <2; therefore there are at least two classes C and at most three classes. The rest of the argument is an arithmetical study of the equation (30.7).

Case 1: There are two classes of poles of order v_1, v_2. Then (30.7) yields

$$\frac{2}{N} = \frac{1}{v_1} + \frac{1}{v_2}, \qquad 2 = \frac{N}{v_1} + \frac{N}{v_2},$$

and we have $N/v_1 = N/v_2 = 1$. This case occurs if and only if $\mathfrak{g}$ is cyclic.

Case 2: There are three classes of poles of orders v_1, v_2, v_3, where we may assume $v_1 \leq v_2 \leq v_3$. Then (30.7) implies that

$$2 - \frac{2}{N} = \left(1 - \frac{1}{v_1}\right) + \left(1 - \frac{1}{v_2}\right) + \left(1 - \frac{1}{v_3}\right)$$

or

$$1 + \frac{2}{N} = \frac{1}{v_1} + \frac{1}{v_2} + \frac{1}{v_3}.$$

Not all the v_i can be greater than 2; hence $v_1 = 2$ and we have

$$\frac{1}{2} + \frac{2}{N} = \frac{1}{v_2} + \frac{1}{v_3}.$$

Not both v_2 and v_3 can be ≥ 4; hence $v_2 = 2$ or 3.

Case 2a: $v_1 = 2, v_2 = 2$. Then $v_3 = N/2$, and in this case $\mathfrak{g}$ is the dihedral group.

Case 2b: $v_1 = 2, v_2 = 3$. Then we have

$$\frac{1}{v_3} = \frac{1}{6} + \frac{2}{N},$$

and $v_3 = 3, 4,$ or 5. For each possibility of v_3 we have:

$v_1 = 2, v_2 = 3, v_3 = 3;$ then $N = 12$ and $\mathcal{G}$ is the tetrahedral group $\mathcal{J}$.
$v_1 = 2, v_2 = 3, v_3 = 4;$ then $N = 24$ and $\mathcal{G}$ is the octahedral group $\mathcal{O}$.
$v_1 = 2, v_2 = 3, v_3 = 5;$ then $N = 60$ and $\mathcal{G}$ is the icosahedral group $\mathcal{J}$.

EXERCISES

1. Let V be a real vector space with an inner product.
   a. Prove that, if T_1 and T_2 are reflections with respect to the same hyperplane H, then $T_1 = T_2$.
   b. Prove that, if T is an orthogonal transformation that leaves all elements of a hyperplane H fixed, then either $T = 1$ or T is the reflection with respect to H.
   c. Let T be the reflection with respect to H and let $x_0 \in H^{\perp}$. Prove that T is given by the formula

   $$T(x) = x - 2 \frac{(x, x_0)}{(x_0, x_0)} x_0, \qquad x \in V.$$

2. Let $\mathcal{G}$ be a finite group of orthogonal transformations and let $\mathcal{K}$ be the rotations contained in $\mathcal{G}$. Prove that $\mathcal{K}$ is a subgroup of $\mathcal{G}$ and that if $\mathcal{K} \neq \mathcal{G}$ then, for any element $X \in \mathcal{G}$ and $X \notin \mathcal{K}$, we have

   $$\mathcal{G} = \mathcal{K} \cup X\mathcal{K}, \qquad \mathcal{K} \cap X\mathcal{K} = \varnothing.$$

3. Let $\mathcal{G}$ be an arbitrary finite group of invertible linear transformations on R_3. Prove that there exists an inner product $((x, y))$ on R_3 such that the $T_i \in \mathcal{G}$ are orthogonal transformations with respect to the inner product $((x, y))$. [*Hint:* Let (x, y) be the usual inner product on R_3. Define

   $$((x, y)) = \sum_{T_i \in \mathcal{G}} (T_i(x), T_i(y))$$

   and prove that $((x, y))$ has the required properties. Note that the same argument can be applied to finite groups of invertible linear transformations in R_n for n arbitrary.]

4. Let $\mathcal{G}$ be the set of linear transformations on C_2 where C is the complex field whose matrices with respect to a basis are

   $$\pm \begin{pmatrix} 1 & 0 \\ 0 & 1 \end{pmatrix}, \quad \pm \begin{pmatrix} 0 & 1 \\ -1 & 0 \end{pmatrix}, \quad \pm \begin{pmatrix} 0 & i \\ i & 0 \end{pmatrix}, \quad \pm \begin{pmatrix} i & 0 \\ 0 & -i \end{pmatrix}.$$

Prove that $\mathcal{G}$ forms a finite group and that there exists no basis of C_2 such that the matrices of the elements of $\mathcal{G}$ with respect to the new basis all have real coefficients. (*Hint:* If such a basis did exist, then $\mathcal{G}$ would be isomorphic either with a cyclic group or with a dihedral group, by the results of Section 26.)

BIBLIOGRAPHY

Albert, A. A. (Ed.), *Studies in Mathematics*, Volume II: *Studies in Modern Algebra*, Mathematical Association of America, Buffalo, 1963.

Artin, E., *Geometric Algebra*, Interscience, New York, 1957.

Birkhoff, G., and MacLane, S., *Survey of Modern Algebra*, rev. ed., Macmillan, New York, 1953.

Coddington, E., and Levinson, N., *Theory of Ordinary Differential Equations*, McGraw-Hill, New York, 1955.

Coxeter, H. S. M., *Regular Polytopes*, Methuen, London, 1948.

Coxeter, H. S. M., *Introduction to Geometry*, Wiley, New York, 1962.

Courant, R., and Robbins, H., *What Is Mathematics?*, Oxford University Press, New York, 1941.

Jacobson, N., *Lectures in Abstract Algebra*, Volume II: *Linear Algebra*, Van Nostrand, New York, 1953.

Landau, E., *Foundations of Analysis* (English translation), Chelsea, New York, 1951.

Polya, G., *How to Solve It*, Princeton University Press, 1945.

Schreier, O., and Sperner, E., *Modern Algebra and Matrix Theory* (English Translation), Chelsea, New York, 1952.

Synge, J. L., and Griffith, B. A., *Principles of Mechanics*, McGraw-Hill, New York, 1949.

Van der Waerden, B. L., *Modern Algebra*, Volumes I and II (English translation), Ungar, New York, 1949 and 1950.

Weyl, H., *Symmetry*, Princeton University Press, 1952.

INDEX